Through Martha's Eyes

Corinne Brixton

Through Martha's Eyes

One woman witnesses
the greatest event in history

Corinne Brixton

Matador
9 Priory Business Park,
Wistow Road, Kibworth Beauchamp,
Leicestershire. LE8 0RX
Tel: 0116 279 2299
Email: books@troubador.co.uk
Web: www.troubador.co.uk/matador
Twitter: @matadorbooks

ISBN 978 1788036 283

British Library Cataloguing in Publication Data.
A catalogue record for this book is available from the British Library.

Printed and bound by CPI Group (UK) Ltd, Croydon, CR0 4YY
Typeset in 11pt Aldine401 BT by Troubador Publishing Ltd, Leicester, UK

Matador is an imprint of Troubador Publishing Ltd

To my friends Jamie and Lucy, Lynda and Lisa,
and others at St John's Church, Buckhurst Hill,
who were the inspiration for this book.
May it help you to read and understand
the greatest book of all.

'This book is a bit like an enjoyable film which vividly retells the story of Jesus. It brings together biblical texts, lots of historical and social background, and plenty of intelligent imagination filling out the story. Jesus was a real person living in a real historical world among real people, and this book helps bring his story alive for us by suggesting how Martha might have experienced it. I am glad to commend it warmly.'
Revd. Dr. David Wenham, *MA, PhD, Tutor in New Testament, Trinity College Bristol;*
author of "The Parables of Jesus", and "Paul and Jesus: The True Story"

'Corinne Brixton is a wise and experienced guide to the Christian life. This is a book which I hope will introduce many to the riches of the Bible, and help them to understand it better.'
Rt. Revd. Graham Tomlin, *Bishop of Kensington and President of St Mellitus College;*
author of "The Seven Deadly Sins and How to Overcome Them", and "Looking Through The Cross"

'This book achieves its goal of providing a readily accessible background to the gospels for newer Christians. In reality, its appeal is much broader— it is an easy read which will bring the gospel stories into a fresh focus.'
Christine Fry, *Member of Church of England General Synod.*

Acknowledgements

I would like to thank all those who have in any way helped this book to be written. I am grateful to Rt. Revd. David Hawkins, for encouraging me to write when he was Bishop of Barking, and to Revd. Dr. Ian Farley, for giving me time to do so when he was my boss. Thanks also go to Clive Gardner and Angie Blanche, who read and commented on the manuscript as it was evolving, and to Kathy Horstman for her numerous suggested improvements to the completed draft. I also wish to thank Nick Page, both for his excellent books which helped the research, and for giving permission for the map of Jerusalem to be reproduced. And finally, I will always be grateful to my mother, not only for her skills in proof reading, but also for passing on the writing gene.

Foreword

The Bible is a big book – and an old book. Even the *New* Testament was written the best part of two thousand years ago. But it is still a best-seller today, and is read and re-read across the world. It can, nevertheless, present challenges to modern readers unfamiliar with the whole story of the Bible and its historical setting. It uses terms – Tabernacles, Messiah, Sabbath – which may be unfamiliar. It refers to groups or individuals – Pharisees, Sadducees, Pontius Pilate – whose politics and purposes can be a mystery. It is set in places – the temple, Jerusalem, Galilee – whose geography and significance are possibly unclear.

The primary aim of *Through Martha's Eyes* is not to re-tell stories from the gospels. It is to provide the reader with a cultural, historical and religious framework within which those stories might be better understood. To achieve this, the New Testament character of Martha was chosen and a backstory for her created. The telling of her story then becomes the means to describe or explain both various features of first-century Jewish life and the main events of the gospels.

All we actually know about Martha comes from three passages in the gospels, describing three separate events. Firstly, there is an occasion when Jesus stays at what is described as Martha's home, presumably with his disciples. Jesus gently chides Martha for being preoccupied with the tasks of hospitality rather than being with and listening to him, as her sister, Mary, is doing (Luke 10:38-42). Secondly, there is the story of Jesus raising her brother, Lazarus, from the dead. There, we learn that they live in the village of Bethany, less than two miles from Jerusalem, and that Jesus 'loved Martha and her sister and Lazarus'. This implies that they are well-known to him, and he to them (John 11:1-44). And finally, we are told of a meal at Bethany held in Jesus' honour, a few days before his death. Lazarus sits with Jesus at the table, Martha serves, and Mary anoints Jesus' feet with costly perfume. (Matthew 26:6-13 and Mark 14:3–9 are most likely also describing this event.) We also learn at the end of this story that the chief priests are plotting to kill Lazarus, as many Jews are putting their faith in Jesus on account of him (John 12:1-11).

These are the only definite facts about Martha and her siblings. But the implication from the gospels is that Jesus stayed in Bethany (and so probably with them) during the week leading up to his death. It seems likely, therefore, that they would have been, at the very least, on the edge of all the events of that week. At the resurrection appearance on the evening of Easter Sunday, we read of 'the Eleven and *those with them*, assembled together' (emphasis added). Again, it isn't hard to imagine that they may well have been part of that gathering. There must also have been occasions before all these events when they heard Jesus speak or saw him perform miracles. Something, after all, must have prompted Martha to open her home to him. And not forgetting that the meal held at Bethany in Jesus' honour was in the house of Simon the Leper – one can assume that Jesus had healed Simon of that disease!

It was a challenge, however, to decide upon a suitable domestic situation for the family. No indication is given in the gospels of their ages and no reference made to either parents or spouses. They appear to be three single siblings living together. This would be unusual in a culture where people married young and had larger families, so this had to be plausibly explained in the imagined backstory. The home is described as being Martha's, implying possibly that she is the elder of the two sisters, and Lazarus appears to be more passive, and therefore possibly younger. The way in which Martha and Mary describe their brother to Jesus as 'the one you love' (John 11:3), could be seen as a reference to a teenager for whom Jesus had great affection. Jesus would still be able to describe him to the other disciples as 'our friend Lazarus' (John 11:11).

A chronology of Jesus' life was also needed. Although various theories exist for the length of Jesus' ministry and for the year he died, all that is completely certain is that: (a) John the Baptist started his ministry 'in the fifteenth year of the reign of Tiberius Caesar' (Luke 3:1), i.e. sometime in either AD 28 or AD 29; (b) Jesus was about thirty years old when he began his ministry (Luke 3:23), although this allows for a few years' leeway on either side; (c) Jesus must have been born sometime before the death of Herod the Great in 4 BC. A dating that places the death of Jesus in AD 33 has, for various good reasons, been chosen. The years (in our modern form of dating) have been placed at the beginning of each chapter for the convenience of the reader alone. (Any distances are also given in miles for the same reason.)

The research and background reading that preceded

the writing of this novel have, hopefully, enabled a reasonable degree of accuracy in the portrayal of historical details and first-century life.

Finally, there *is* only one place where the true details of Martha and her siblings are recorded – and that is in the gospels. All other descriptions of their lives in this book are a work of imagination.

Map of Jerusalem

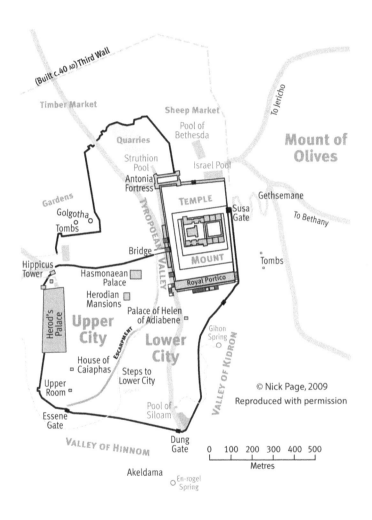

(Built c. 40 AD) Third Wall

Timber Market

Sheep Market

Quarries

Pool of Bethesda

Struthion Pool

Israel Pool

Antonia Fortress

Gardens

TEMPLE

Mount of Olives

Golgotha
Tombs

Susa Gate

Gethsemane

To Jericho

To Bethany

Bridge

MOUNT

Tombs

Hippicus Tower

Hasmonaean Palace

Herodian Mansions

Palace of Helen of Adiabene

Royal Portico

Herod's Palace

Upper City

Lower City

Gihon Spring

House of Caiaphas

Steps to Lower City

VALLEY OF KIDRON

© Nick Page, 2009
Reproduced with permission

Upper Room

Essene Gate

Pool of Siloam

VALLEY OF HINNOM

Dung Gate

0   100 200 300 400 500

Metres

Akeldama

En-rogel Spring

TYROPOEAN VALLEY

ESCARPMENT

The Temple

See picture opposite.

1. The Susa Gate
2. The Royal Stoa (also known as the Royal Portico)
3. The Court of the Gentiles
4. The Court of the Women
5. The Nicanor Gate
6. The Court of Israel/The Court of the Priests
7. The Sanctuary
8. The Antonia Fortress

(There are also family trees for Martha and other main characters at the back of the book)

Prologue

The day our world changed

'See, I am doing a new thing!' (Isaiah 43:19)

Spring AD 30

'Martha!' My name was yelled rather than spoken. 'You must come! There's something you've got to see.'

Lazarus stood outlined in the doorway, sunlight streaming in around him. Mary's head appeared almost immediately at my brother's side. On their faces was the same look of almost wild excitement. Both were breathing heavily, presumably from the exertion of having run back from wherever they'd been.

I brushed an arm lightly dusted with flour across my forehead, to move the hair out of my eyes where it had fallen as I'd pounded the large batch of dough on the table. 'Can't it wait?'

'No!' exclaimed Lazarus, his eyes shining in a way that I hadn't seen for a long time – probably since before our father died. But interrupting the task of baking bread for the family still needed a good reason.

'What is it?'

'You'll see.' My sister's enigmatic response was followed by a knowing look between her and Lazarus.

Any choice I had in the matter vanished as they both grabbed my arms, clearly intent on dragging me (should I refuse their summons) to wherever they wanted to take me.

Lazarus began to pull me. 'Come on.'

'If you'd let go of me so I can wash my hands and make myself respectable, it would help.'

I hastily removed the worst of the dough and flour and then snatched the pale blue embroidered head-covering that I wore outside. But even that short delay seemed almost too much for my brother to bear. '*Martha* – come *on!*'

Despite their best intentions to keep their secret until I could see it with my own eyes, Lazarus wasn't entirely successful in containing himself. He was finding it hard enough not to break into a run as we hurried along the dusty street, towards the small square which marked the centre of Bethany. The shower of rain that had earlier forced me inside had long since disappeared, and there was now no trace of any moisture on the dirt road. But the weather's variability was instantly forgotten when my brother suddenly blurted out, 'It's Simon!'

Mary shot him an exasperated glance to silently chide him for his inability to keep quiet – at the age of thirteen he wasn't a child any longer. I looked at him with a certain amount of confusion. 'Simon son of Judah?'

Lazarus rolled his eyes as if I had missed the blindingly obvious, despite there being more than one man with that name in our village. 'No, Simon the Leper,' he replied.

'What about him?'

'You'll see.'

I contented myself with muttering under my breath, 'He wasn't always called that, you know.'

But Lazarus just ignored the superior knowledge that came from my greater years, and gave me a strange little grin. 'Come on.'

It had always seemed so cruel to me that Simon the Silversmith (as I had known him in my earliest years) should come to be defined by his hideous illness. It had struck him down three months before my ninth birthday, when Mary was barely two and my brother not yet born. *Simon the Leper. What a name for the man I had grown up treating like an uncle!* He and my father, Heli, had been great friends, but the dreaded skin disease that he contracted drove him from the heart of our community and onto its edges. To my brother and sister, he was never more than a man to be avoided and kept at a distance.

As we neared the square, I saw a large gathering of people, all in animated, excited conversation. We quickly reached the edge of the crowd, and I craned my neck, trying to get a better view of what others were seeing. My brother was about to start worming his way through the tight mass of people, but then the crowd began to part to allow someone through. As the familiar figures of friends and neighbours moved aside, I finally caught sight of the person at the heart of the commotion. And I gasped.

There before me was Simon – the man I had known all my life, the man whose family home was three houses away from ours, the man who had suffered from leprosy since my childhood. Except that now he was different. His skin looked like that of a child: clear, unblemished, and completely devoid of the ugly ravages of the dreaded disease.

And by my side, my brother quietly breathed out the words which our hearts and our eyes knew to be true: 'It's a miracle.'

Chapter 1

The Rock from which I was hewn

'Look to the rock from which you were cut and to the quarry from which you were hewn; look to Abraham, your father, and to Sarah, who gave you birth.' (Isaiah 51:1–2)

AD 6-AD 12

If good fortune were measured only in silver Roman denarii, then we were fortunate indeed compared to most in our village. And at least in my early years, our family did seem blessed in all ways. Blessed as a family as we were blessed as a nation: God's people living under God's favour. It was only as the years passed and my age increased that I learned the significance of the soldiers who marched through our land of Judea, and, with it, a troubling truth. Despite being the apple of God's eye, we were also the vassal of Rome's power. The years also taught me that, from another perspective, it could appear the Hand of Providence was against our family. And yet I grew up happily enough, at least in those earliest years.

I was the eldest, the firstborn. My father Heli (like all Jewish men) would, of course, have liked a son as his firstborn. But if there were any genuine disappointment

– however small – on his part, then I was never aware of it as I grew up. I only knew my father as the one whose loving generosity and habitual laughter brought sunshine into my young life day after day.

We lived comfortably in a house that was considerably larger than many others in Bethany. Not that life under Roman occupation was easy. I was born in the thirty-third year of the reign of Caesar Augustus, a time when Roman rule weighed heavily upon most Jews living in Judea. The emperor's substantial taxes and our lack of power to determine our own fate seemed to fly in the face of our destiny as the people of God. And yet it was not the first time in our history that foreign powers had played an unwitting role in the unfolding plans of the Almighty. Egypt, Assyria, Babylon and Persia had all been there in the telling of our nation's story, and now Rome was added to that list.

My childhood, however, was mostly lived in blissful ignorance of these harsh realities. My only real awareness of our plight in those early years was the sight of the Roman soldiers passing through our village, usually on their way to or from the Antonia Fortress, situated less than two miles away in the city of Jerusalem.

Jerusalem. The spring day on which I went there with my father and mother is my earliest childhood memory. I know that they had often taken me to the city before, but that particular day – half way through my fifth year – left a fragment in my mind that is still there, even now, many years on. The sun was shining as I sat high upon my father's shoulders as we went over the brow of the Mount of Olives.

'Look, Martha – can you see the temple?'

I followed the direction of my father's pointing,

across the tops of the olive trees which lay like a dark green rug over the downward sloping hill, and nodded solemnly, 'Yes, Abba.' Although in truth I wasn't entirely sure what I was supposed to be looking for. I had been inside the temple with my parents on many occasions, but had never quite made the link in my child's mind with what could be seen of it from a distance. Young as I was, it wasn't difficult to conclude, however, that the huge structure that dominated Jerusalem and its skyline was the building to which my father was referring. The vast walls of the Temple Mount resembled huge, sheer cliffs, rising from the bottom of the Kidron Valley which ran along the length of the city. And there laid out before me was the huge temple complex, at the centre of which was the Sanctuary itself.

The tall, elegant building, which lay at the heart of not only the temple but also our faith, rose high and proud in the middle of the rectangular open space of the temple courts. Its white marble and gold decoration were shining almost as brightly as the morning sun, already beating down on my back. My mother smiled up at me and I beamed back, feeling very important at being able to recognise what I came to know later as the pride and joy of Jerusalem. Whatever else happened on that distant day is lost in my memory. But that vision of the temple, rising resplendent in the sunshine above the rest of the city, is still etched on my mind.

I was taught from my earliest days that we were special, that God had chosen the Jews to be His own. He had blessed us and given us the land in which we lived. It was the fulfilment of His gracious promises to my distant father Abraham, who had walked the land two thousand years before my chubby little legs took their first uncertain steps. Being God's chosen people was woven into the rich fabric of our daily lives, from the food that we ate to the prayers that we prayed. Our days, weeks and seasons were all ordered by the rhythms of our deeply held faith – our rituals, our worship, our festivals. And inextricably linked with that faith was my family.

My father and mother – Heli and Susannah – had been married for almost ten years before I arrived. Some twenty-five years earlier, shortly after my mother was born, her parents had moved down from Galilee in the north, as had many other families. And they'd settled in Bethany, only a mile and a half from Jerusalem. The reason for the move was simple. Herod the Great (though many would question that later title, given his brutality) was beginning his ambitious transformation of the temple – and my mother's family were stonemasons. It was said that Herod may have trained as many as a thousand priests to rebuild the Sanctuary itself. But for others like my grandfather Eleazar, there was still plenty of work to be done on the outer courts. Not to mention Herod's other building projects elsewhere in Jerusalem. And so it was that Eleazar and his wife, Rebekah, made their home in the village where I would be born and raised, bringing with them their three sons and baby daughter. Their eldest – my aunt Tabitha – remained in Galilee where she had recently, at the age of fifteen, been married.

My father's family, however, had for several generations been living in Jerusalem, where my other grandfather, Saul, was a perfumer. It was a profession of which he was rightly proud, being able to trace its roots back to our birth as a nation. Then, his forebears had crafted the fine anointing oils and incense commanded by God Himself for His people's worship. My father and his two brothers had all followed in their father's footsteps. Whilst my uncle Matthan decided to ply his trade in Jericho, some twelve miles to the north-east, my uncle Jacob and my father worked together, running the family business in Jerusalem. Their workshop was always busy, providing the raw materials for the sacred oil and incense used at the temple in whose shadow they worked, and perfumes, fragrant oils and other potions for the more wealthy in the prosperous city. Although my grandparents lived in the Upper City in Jerusalem, my father had decided not to stay there when it came time for him to be married.

My two grandfathers had met in Jerusalem and become friends. When a wife was needed for my father, it seemed natural to both men that Eleazar's youngest daughter, Susannah, would make a good match. But rather than settle in the busy and overcrowded city, my father had chosen to set up his home in Bethany, near his new wife's family, boosting the population of the growing village further. It was close enough to Jerusalem that he could walk there in not much more than half an hour. He always claimed, however, that the cleaner air of our village was *better for the delicate nose of a perfumer* – the words spoken with a twinkle in his dark eyes.

And so after my birth, and almost as soon as I could understand the words, I began learning the genealogy of our family. I was Martha, daughter of Heli, son of Saul, son of Jacob, son of Matthan, son of Simeon, son of

Eleazar – and as many as I could remember before my father had to correct me. He would then continue to recite the list of names that went back eventually to Judah, the son of Jacob, the son of Isaac, the son of Abraham. We were the latest to stand in the long line of those descended from our father Abraham, to whom God had promised offspring so numerous that they would become a great nation. And on each new generation rested the solemn responsibility to live out the faith of our fathers, thereby honouring the Lord of history. And I learned that faith from my parents.

I could never remember a time when I didn't know God. He was there as the unseen rock on which my family was built – spoken of with reverence, prayed to with confidence, and trusted with a love and devotion I hoped I could one day emulate. Both my mother and father were deeply devout, and yet so different from many of the religious men in their robes or their prayer shawls who we encountered in the holy city. As a small child, their stern exteriors made me want to hold the hand of my father or mother more tightly. I would avert my gaze in case their piercing eyes discovered something deficient or unpleasing within me. My parents, however, surrounded me with a love that nurtured the deep conviction that, even when I had done wrong, I was still their treasured child.

It was in this setting of a deep faith lived out that one day, as I walked with my hand in that of my father, I asked him with the innocence of my young age, 'Abba – is God like you?'

Where others may have reacted with a strict rebuke,

my father knew that no disrespect of the Divine was intended. So he put back his head and roared with laughter. My face must have looked puzzled at this outburst, because when he had finished laughing he smiled down at me, shaking his head several times before he spoke. 'No, my sweet one, but I hope that I may be found to be at least a little *like Him.*' Then, as he did so often and so well, he quoted from the vast wealth of Scripture that was stored in his memory: '*The LORD is compassionate and gracious, slow to anger, abounding in love... For as high as the heavens are above the earth, so great is his love for those who fear him.* How, my dear Martha, can a small man on the Lord's vast earth be large enough to contain that measure of love? And how can a man as imperfect as your father be anything more than a tiny reflection of that love?' And with that, he scooped me up into his arms, so that I could wrap my legs around his back and my arms around his neck, as he continued his impromptu lesson in the Word of the Lord. '*As a father has compassion on his children, so the LORD has compassion on those who fear him; for he knows how we are formed, he remembers that we are dust.* You and I are but dust compared to Him – but we are dust that He treasures! Never forget that, Martha – never forget.'

'I won't, Abba – I promise.'

So the truths of our faith remained as constants, unshakable as the mountains, as they always had done throughout the turbulent history of our people. And our own times were no less turbulent. The year of my birth was not only a time of upheaval for my parents. It was also a time of great change for the land of Judea.

The name *Archelaus* never meant anything to me, but it was a name that brought fear to those old enough to understand the meaning of the word *tyrant*. He was a son of Herod in every sense. He and two of his brothers had been granted control by Rome of different areas of their father's kingdom upon his death. Antipas and Philip were given regions to the north and east, but Judea and the lands around it came under the rule of Archelaus. Had I been born a few years earlier, I might have heard the conversations between my father, uncle and grandfather, conducted in lowered voices after a shared meal. Concerns were voiced about the possibility of a revolt, and questions raised about the dire outcome of such an action. But the whispered conversations that must have been repeated across our land found a powerful voice in the wealthy. After Archelaus had been in control for ten years, Rome and Caesar Augustus himself were finally warned of his brutal ineptitude and its possible consequences, and the response was swift. Gaul, rather than Judea, became the place where that son of Herod lived out the rest of his life at the emperor's pleasure. And Rome took back direct control of our province and Coponius became the first Roman prefect to govern there.

But I would slowly learn, with my growing years, that not even our beautiful temple was free from the politics of power and self-interest. The year of my birth was also the time of a new high priest – the lofty office first held by Aaron, the brother of Moses. It was, however, also the most powerful position in the temple and in Jerusalem. A new dynasty was born even as I was drawing my first breaths – and the name *Annas* would become familiar to me. Five of his sons and a son-in-law would become high priest after him, keeping that role within their grasp for close on sixty years.

But neither my parents nor anyone who knew us would have guessed, then, a terrible truth. That, in the years to come, the death of the only son of Heli and Susannah of Bethany would be sought by that family of supposedly godly men.

Chapter 2

Our daily bread

'Give me neither poverty nor riches, but give me only my daily bread.' (Proverbs 30:8)

AD 13

'Martha, you can be Goliath.'

'But I don't want to be Goliath!'

Benjamin, the older brother of my closest friend, Abigail, stood looking at me with his hands on his hips. 'How can we tell the story of David without someone being the Philistine?'

The slight chill of the fading afternoon in the final days of February made me shiver slightly. I looked over towards James and had the inspiration for the perfect solution. James was the son of my father's good friend Simon the Silversmith, and was twice my age and almost twice my height. 'Why can't James be Goliath?'

'Because James is going to be King Saul,' replied Benjamin, 'and Saul has to be tall.'

I tried again, not liking the prospect of the inevitable stone being thrown at me in the course of acting out the famous victory of the shepherd boy, who went on to become Israel's greatest king. It seemed a ridiculous idea, anyway, for me as the youngest to play David's nine-foot-

14

high opponent, even if I was tall for my age. 'But I'm too little to be Goliath.'

Abigail, almost a year and a half older than me but still the same height, nodded enthusiastically in agreement, instinctively coming to my support. 'She's right, Benjamin!'

But her brother wasn't about to be swayed from his decision. 'There's a large stone over there – you can stand on it.'

The truth of the matter was, of course, that no-one wanted to play the enemy – the arrogant Philistine who defied the armies of the living God, but was felled by a single small stone from the sling of Israel's unlikely hero. I was the youngest, and therefore the one with the least say in apportioning the roles in our latest re-enactment of the story.

I decided to adopt a different, if futile, approach. 'Why can't I be David?'

Levi, who was two years my senior and standing at the edge of the small group, replied with derision, 'Because you're a *girl*!'

'But *Goliath* wasn't a girl,' reasoned Abigail. I smiled appreciatively at her for stating the obvious but seemingly overlooked fact. She followed it with a further proposal that emphasised our solidarity as girls but which would have been beyond my ability to suggest. 'Why don't we do the story of Esther – like we do at Purim?' She turned towards her brother and said rather pointedly to him, 'And you could be Haman.'

The festival of Purim always involved the re-telling of the wonderful story of Esther. I loved hearing about the Jewess who became a Persian queen. Through her beauty and her bravery she saved the people of God from almost certain annihilation at the hands of their enemy, Haman. It was, of course, perfectly well known to all of us that the climax of the story involved the hanging of Haman on the gallows that he himself had built for Esther's wise uncle, Mordecai.

I never got to hear Benjamin's response to his sister's slightly unkind suggestion – though no less kind in my six-and-a-half-year-old mind than his suggestion that I be Goliath.

'Martha!'

On hearing my mother's voice in the distance, I bade a hasty farewell, only hoping that Abigail wouldn't suffer in my place the fate that I'd seemed destined to endure. I ran past the almond trees that were heavy with blossom, and back to our family home.

My mother looked tired as she stood in the entrance to our courtyard, the ninth month of her pregnancy weighing heavily upon her. 'The Sabbath will soon be here, Martha. Could you help me finish the meal please?'

'Yes, Mama,' I said happily. What was being asked of me was no hardship and a welcome alternative to the inescapable doom of the Philistine champion.

If I had a favourite room in the house, then it was the one to which I was now being summoned – the kitchen. Our home had a central courtyard which was open to the air and paved – one of the benefits of having stonemasons in the family. Among other things (notably the chickens), it had a brick oven, an open fire and heavy mill-stones for grinding grain. The kitchen was a reasonably-sized room off the courtyard, and was certainly big enough for two people to work comfortably side by side. Its furniture was simple but sufficient: a large sturdy wooden table in the centre of the room, a smaller table by one of the walls, and two or three stools. The utensils and pots, however, were anything but scant. Some of the larger pots rested on the floor. Others stood in neat lines on thick wooden shelves mounted upon the walls, where the wide-necked cooking pots also hung by their handles from hooks.

I quickly learned the contents of each of the pottery jars on the shelves. My job was often to climb onto my small three-legged wooden stool to carefully retrieve whatever had been requested by my mother as she cooked.

'Could you reach down the lentils for me please, Martha?'

The lentils, chickpeas, beans and other dried peas were to be found on the bottom shelf in the larger containers, next to the bowl of eggs gathered from our chickens. The large, pungent bulbs of garlic could be found in the pot next to the small jar that contained salt and which stood at the end of the shelf. The small stool scraped across the floor as I positioned it near to the wall. I stood on it, and carefully took hold with both hands of the jar containing the small green-brown lentils which were often an addition to my mother's cooking. But my knowledge of the pots was certainly not confined to the bottom and most easily reached shelf.

The middle shelf was my favourite one. It had jars of juicy dates and cakes of pressed figs, smaller pots of walnuts, almonds and pistachio nuts – to be eaten raw or included in the spicy stews that my mother prepared. There was also the jar of pickled olives, and the bowls of fresh fruit that held whatever was in season – whether grapes, pomegranates, peaches or figs – although the larger melons were usually left on the smaller of the two tables. And then the sweetest of delights: the jar of honeycomb into which I would occasionally be allowed to dip a tiny clean spoon when my behaviour had merited a special reward.

I put the jar of lentils on the table by my mother, whose hands were by this time covered in a floury paste. She glanced up from the dough she was mixing. 'Take two measures, my love, and add them to the cooking pot please.' I duly obeyed, scattering the chickens in the courtyard as I scurried out to where the meat had already been stewing for some time over the open fire, and then hurried back again. 'And could you clean the mortar for me please, Martha?'

I learned from my mother that the Lord had blessed us, not only with meat, vegetables and fruit, but also with a wonderful array of herbs and spices. And so there was never any excuse (in her mind, and then mine) for serving food that was anything other than tasty and enjoyable. Mint and dill, coriander and rue, could usually be picked fresh from outside the house. But they – and other herbs – also hung dried on the walls. Seeds and spices were stored in small pots, next to the stone pestle and mortar on the top shelf (only reached, at least in my earlier years, by my mother's longer arms). On this occasion, she had already ground to a paste in the mortar a collection of fresh herbs with some cumin and mustard seeds, and added them to the cooking pot. The little stone bowl now lay empty near the edge of the table, and a quick sniff told me that mint and garlic would be flavouring our evening meal. As I washed it, I ran my fingers over the smooth stone, enjoying its silky feel. Unlike many others in our village, we could afford a number of the more expensive limestone bowls and dishes rather than the cheaper pottery ones. The advantage of stone was that if it became ritually unclean it could be washed and cleansed. The rules stated that pottery, being porous, could only be discarded and broken.

I looked up as my mother reached for the glazed jug that was never far away. She added to the dough a little more of the rich green liquid on which so many of our comforts depended. The Lord of creation had provided us with streams of water to quench our thirst, and vines with grapes for the wine that made our hearts glad. But equally importantly, he had also blessed our land with bountiful olive trees whose small, hard fruit were an unlikely treasure. From these flowed the oil that lit our homes and made our hair shine, that softened our work-hardened hands and our sun-weathered faces, and that both enriched and cooked so much of the food that we ate day by day.

'What next, Mama?' I asked as I dried my hands.

'The onions need their skins removing, please,' she replied, without glancing up from her task.

As well as being instructed how to recognise and use the bounty of our land, I also learned from my mother the practical knowledge of any kitchen. As I grew, I was constantly adding new skills to the ones I had already mastered: how to peel (and later slice) onions, how to prepare carrots and turnips, radishes and lettuce, squash and cucumber. I was taught the difference between those vegetables that could be eaten raw and those that needed to be cooked, and those which could be used in either way, depending on the dish. I learned, in time, how to stew or to boil or to roast the lamb or the goat that would often be part of our more special meals. I was shown how to divide up a chicken or a pigeon, and how to separate a fish, bought from the market in Jerusalem, from its bones. I watched and copied as my mother collected the milk from the goats that we owned and turned it into curds, to be eaten or further transformed into cheese. And as I was taught each skill and learned about every food, I was also educated in the weightier knowledge of which foods were allowed and which forbidden in the Law of Moses.

In the days after our people had left Egypt in the Exodus, they had wandered in the desert, being fed manna – the bread of heaven – by the hand of God. But the Lord had also given us the laws that would set us apart from other nations and which would bring us life. The Almighty had told us that man does not live on bread alone, but on every word that comes from His mouth.

'And yet,' as my father had once observed at a meal, 'the Lord has still blessed me with a wife who bakes the best bread in Bethany.'

My mother chided him playfully. 'Heli, son of Saul, are you telling me that you have tasted the bread made by *every* woman in this village?'

And as I giggled at their exchange, my father had winked at me and exclaimed, 'A man does not have to ride every horse to know which of them will win the race!' And he was right. My mother made her bread with the lightest of touches, and the wonderful smell of it baking would permeate our house each day before filling and delighting our hungry mouths. And I was fortunate that my mother graciously passed those skills on to me.

Bread was one of the first things that I learned how to

cook as I grew up. Although grain stood in large, round ended-jars that were propped up against the wall in the kitchen, we were fortunate to be sufficiently well-off that flour could be bought already milled. This meant we didn't have to rise even earlier each day, as so many wives and daughters did, to grind the wheat or barley that would be needed for baking that day's bread. Even so, my mother wisely decided that no daughter of Israel should grow up without the skill of knowing how to turn kernels of wheat into flour. And flour that was sufficiently fine for the bread that was so much a part of each and every meal. And so I was taught how to set the heavy upper millstone turning on its base. It required my mother's strength in the earlier years and my sister's help later. I was shown how to feed the grain into the hole at the centre of the millstone from where it would fall between the two stones and be ground into flour.

I learned how to mix the flour with water, olive oil and yeast as my mother was now doing, how to leave it to rise, and how to then make the round loaves that were cooked on the hot oven floor. I could also make the larger, flatter breads, baked on the outside of a metal dome heated over a fire. And I learned how to set aside a lump of freshly made dough with its yeast, so that it in turn would become the raising agent for the next batch to be made. And with every lesson learned, my longing grew to be able to cook as wonderfully as my mother.

As the afternoon lengthened on that particular day, my mother allowed me to knead a small amount of the dough alongside her. I worked the yeast through the mixture by pushing it out with the heel of my hands, folding it over and watching it spring back again and again. And

21

as the light began to fade, the yeast and the oven finally performed yet again the everyday miracle of turning dry flour and water into warm, soft bread.

The smell of freshly baked bread was all around us by the time we heard the first blast of the trumpet. I knew that Joseph, the scribe who was our synagogue attendant in Bethany, would be standing on the roof of the synagogue, trumpet in hand, to announce to our village the impending arrival of the Sabbath. The first blast was to let us know that the Sabbath was imminent, and to give us the opportunity to finish any last tasks that still required completion. My mother had just taken the bread out of the oven and laid it in a basket, covering it with a cloth to keep it warm, as the second trumpet sounded to announce that all work must cease. She turned to me. 'Martha, would you light the Sabbath lights for me?'

'Yes, Mama.' I suddenly felt very privileged to be entrusted with the task usually done by the mother of the household.

Earlier in the afternoon, after cleaning the house, my mother had re-filled each of the small clay lamps with olive oil and trimmed their twisted wicks. As my father joined the two of us in the living area, I took a small taper, and carefully moved around the room, lighting the lamps in the alcoves as my mother said the blessing. 'Blessed are You, O Lord our God, King of the Universe, who has sanctified us by His commands, and commanded us to kindle the Sabbath lights'. And as the last light of the day faded in the sky, the trumpet sounded for a third time, announcing to the whole of Bethany that the Sabbath had begun.

Our evening meals were special times, when our small family and any guests relaxed over shared food, and talked and told stories. It was not unusual for singing to accompany our gatherings, especially on the Sabbath.

Shortly after the last trumpet, we were joined by Simon and Rachel, both neighbours and good friends, and their son James, who had been destined to play King Saul in our earlier re-enactment. Though I never did ask him whether David ever found a worthy Goliath that day. James, being thirteen, was – despite still joining in our games at times – now considered an adult. He had clearly decided to behave as such that evening, listening intently to the conversation of our parents and joining in as often as he could.

Our two families often spent the Sabbath eve together, and we shared not only good food but also the events of the past week. Although the indignities or cruelties of life under Roman rule would occasionally creep into the conversation, they would not be dwelt on in the presence of children – or on God's holy day. Besides, Simon and my father could never stay serious for long. I loved hearing them laugh as they shared a joke or some observation on what they had seen in Jerusalem, where their workshops were almost side by side. And when they weren't talking – or laughing – their rich, deep voices would often blend together as they sang the songs of Israel, which their fathers and their fathers before them had also sung.

That evening, after my father had poured the wine (mixed with water as was our custom), he raised his voice and gave the blessing over the cup. 'Blessed are You, O Lord our God, King of the Universe, Creator of the fruit of the vine.' And then he began the evening meal as he always did, standing with his hands raised and his eyes lifted to heaven. 'Blessed are You, O Lord our God, King of the Universe, who brings forth bread from the earth.' And I sat snuggled close to my mother, with a hand resting on her swollen belly, trying to feel the movement of the baby that would soon be my brother or sister.

Rachel began serving the food, so that my mother could rest. 'You should have come to us this night, Susannah. Your baby is close.'

My mother smiled, 'Yes – a week now, maybe two,' and added with a laugh, 'but until the child comes I am perfectly capable of preparing a meal…with a little help maybe.'

My mother's hand caressed my head and the eyes of each person in the room were upon me. My heart warmed, knowing that I had a place in the world and in my family that was valued. My mother laid her other hand over my small one, still resting on her stomach, and I glanced up and caught her smile, unaware, however, of the pain that lay behind it. I was too young to remember the miscarriage that came two years after my birth, and oblivious to those in the first ten years of my mother and father's marriage, before my arrival. They also accounted for the fact that, although my parents were roughly the same age as our guests, Simon and Rachel had two older daughters who were both recently married.

Rachel continued, 'I do not doubt your capabilities, but why not join us tomorrow after synagogue anyway? There is always a place at our table for you.'

'That's kind, Rachel, but Judas and Salome have already invited us.'

I smiled happily at the thought of a meal and an

afternoon spent with Abigail and her parents, even if that did mean putting up with her brother, Benjamin, too.

But Rachel was not to be put off, and as she offered the basket of fresh bread to her husband, she continued, 'Then join us next Sabbath eve.'

My father interjected as he raised the cup of wine in his hand towards his lips, 'And what if my next child has already arrived by then?'

Simon dipped a piece of the bread in the spicy lamb and lentil stew, and laughed. 'If the child has arrived, then the whole village will be here to feed you!' And with that he smiled, popped the bread in his mouth and ate.

And at that moment, my hand felt a kick from the unborn child. I wondered how long I would have to wait for my first brother or sister – and what would happen if they were born on the Sabbath.

Chapter 3

The seventh day

*'For in six days the L*ORD *made the heavens and the earth…but he rested on the seventh day.*
*Therefore the L*ORD *blessed the Sabbath day and made it holy.' (Exodus 20:11)*

AD 13

Our leather sandals slapped against the wood of the stairs in the synagogue as my mother and I climbed slowly up to the gallery. 'Shalom, Susannah,' said a voice behind us. We both turned to see who had spoken the customary greeting, wishing us peace and well-being.

'Shalom, Miriam!'

Miriam, our local midwife, scrutinised my mother's belly, smiling. 'I'll be visiting you soon, I see.'

'The sooner the better,' laughed my mother, turning to continue her laborious ascent to the upper floor.

All of the faces around us were known and familiar to me, as was the pattern of the day. The Sabbath, which had begun at sunset the previous evening and which would continue until sunset that day, was our day of rest, ordained by the Almighty when He Himself ceased from His work of creation. Its pattern of worship and relaxation was the same as it had always been from the earliest days of our people. It was a time for celebration and joy, free from the work which accompanied most of the daylight hours of the other six days.

And yet despite all this, there was always a slight fear lurking in the back of my mind. It was a fear that I would unwittingly transgress the command to refrain from working on the Sabbath. There were myriad tasks – such as watering a plant or picking small bones from a fish – that we were told counted as work. But at least that fear receded whenever we were at synagogue. There, we were in perfect obedience to the will of the Almighty, hearing His Word and proclaiming His praises.

Our synagogue – easily the largest building in Bethany – was, as always, packed that Sabbath. My father was an elder, even though he was not yet forty, but his education, profession and wealth made him respected among the citizens of Bethany. Being from a more prosperous family, my father had been able to stay in education at one of Jerusalem's synagogues longer than many of his peers. He was blessed with both aptitude and freedom from having to work the land for the family as many did from an early age. So he had been able to study the Scriptures for longer, as had Simon, who was also an elder and for similar reasons.

My mother and I joined the other women and girls in the gallery, together with the boys twelve and under. Her condition meant that space was made for the two of us on one of the front benches set out there, giving me an unobstructed view. Down below, my father and the other elders went forward to join Jonathan, who worked as a physician and had been chosen from among them to be the ruler of the synagogue. Together they began to sit down facing the gathering in ornately carved chairs – the so-called *Seats of Moses*. Behind them was the ark, the cabinet set into the wall of the synagogue nearest Jerusalem, which contained the scrolls of hallowed Scripture. In front of them was the wooden platform from which those Scriptures would be read. The rest of the men, together with the boys over twelve, were always seated on the benches on the ground floor. These stood, similar to most synagogues, between and to either side of the two rows of pillars which ran from front to back in the long room.

My mother leaned across me and whispered to Jonathan's wife, Naomi, 'Have we a visitor speaking to us today?'

'Yes,' she replied. 'Jonathan's cousin from Galilee is with us – he's a scribe and the ruler of the synagogue at Japhia.' I recognised the name of the large village where my aunt Tabitha lived, and craned my neck to see if I could spot our guest speaker. *Ah! The tall man to the right of the platform.* He was standing in conversation with Joseph, our synagogue attendant who had sounded the trumpet the previous evening. Joseph was also a scribe and the two of them, in their long scholar's robes, looked from head to toe the men of learning I knew them to be.

To be a scribe you had to be clever – of that I was sure. They knew how to read and write, and they were the ones who often kept records or wrote official documents for our leaders. Others sold their services in the markets, reading or writing letters for the not-so-able. But they were also experts in the Law. I had once asked my father what that meant, and he had tried to explain as best he could. 'We have God's unchanging Law to tell us what is right and wrong, Martha. But the experts in the Law are those who can tell us exactly what God's Word means and how we are to understand it in our daily lives.' I must have looked bemused because my father continued with an example. 'God's Law tells us, for instance, that we must not work on the Sabbath, but what is work and what is not?' My brow furrowed as I applied my young mind to that problem. But before I made any progress on the perplexing issue, my father continued: 'That is the sort of question to which the scribes give the answer.'

'And what is the answer, Abba?'

My father had laughed. 'It is a very long one, Martha! But it helps us to be sure that we're in no danger of breaking God's Law and that we're keeping the Sabbath holy as the Lord requires.'

My brow remained furrowed however. 'But how do *they* know the answer, Abba?'

My father swept me up into his arms and sat me on his knee. 'They talk and they question and they debate, and then they decide between themselves what is right and what is wrong – although even then they don't always agree. But it is the job of the scribe to remember all that the different rabbis say…'

'So that they can tell us?'

My father had laughed again, 'Yes, Martha, so that they can tell us, and so that we can walk righteously in all the ways of the Lord.'

The two scribes were still deep in conversation. I was glad that it was not Joseph giving the talk. I could rarely understand what he said. Often whilst he was addressing the congregation, I would try to amuse myself in other ways. I'd count the pillars in the synagogue – there were ten, although others supported the gallery beneath where we sat. Or sometimes I would see how many little bells I could spot sewn onto the embroidered curtains of the ark. Or try to guess in advance which scroll of the Law or the Prophets would be read from (although my knowledge of the latter was still shaky). I was not sure if this visitor would be any better, but at least it wasn't Joseph.

The chatter began to fade away as Joseph had stepped up onto the platform, and the congregation prepared itself for the start of the service. Our visiting scribe sat down on one of the chairs that were usually reserved for the more honoured members of the congregation.

Although it was Jonathan's responsibility to organise our services, it was the synagogue attendant who conducted them. 'Shalom, friends,' began Joseph. 'We are honoured today to have with us Jacob son of Simeon, from the synagogue in Japhia. He will be teaching us from God's Law. But first Simon will lead us in our prayers.'

Our neighbour rose and went up to the reading desk on the platform. He began the introduction to the prayers in perfect Hebrew, using the words with which every Sabbath service commenced: *With great love have you loved us, O Lord our God, and great and overflowing tenderness have you shown us.* Although my Hebrew was not as good as the Aramaic I spoke every day, I had been hearing the ancient language every Sabbath for as long as I could remember. I knew that Simon would go on to thank God for giving Israel His teaching, and would ask the Lord to enable us to understand, teach and perform all of His Law. He then recited the prayer that was etched on to all of our hearts: *Hear, O Israel: The LORD our God, the LORD, is one. Love the*

LORD *your God with all your heart and with all your soul and with all your strength.*

I glanced around the synagogue, proud to be part of the gathering, and grateful that I was a daughter of Abraham and one of the people to whom God had revealed Himself. Simon's voice rose strong and clear again, as he concluded with a blessing in his lilting Hebrew: *True and firm is your word to us for ever and ever...*

The opening prayers finished, Simon then led us all in the benedictions which we recited together. Although the prayer was again in Hebrew, I was beginning to be able to remember it. I spoke every word as best I could, even if in the middle of the prayer some of my words were lagging just slightly behind. Other words of which I was unsure were mouthed without sound. I loved, however, the opening words. They gave me a sense of history and of connection with my ancestors from centuries before: *Blessed are You, O Lord our God, and the God of our fathers, the God of Abraham, the God of Isaac, and the God of Jacob.* I looked around again with joy as together we declared, following our fathers before us, the great truths we believed about our God. *The great, the mighty and the terrible God, the most high God, Who shows mercy and kindness, Who creates all things, Who remembers the pious deeds of the patriarchs, and will bring a redeemer to their children's children for Your Name's sake.* And not for the first time, I wondered who this promised redeemer would be.

We sat once again, and my heart swelled with pride as my father rose to read from the Law, a scroll of which was handed to him by Joseph. The words were again in Hebrew, but this time Joseph stood near the desk. Every couple of verses, he translated the ancient words into

Aramaic, so we could all understand the sacred writings. The reading finished, my father handed the scroll back to Joseph. Simon then returned to the desk to read from the prophets, receiving a different scroll from the ark. There was then an air of expectation as our guest was invited up onto the platform to address us all.

If I'd hoped for better than Joseph, I was to be disappointed, however. Although Jacob son of Simeon spoke in Aramaic, the words of the scribe were no more intelligible to me than the more obscure Hebrew in the prayers. As far as I could tell he was speaking about oaths made to God, and was saying something about the altar in the temple and about Jerusalem. As usual the names of various rabbis were mentioned. So I went back to counting the pillars of the synagogue. There were still ten.

I was grateful when the time came to stand for the words of the closing benediction, and judging by the weary look on my mother's face, I wasn't the only one. A general hubbub of lively conversation broke out across the large building as the service ended, and my mother began chatting to Naomi and to Esther, the wife of Matthias, a priest living in Bethany. The synagogue was not just a place of worship – it was a gathering place of friends. It was where the community shared its joys and its sorrows, its news and its stories. I could see my aunt Elizabeth a little way off – she was married to my mother's brother John. They were our closest relatives left in Bethany, her other two brothers having returned to Galilee with their families.

'Martha!' I looked around, and saw Abigail waving madly at me from a corner of the gallery. 'Over here!'

'Come on, Tamar,' I said to Esther's daughter, also in her seventh year, and we began weaving a path between tunic hems and sandalled feet.

'Did you hear what Benjamin did yesterday?' began Abigail mischievously as we reached her. Soon the three of us were sitting on the wooden floor, chattering away happily, telling stories and laughing together.

But eventually I heard my mother's voice beckoning us. 'Martha, Abigail – we're leaving now.' After saying our farewells, we clattered down the stairs to the ground floor, Abigail and I still chattering, and began to make our way to the house of our friends.

At least three men in Bethany were called *Judas*. The name was a common one, although I would – much later – meet another man of that name who would give it a new, darker association. But it was *Judas the Potter* (as Abigail's father was known) whom I viewed as almost another member of the family. His profession as a potter was an honourable but humbler one, a fact that was reflected in their house. It had fewer and smaller rooms than our own, but any inadequacy in size was more than made up for by our hosts. Judas, with his ready wit and seemingly never-ending wealth of stories, reminded me of my grandfather Saul. But he more than met his match in his wife, Salome. Between the two of them, there was barely a pause for breath.

That afternoon, as we sampled Salome's cooking (all prepared before the Sabbath), my mother was content to spend much of the time resting her tired head against the wall behind her, listening with her eyes closed to the conversation around her. As was often the case, that morning's address was one of the topics of discussion.

'I didn't understand what he was saying. It sounded so confusing,' said Abigail. I agreed whole-heartedly, but not out loud.

Benjamin was eager, however, to reveal his superior knowledge as not only a boy, but also one who had almost reached the exalted age of eleven. He had obviously been paying attention that morning when I had not, and was keen to share his newly acquired understanding. 'Whether you are bound by an oath,' he began, 'depends on what you swear by. It makes a difference whether you swear by the altar or by the gift on the altar, or whether you swear by Jerusalem or by the temple.'

'Why can't people just say what they mean?' protested Abigail, and I was once again grateful to her for voicing my unspoken question.

'Girls aren't expected to be able to understand these things…'

'Benjamin! Don't be unkind to your sister,' chided Salome, although her swift rebuke didn't entirely remove the patronising look from his face. She then, however, put herself firmly on the side of her daughter. 'It sounded to me very much like a way of getting out of a promise you don't want to keep.'

My mother's eyes remained closed as she added, 'Sometimes I wonder if we've made God's truths too complicated.' Judas raised an eyebrow and gave a little smile and nod, agreeing with her contribution to the lively debate.

My father rubbed his beard thoughtfully, and then added rather jokingly, 'Judas – it seems that the women among us might be the wise ones today.'

'Ha!' exclaimed Salome, with the look of someone

who feels they have a won a small victory. 'Don't ever think you men are the only ones who can speak sense or see what is right. Just think of Deborah – '

The mention of the prophetess who steered the Israelite army to a great victory immediately put me in mind of the events of the previous day, and I piped up, 'Or Esther!'

The finer points of oaths and of that morning's address were suddenly forgotten. The two women in the Scriptures about whom great tales were told were of far greater interest. It moved us on to what was often my favourite part of the Sabbath. Abigail eagerly said to her father, 'Tell us a story, Abba!'

There was no better storyteller in the whole of Bethany than Judas the Potter. He may not have had the same formal education in the Scriptures as my father, but he carried the stories of God's Word around in his heart, and when he told them, they came alive. I often wondered what it would be like if someone like Judas gave the talk in the synagogue rather than men like Jacob son of Simeon or Joseph. It was only years later that I discovered the answer to that particular musing.

Judas told the stories of our ancestors with passion and zeal. We would sit listening to him, wide-eyed, as he told us of Noah or Joseph, of Moses or Joshua, of Gideon or David, often with sounds and actions, not only from him, but also from Salome. But he also recounted tales from our history that were not part of Scripture. Like the heroic exploits of his namesake, Judas Maccabees, who had, some one hundred and seventy years earlier, triumphed against the foreign ruler who had desecrated our temple.

It was these stories that so often fuelled our imaginations and our games as we played together as children, reliving for ourselves the stories of our heroes from of old. And foremost for me among those heroes was David. Despite the experiences of the previous day, I loved the young man who had, a thousand years earlier, stood fearlessly against the terrible giant who had threatened to take his life. A shepherd boy with nothing more than a sling and five smooth stones to fight the towering opponent armed with sword and spear. I loved the fact that this youngster, who had been written off by his brothers, had defied all expectations to become the mighty conqueror. And I loved the way in which God had protected his chosen king, despite all the enemies who came against him, so that eventually he became the greatest king that Israel – *no, the whole world!* – had ever known.

And for me, the stories of David began to be woven together with one of my father's favourite phrases: *When the Messiah comes…* It was his answer to all the world's ills and to all of Rome's crimes. I began to understand from my father and men like him that God had promised another king, a descendant of David, who would rise with a greatness that the world had never before seen. He would not only deliver God's people from their enemies but also establish, for ever, His kingdom on earth. And I, like my father, began to long for the coming of this Son of David who would change everything.

The shadows began to lengthen as the sun dropped lower in the sky. The time was approaching when Judas would say the blessing that closed the Sabbath. He would thank

God for the distinction He had made between the holy and the profane, between light and darkness, between Israel and the heathen nations, and between the seventh day and the rest of the week. Another conversation occurred first, however, as talk of the Messiah had stirred a memory deep within my father, and he suddenly became pensive. He turned to Judas. 'Do you remember that story Matthias told of one of the other priests at the temple?'

A look of innocent amusement crept across Judas's face. 'A story told by Matthias the priest about another priest at the temple? You will have to narrow it down, Heli, my sweet-smelling friend.'

My father ignored the reference that Judas often made to his profession, and continued. 'It concerned one of the priests in the division that was serving at the temple the week before him – ' My father paused to think. ' – it must have been, what, sixteen or seventeen years ago? I remember because Susannah and I had only recently wed and moved to Bethany, and it was one of the first tales he ever told me.'

'You're still not narrowing it down much...'

'Be patient, Judas, and you will hear. He told me a priest had a vision in the temple – ' My ears pricked up, suddenly excited by the idea that the God of history may have not finished telling His story.

Salome interjected: 'I remember! It was while the priest was burning incense in the Sanctuary. Matthias said that he was struck dumb after seeing an angel.'

My father continued, 'Yes, but not before the angel had apparently told him that his wife would bear him a child – a son.'

My excitement, if anything, grew even greater. My

mother, however, with her eyes still closed and both her hands clasped over her sizeable belly, added with a smile, 'A woman having a baby? There's nothing unusual there – well, apart from the appearance of an angel.'

'Ah, but there was,' continued Salome. 'If I remember rightly he was getting on in years, as was his wife, and she was barren.'

'Precisely,' said my father.

I felt at last that I had something to contribute to a story that had me sitting up expectantly in my cross-legged position on the floor. 'Like Abraham and Sarah?'

'Yes, Martha,' replied my father. 'He was also told that the child would be great in God's plans.'

'And?' asked Benjamin, as eager as I was to know how the tale continued.

'A son was born and the priest spoke again – that's all Matthias said.'

Judas let out a deep breath. 'Did you ever find out what happened next?'

My father shook his head. 'No. I don't even know what the priest's name was. But it can only have been a year or two later when we had that strange business with the Magi.'

Salome nodded. 'A group from the East turning up in Jerusalem and asking Herod about the birth of a new king was always going to cause an uproar – '

'An uproar and an evil,' said my mother quietly, a look of deep sorrow passing briefly across her face. Neither she nor any of the other adults would elaborate, however, as to the nature of the evil to which she alluded. I would later learn of the edict of Herod that resulted in a massacre of children in the nearby town of Bethlehem, the recollection of which had troubled each of the adults that day. All I knew, however, was that it ended any further discussion of those strange events that afternoon. I was, however, left wondering about the dumb priest and his mysterious son. But any questions about the one born after the angelic visitor were soon forgotten in the pain and the joy of another birth.

Chapter 4

Moulded by the Craftsman

'We are the clay, you are the potter; we are all the work of your hand.' (Isaiah 64:8)

AD 13

Rachel's kind offer of hospitality the following Sabbath was never taken up, for that was the day my sister decided to enter this world, after nine months of safety within our mother's womb. In the middle of the afternoon before the sunset that heralded the Sabbath, the first signs of labour came upon my mother. James – Simon and Rachel's son – was sent to run into Jerusalem to pass on the news to my father. And before the first of the Sabbath trumpets sounded, he had returned, bringing with him my only remaining grandmother: Anna, Saul's wife. Miriam, the midwife, and my aunt Elizabeth had both been called, and the two women attended my mother throughout the travail of birth.

That evening, I prayed as I had never prayed before, that the Lord would save my mother, for to my ears it sounded at times as if she was surely dying. And, although I was young, I knew enough of my world to know that mothers sometimes died in childbirth.

After the supper that had been hurriedly prepared by

my grandmother, my father sat in the corner of our living area or paced around, often leaving the room to stand by himself in the courtyard in the cool night air. My place of solace and comfort, however, was in the embrace of my elderly grandmother. Her wizened arms were wrapped around my body as I sat curled up on her lap. Sometimes when I looked up into her old and kindly face, I would catch her lips moving, although I could not make out the words.

Another cry of pain from my mother in the room nearby must have brought a look of fear to my face, because my grandmother began to gently stroke my head. She said with a smile, 'Do not fear, Martha. It has been this way ever since the time of Eve, when the Lord Himself spoke of the pain of every childbirth. Eve's first child was born in pain, and it was the same when your mother bore you.' She put a finger underneath my chin to turn my face slightly towards hers, and she smiled reassuringly. 'But we will pray together to the Lord, and he will hear us.' I closed my eyes, and rested my head against her breast again, feeling the comforting beat of her heart and hearing the comforting words that flowed from her lips. 'God of Abraham, Isaac and Jacob – you are also the God of Sarah, and of Rebekah, and of Rachel. Protect and strengthen your servant Susannah, your daughter of Abraham, as she labours to bring forth the life you have ordained to fill this earth. Bring safely into this world the child you have formed within her womb, and may the pain of birth be soon overtaken by the joy of new life.'

I never knew whether this was a prayer that was always prayed by the women of Israel as birth approached, or whether it was one of the prayers that seemed to flow effortlessly from my grandmother's deep faith. Either way, her gentle words and comforting prayer loosened the suffocating grip of dread on my heart. It also gave me the courage to voice another lurking fear. I glanced up again. 'Nana, God has told us not to work on the Sabbath, hasn't He?'

'Yes, my child.'

'But Miriam and Mama – they are working, aren't they? Is that a sin?'

My grandmother smiled as if my question had amused her. 'Such deep thinking for one so little! You need not worry, Martha. The labour of a mother and the help of a midwife are never seen as breaking the Sabbath. If it were not so, then you can be sure that the Lord would never ordain a child to be born on that day. For it is He that calls us forth from the womb – neither the child nor the mother chooses the day of the birth.'

I doubted neither the wisdom nor the truth of her words, and laid my head back down on her chest once more, my troubled thoughts replaced by a sense of peace. My mother had, as usual, filled and trimmed the little oil lamps in the alcoves of the walls earlier on, and the shadows from the Sabbath lights danced upon the walls as the lamps burned ever lower. The lateness of the hour, and the comfort of snuggling down into my grandmother's arms, allowed sleep to draw me into its peaceful oblivion. I woke some hours later, when the lamps had gone out but the light of a new day had just begun to creep in through the window. The air was pierced by a different cry to the one that had filled my ears as I had drifted off.

My grandmother was smiling broadly. 'Would you like to meet your new sister, Martha?'

I yawned, climbing clumsily off her lap and onto my feet, and we walked hand in hand into my parent's bed-chamber. My father was already sitting on the bed with my mother's hand in his. Her other hand cradled a little bundle against her breast, a weary but happy smile upon her face. I clambered up onto the bed beside her, and gazed for the first time upon the face of my sister. 'What's her name?'

Unlike boys, girls were named at birth, and I could hear the joy in my father's voice as he uttered the words, 'Mary – her name is Mary.'

'That's like mine!'

'Yes, Martha,' said my mother softly, 'and she looks like you did when you were born.'

The little wrinkled face was screwed up as another cry came from the lungs that had so recently drawn their first breath – and I tried to imagine having once been as small as her. I had wanted to have a brother, so that I could be like my best friend, Abigail. But then I thought of Benjamin and of James and Levi, and was suddenly glad that I had a sister.

The prediction that Rachel had made the previous week turned out to be correct. We had no need to be concerned about food that Sabbath – or for several days after. The women of Bethany who knew us well arrived day after day, their earthenware pots containing a variety of dishes: spicy chickpeas cooked with carrots and turnips, a fish stew with onions and garlic, roasted pigeon with chopped radishes, lettuce and cucumber. And with every meal, freshly baked bread.

As the days went by, our house began to resemble a Sabbath-day synagogue. My aunt Elizabeth came almost daily, often accompanied by my cousins Matthan, Eliakim and Seth. And in addition to the familiar faces of Bethany I knew so well, we had visitors from Jerusalem: my uncle Jacob and his family, and my grandfather, Saul, with his mischievous smile and frequent laughter.

I began to learn the skills that any mother should know. 'Why don't you help me with the swaddling cloth, Martha?' my mother asked as I watched her tending to my sister.

'What should I do?'

'I'll hold Mary. See if you can undo the cloth.' I began rather awkwardly to unwind part of the long strip of linen that was wrapped round and round her, from her middle to her feet. After she was unbound, my mother then held up the soiled square of cloth that the swaddling cloth held in place. I wrinkled my nose at the unpleasant smell. 'Would you like to wash it for me?' she asked with a twinkle in her eye.

'No!' I shrieked, and then giggled.

My mother laughed, 'I thought not.' She then washed my sister, and used olive oil to clean her, dusting her with powdered, dried myrtle leaves, before binding her up again with the swaddling cloth.

The novelty of caring for my new-born sister soon wore off, however, and I was glad when Salome arrived one day with Abigail. The two of us soon tired of the adult conversation, and Salome must have seen it in our eyes. 'Abigail – why don't you take Martha to your father's workshop? I'm sure he would love to have your company there.'

'I'll race you!' said Abigail as we both jumped to our feet.

Seconds later, the two of us were running madly – and happily – along the streets of Bethany to the potter's house, impatient to be in one of the places we loved the most. And eager to discover who could run the fastest. On this occasion, my longer legs triumphed over Abigail's greater age – but only just. We found Judas working outside on the wheel in front of his workshop – always preferable to him when the weather allowed. But before he was aware of our presence, I thought for a moment that he looked sad and weary. I was too young to understand that the burden of Roman taxation (and the anxiety that went with it) could often rob our less well-off neighbours of sleep at night. However, the look on Judas's face was gone by the time he glanced up at the sound of our breathless approach.

The potter's wheel – and the clay on it – were brought to a swift halt. 'Ah! The two prettiest girls in the whole of Bethany! How am I ever going to be able to concentrate on my work now?' I giggled as Judas winked at me, whilst Abigail ran over to the little hut where her father kept his potter's supplies and equipment, and found two small stools just inside the door. We both seated ourselves as close to the wheel as we dared as Judas started it spinning again. We didn't want to be splashed by any watery clay that might happen to fly off in our direction as he deftly turned the small round table in front of him.

Although Judas owned a wheel that he could turn slowly using his hand, that day he was using the faster one that fascinated us. The wooden table on which the soft clay sat was connected to a larger, flat wheel in a hollow dug into the ground. Judas, sitting on a small bench above the hollow, could kick the wheel, so that it spun at ever greater speeds as his foot propelled it again and again, spinning in turn the upper table with the clay. Despite his implication that our presence would be a distraction, a large clay pot rose perfectly symmetrical out of the lump of clay as he turned it with the precision of a skilled craftsman.

'And how is your new sister, Martha?' asked Judas, without taking his eyes off the pot.

'She cries a lot.'

Judas smiled, and quickly picked up a small wooden tool. 'You'd better get used to it,' he said, holding the tool against the inside of his handiwork, to smooth the inner surface of what appeared to be destined to become a large mixing bowl. Still concentrating on what his hands were doing, he suddenly asked, 'Have I ever told you, Martha, that God is a potter?' Abigail's expression told me that it was not the first time that she had heard her father make this surprising and intriguing observation.

I shook my head and answered, 'No,' my eyes wide with wonder as I waited eagerly for his explanation.

'The Lord, when he created Adam, took dust from the ground – just like we do with clay – and from it he formed a man and breathed life into him.' I nodded, familiar with the story, but not entirely convinced that this made God a potter. 'And he forms *each* of us in the womb, just as he has done with your baby sister. He is a craftsman.'

My brow furrowed slightly, 'But Mary's not made out of clay…'

He looked up, and the wheel and pot began to slow. 'You're right, Martha – the Lord uses different materials for all his different creations. But hundreds of years ago, when the descendants of David sat as the last kings on the throne in Jerusalem, the Lord sent the prophet Jeremiah to watch a potter at work. But the potter wasn't as good as me…' Judas paused to wink at me again before continuing. 'The pot that he was turning on the wheel became out of shape and was spoiled. But the potter was clever. Can you guess what he did next?'

'He threw it away?'

Judas shook his head, and Abigail – knowing the story well – gave the correct answer. 'He started again with the same clay, and made it into a different pot.'

'Ah, my little Abi – you have listened well to your father! He did indeed shape it into a different pot. Then the Lord told the prophet that *He* was like a potter and His people were like clay in His hands, and that He could shape them in the way He wanted, even when they went wrong.'

The wheel finally came to a standstill, and Judas then carefully removed the pot and placed it on the ground to dry before firing. I tried to remember all the stories that I had heard at home and at the synagogue. 'And *did* they go wrong?'

Abigail was quick to answer, familiar with her father's stories. 'One of the kings didn't like what Jeremiah was saying and threw him down a well.'

'No!' I was shocked and horrified. I found it inconceivable that anyone could treat God's prophet with such great disdain or with so little fear. But worse was still to come, when I heard the reason for the prophet's mistreatment. Although I knew that we were not perfect and that we all committed sins, it had never entered my head that the Jews could reject their own God – the Lord of creation. The thought filled me with perplexity and

I felt deeply unsettled, even at my young age. I could understand the enemies of Israel rejecting the one true God, *but how could God's own people turn their back on Him?* The thought seemed utterly foreign and troubling. I had heard the words *the exile* before, and had had some vague awareness that our people had lived for a while in another land. But I had not understood that this had been God's punishment and discipline for their continued rejection of Him and His laws.

Judas must have sensed that I was unsettled, because, after assuring me that Jeremiah was rescued, he then gave both Abigail and me a small lump of soft, pliable clay. 'Why don't you make something for your new sister, Martha? What do you think Mary might like?'

The worrying thought that God's people could reject their God was soon gone, lost in the joy of pinching and poking and pulling the grey-brown clay in my hands. I quickly decided that Mary would like a little pot with a lid. Once roughly fashioned, Judas put a little pointed stick into my hand, with which I could mark out a pattern on my masterpiece. My crude efforts could not match the dexterity that Abigail's extra eighteen months had bestowed on her. But still, I was proud of my little pot.

Judas smiled approvingly when I presented him with my finished object. 'I think Mary will love that pot,' he said, 'when she is old enough to appreciate its beauty. But we can't give it to her just yet.' He crouched down to be on my level and whispered (as if telling a great secret), 'Clay is one of the most wonderful and mysterious things in the whole of God's creation.'

I stared at the little dull lump in my hand and was not convinced.

His eyebrow arched up. 'You don't believe me?' I shook my head. He took the little pot from my hand. 'You see, Martha, like this, a pot would be useless. It wouldn't hold its shape and if you put oil or water into it, it would turn them brown. But bake the clay in a special oven' – Judas's eyes became bright and keen – 'and it turns almost miraculously into something quite different.'

'Like baking bread?' I offered.

'Yes, but bread becomes soft and light; clay becomes hard and strong. And *that* is what is going to happen to your little pot, after I have glazed and fired it for you.'

It was the following Sabbath, a week after Mary's birth, that I next saw my little pot. Girls had no special rite as baby boys did on the eighth day, but they were always presented at the synagogue on the Sabbath after their birth. As our family of four walked into the familiar building, we were greeted warmly. Judas wove his way through the crowd until he had reached me. He bent down and pressed a small glazed pot into my hand.

'Here you are, Martha. What do you think of your present for Mary now?' I was amazed. He had found a pretty glaze for it, and the dull clay had been fired and transformed into something truly beautiful in my eyes, despite its slightly misshapen lines.

My mother proudly carried my sister, with my father beaming at her side, and we were formally welcomed by Jonathan, the synagogue ruler. Mary was then held by Matthias the priest, and the familiar words of the priestly blessing rang out in Hebrew: '*The* LORD *bless you and keep you; the* LORD *make his face shine upon you and be gracious to you; the* LORD *turn his face towards you and give you peace.*'

And in my heart I longed for my little sister to know God smiling upon her.

Back upstairs, my mind wandered happily for most of the service – until Jonathan stood to read from the Prophets. He was handed the scroll of Isaiah, and began to read some words that I struggled to follow. Joseph started translating the words: '*Yet you, LORD, are our Father.*' But I gasped when he continued: '*we are the clay, you are the potter; we are all the work of your hand.*'

Down below, Judas turned his head and looked upwards, and when he found my face in the gallery he gave me a little grin and a knowing look. I fingered the pot in my pocket, eager to give it to my sister after the service. But as I did so, I also thought once again about Jeremiah the prophet. I determined that if God were ever to send another prophet, then I would not reject him, even if others did.

Chapter 5

The city of the Great King

'Beautiful in its loftiness, the joy of the whole earth…is Mount Zion, the city of the Great King.' (Psalm 48:2)

AD 14

It was strange that my sister should be called Mary. Behind the meaning of her name was a Hebrew word for bitterness, a trait that could not have been further from her nature. Even as a child who was only four months beyond her first birthday, her disposition was one that brought even more sunshine into those hot, dry months of summer, pattering around in our lives on her newly discovered feet. Whereas I could often be found with a furrowed brow, she never seemed to know the meaning of those words. A lack of years never stopped me from pondering matters too great for me. But Mary began as she then went on: a care-free child with a smile that constantly lit up not only her face, but also the lives of those around her. She could usually be found, however, following me around wherever I went. As soon as she found out the true purpose of her legs, she used them to become my shadow. Although a younger sister under my feet could be an irritation at times, it brought joy to my heart to know that she adored me.

The sixteen months since her birth had been busy ones for me. I had helped my mother more than I'd ever done before, learning new skills and taking over simple tasks from my mother, as much of her time was taken up with caring for Mary. I never complained or even questioned what she asked of me. Instead I delighted in the new responsibilities that were placed upon my shoulders, and even thought – as every girl in Judea did – of the time when I would have a household of my own to run. But I still hadn't even reached my eighth birthday, and my mother never lost sight of my needs as a child. So, one hot day in July, as the grapes were being harvested in some of the fields nearby, she asked me if I would like to go with my father into Jerusalem the following day. She asked with a smile on her face, because she knew without a shadow of a doubt what my answer would be.

The day dawned much like any other at that time of year, with cloudless blue skies and the promise of heat. On the short but early walk into Jerusalem, my father and I were accompanied (as I had expected) by Simon and his son, James. As their silversmith's workshop was close to my father's, they were frequent companions on the morning walk. I held my father's hand and listened (as James did) to the adult conversation.

'Has the price of silver stayed the same?' asked my father.

'A little higher,' replied Simon. 'But Pentecost was good for us as usual.'

'As for every business in the city, my friend.' A little over a month earlier, Jews had flocked into Jerusalem from far and wide within the Roman Empire for the Feast of Weeks, or Pentecost as it was also known. It celebrated the start of the harvest, the first-fruits of which were offered to God. Although it never drew quite the same crowds as the longer festivals of Passover and Tabernacles, any increase in the population of Jerusalem – even for a day or two – was always good for trade. And as the men talked together, the great city came into view. The rising sun was catching and reflecting off the highest parts of the city, the foremost of which was, of course, the temple sanctuary.

As we began the descent down the Mount of Olives, the discussion of money and profits soon turned, as it did for so many Jews, to the payment of taxes to Rome. 'Rome may bring us its roads, its order and a peace of sorts, but there is still a high price to pay,' said my father.

'You are, as ever, right, Heli my friend,' responded Simon. 'But the alternative is far worse, and the cost far higher – as Judas of Gamala should have known.'

James looked enquiringly at his father. 'Who?'

Simon shook his head and sighed, conveying something of his disapproval for the man to whom he had referred. 'One of the Zealots, who thought – as they all do – that the path to freedom for the Jews is to throw off the yoke of the Romans. Coponius, the Roman governor, soon put a stop to it.'

A grim expression came to my father's face as they continued to discuss the Jewish revolt that had happened around the year of my birth. 'The Zealots are fools! No one doubts their passion for our nation, but they are wrong to believe that they can bring about God's kingdom with their swords.'

'He is indeed a fool who tries to resist by force the

census and taxes imposed by Rome – and a fool who ends up on a Roman cross…'

Both men fell silent – and I shuddered. Crucifixion was an inescapable horror that blighted our lands – as it did all lands within the empire. Mothers would seek to shield their children from the sight, but the Romans had a deliberate habit of crucifying their victims in the most public of places. They had little care for the sensitivities of the young. Our pagan rulers wanted all, even from the earliest age, to understand the simple truth: rebellion against Rome ended only one way. Added to that, boys like Benjamin (when Judas and Salome weren't in earshot) had a grotesque fascination with its details. And so I found myself unwittingly and unwillingly exposed to the grisly facts that I wished could be erased from my young and impressionable mind. And those facts were these. Transgressors were first stripped naked, and then nailed through their wrists and feet to the rough wooden cross upon which they'd been laid. Their torment was multiplied as the cross was then lifted up. Finally, they were left to hang in hopeless agony and utter humiliation for all to see – and for the birds to ravage after death eventually came. Although the birds did not always wait that long to perch upon the victims and start their feasting. My insides lurched as an image of the unknown Judas of Gamala upon a cross drifted, unbidden, into my thoughts.

My father, however, dispelled the image and any gloom in his usual way. 'Ah, but when the Messiah comes, then – and only then – will God bring about His kingdom on earth, and our only human ruler will be the Son of David on his rightful throne.'

Simon's face lit up. 'And Heli, we will watch and pray that the Lord will hasten that time.'

I felt my father squeeze my hand and I looked up to see him smiling broadly down at me. 'And who knows, Martha? Maybe in my lifetime – or if not, then maybe you and James will live to see him!' And as the walls of Jerusalem began to loom large above us, I longed for the time when the coming of God's chosen king would surely herald an end to the horror of crucifixion.

Our small party of four finally reached the bottom of the Kidron Valley. Once again we were in shadow, as the sun had not yet risen above the top of the hill that we had just descended. And the Susa gate rose above us in all its grandeur in the eastern wall of the city. We began ascending again as the road snaked up the other side of the valley, until we reached the steps up to the gate, which would not only give us entrance into Jerusalem, but also access to the Temple Mount. And once again my heart swelled with pride. The sun was just peeking above the top of the Mount of Olives as we reached the gate, bringing out the beautiful cream colour of the huge limestone blocks from which the vast wall was constructed.

The only reason that I knew they were limestone was, of course, because my uncle John had told me. Being a mason, he delighted not only in telling me the type of stone, but also in passing on any details of his craft to any young minds that were able to appreciate them. One Sabbath afternoon, he'd drawn a simple picture in the dirt (for the boys of the family) to explain how the blocks were made. These details were, of course, seen as unnecessary for a girl, but I had still listened in fascination. He explained how a groove would be made in a large piece of limestone, along the lines of the stone, and then a dry wooden beam inserted into the groove. He'd then described how water was poured on the wood, which would then expand and crack the stone along clean, straight lines.

Looking – as I did that morning – at the smooth limestone wall with the sun reflecting off it, I marvelled at the ingenuity of the minds given to us by the Creator. Although I didn't worry myself about how the enormous stones had been manoeuvred into place.

We were soon walking up steep steps, emerging (somewhat breathless) a short while later into the wide open area of Court of the Gentiles, which was bathed in sunshine. I glanced around the huge open space, already bustling with people despite the relatively early hour. The temple never ceased to fill me with a sense of awe. This was the place where the very presence of God dwelt, and we, His people, were the privileged ones who could draw closer to Him than any other nation on earth.

Any further pondering of that breath-taking truth was curtailed, however, by my father tugging gently on my hand. 'Come on, Martha.' Our purpose in being in the temple courts that day was purely a pragmatic one. There were only a very limited number of gates giving entry to Jerusalem through its high walls, and passing through the Susa gate and crossing the Temple Mount was the quickest way to reach my father's workshop. *But then again, why would a person not want to walk through those blessed courts as often as they were able?*

My father smiled at my wistful expression. 'Maybe later. If Thomas has come with your uncle Jacob today, then he might be persuaded to bring you back up here this afternoon.'

Unlike many of the boys in Bethany, my cousin Thomas always treated me kindly – and I adored him. He was a little over three years my senior, and had already reached the age of eleven. He was beginning to learn the family trade: that of a perfumer. Often when he was not at school at the synagogue, he was in their workshop, slowly acquiring the skills which would last him a lifetime. Much as James did with his father, Simon, or I, with my mother in the kitchen. Thomas's sister, Hannah, was born within two months of my birth and, next to Abigail, she was the friend I delighted in most. Though with Hannah living in Jerusalem, it was a less frequent pleasure. It was, therefore, with the happy and hopeful prospect of seeing my cousins that we crossed to the south-western corner of the temple, and then went out onto the grand stone staircase that arched gracefully over the Tyropoean valley. Having crossed it, the stone steps descended, before turning left and south halfway down. At the bottom, we found ourselves in the paved street that followed the valley, which ran from north to south through the centre of Jerusalem, along the western side the Temple Mount. We passed various booths and stalls as we walked down the street a short way southwards into the Lower City, soon reaching my father's workshop. Simon and James then left us, to walk the short distance to where their own workshop was situated.

I smiled when I saw the little wooden plaque above the door. Although I could not read, I was perfectly well aware of what the characters spelled out. My father had delighted in having words of Scripture from the wisdom books carved on the wood, for all who entered his workshop to see. And they were words that I heard him repeat with great relish many times during my childhood.

'*Perfume and incense bring joy to the heart,*' I said, pretending to read.

'Clever girl!' he said, but was clearly not fooled. And we passed under the words and went through the open door, finding my uncle Jacob and Thomas already there. 'Shalom, my brother – and my nephew!' Living in the Upper City in Jerusalem, it was, of course, a much shorter walk for them each day.

That morning, the door that opened into the small courtyard at the back was also wide open, ensuring there was plenty of light for them to do their work. Tiny specks of dust swirled around in the sunlight that was streaming in through the high windows in the walls.

Similar to my mother's kitchen, there were shelves everywhere and pots on those shelves. Though far greater numbers of both. I was fascinated by the seemingly endless collection of anything fragrant, including powders, spices, oils and resins, or the seeds, leaves and bark of plants and trees. However, unlike the pots that lined my mother's kitchen, many of these earthenware vessels contained perfumes or gum-resins of great value. Only Thomas, with his greater height and greater age, could reasonably be trusted with retrieving the precious ingredients from their places. Although, even then, neither my father nor my uncle would place upon his young shoulders – yet – the responsibility of handling the most expensive elements of their stock.

'Any customers yet?' my father asked.

'I sold a jar of lavender oil just before you arrived, Uncle,' replied Thomas, 'and one of rosewater before that.'

'Good! Either everyone is up particularly early today

or the summer is already making the city stink.' My father smiled. 'It is good for business either way.'

The family wares were sought by many in Jerusalem and for many different purposes. There were sweet smelling oils to soothe sun-dried skin. These also masked (albeit inadequately) the unwelcome odours of the teeming city, with its limited drainage, over-crowded poorer quarters, abundant refuse and drifting smoke. Not to mention the sweat of a multitude of labourers and the dung of the city's animals. For the wealthy, there were more costly perfumes and ointments, such as myrrh and aloes, sold in tiny-handled pottery vessels or small alabaster jars. Then the anointing oils that were used in the burial of the dead – a frequent occurrence in a city of many tens of thousands like Jerusalem.

My father and uncle were not, of course, the only perfumers in the city and, as was the case with many of the trades, they were grouped loosely together in the same area within its walls. Some concentrated more on the work of an apothecary, since some of the gums and resins used in my father's trade – such as frankincense and myrrh – were also employed in various medicines. Others produced the cosmetics used by the more well-off women of Jerusalem, such as hair dyes, powders and eye-paints. But Jacob and my father were fortunate, however, to also be able to employ their skills for the highest of purposes. The worship of the temple required special oils for the anointing of priests, and fragrant incenses to be burned at the daily prayers and sacrifices. Although the mixing of these was the preserve of one of the priestly families, my father and uncle nevertheless had the privilege of supplying the prepared ingredients. Their profession was, therefore, always viewed with high esteem. They were, of course, paid for their precious wares, but both men considered this work as part of their own devotion to the God of Israel – and one of the greatest honours of their lives.

I learned (when I was older) that the prosperity, not only of my own family, but also of most of the city, came either directly or indirectly from the temple. Jerusalem was a city that revolved, not only spiritually but also commercially, around its place of worship. Much of its wealth and trade were dependent upon the pilgrims who thronged to the Temple Mount throughout the year, and upon the regular festivals and daily sacrifices that were the beating heart of our city. On that particular summer day, however, I was only concerned with the delights of watching my father work, and of smelling the various potions or scents that he was working on.

'So, Thomas, what will we do with that frankincense when you have prepared it?'

My uncle's question was quickly answered by my cousin, eager to show that he was progressing well in grasping the knowledge required to be a perfumer. 'We use it in ointments, but it is mainly used in the incense for the temple – '

'When it is mixed with which other fragrant spices?'

'Stacte and onycha and galbanum – in equal measures.' I was in awe of my cousin's learning and impressed by his answers, and watched with interest as my uncle went to help him.

'Well done, Thomas. And where does frankincense come from?'

'Arabia and India,' he answered, adding with some hesitation, 'brought here along the spice routes?'

Jacob laughed at Thomas's answer as he stood behind him, guiding his arms and hands in the correct motion to pound and then grind the hard resin in the stone mortar. 'You are, of course, right again my son. But that was not the question that your father was asking. What I mean is: how is this hard resin produced in the first place?'

Thomas grinned at his misunderstanding. 'It oozes from a tree as a gum, and then hardens until it become like this.'

My father turned from the task of transferring small amounts of fragrant ointments into tiny stone pots. 'Your son has been paying attention to all you have been saying, Jacob! What more could a father want?' Despite not having a son and heir himself, and Jacob having two, there was no sense of envy or resentment in my father's comment on Jacob's good fortune. Instead, he turned to me with a twinkle in his eye. 'I wonder if my daughter can answer one of *my* questions now. Can you think, Martha, of any of the other perfumes that also come from a tree like that?'

I pondered for a moment or two. 'Myrrh and nard?'

Thomas smiled at me. 'Myrrh does, but nard comes from the dried root and stems of a plant. I think aloes can also come from a gum – is that right, father?'

Jacob laughed again. 'I begin to wonder if there is anything left to teach you.' He grinned at my father. 'Maybe these cousins will set up their own perfume business when we are old and weary, Heli, and provide riches and comforts for us in our old age.'

I giggled at the thought of doing anything other than being a wife and mother, and my father winked at me. 'Ah, brother, but you are forgetting that we will need the best cook in the whole of Judea to feed us!'

My father knew me well, and knew that, however much I enjoyed being in his workshop, my heart lay in the kitchen. But he had a little treat for me. 'Come over here Martha.' I stood up from the wooden stool on which I had been sitting, and moved over to his side. 'Hold out your arms.' I obeyed, and my father pushed up the thin sleeves of the cream-coloured light summer tunic that I was wearing, so that the hems, which I had embroidered simply in blue thread, were up near my elbows. He dipped one finger into a pottery bowl, and rubbed a tiny amount of ointment onto one wrist. He then dipped another finger into another bowl and repeated the action on my other wrist. 'There. You mentioned myrrh and nard. Which is which?' I lifted one wrist and then the other to my nose, breathing in deeply the heady fragrances.

I held up my right wrist. 'This one's myrrh?'

My father turned to my cousin, still grinding the frankincense ever finer with the pestle. 'Is she right?' I held my wrists out for him to smell, and he just smiled and nodded. My father continued, 'Ah – but there is a more important question, Martha.' I looked at him, intrigued. 'Which one do you prefer?'

Jacob laughed. 'Careful, Heli – you are giving your daughter expensive tastes!'

I breathed the perfumes in again, and knew immediately what my answer would be. 'Myrrh!'

'It is a fine choice, Martha – the perfume used to prepare Queen Esther for her king, and to make King Solomon ready for his bride. And how about your little sister, Martha – which one do you think Mary would like best?'

'Nard,' I said, naming the other perfume only so that

62

she would be different to me, although in time I would discover that my answer was correct.

Jacob wagged his finger at my father. 'I warned you, Heli! You'd better start saving for their wedding days.' I blushed slightly at the thought of one day being a bride and a wife.

'I have plenty of years yet to make sure that my daughters have generous dowries for when they wed.' He rubbed the top of my head affectionately, before adding with a laugh, 'But maybe I should get back to work, just to be sure.' And with that he returned to the task in hand.

I then happily watched Jacob and Thomas preparing the ground frankincense and other fragrant spices for the temple incense. And I was fascinated by my father heating oil together with powdered myrrh out in the courtyard, transferring the fragrance to the liquid which would eventually become a perfume.

As the sun reached its zenith, Thomas and I were sent to his home in the Upper City – to be fed by my aunt Ruth, and to collect my cousin Hannah for the special task to be entrusted to us that afternoon.

The Upper City did, of course, require us to ascend through the narrow, teeming streets of Jerusalem. We quickly reached one of the gates in the wall that divided the more prosperous quarters of the city from the lower, crowded areas, where the small houses of the less fortunate were packed closely together. The higher ground not only afforded better views the temple but, more importantly, its air was cooler and fresher. Its elevation also ensured that any rainwater or waste flowed away from the comfortable houses of the rich and powerful, and down into the valley. And of its residents, none had been more rich and powerful than Herod, who had built himself a magnificent palace on the most westerly edge of the Upper City, years before I was born.

I stared at some of the large and lavish houses that we passed, some styled as spacious Roman villas, complete with mosaics and the comforts of the wealthy. My cousins, however, lived in a much more modest house, not too dissimilar to our own.

When we arrived, we found Hannah out in the courtyard feeding her brother Jude, who was several months older than Mary and recently weaned. Her face immediately lit up when she saw us, but before she could speak, Ruth emerged from the kitchen. 'Martha, how lovely to see you!' she exclaimed, and her welcome was quickly followed by a warm embrace. 'How are your mother and Mary?'

'And what's it like having a sister?' chipped in Hannah as Jude threw a piece of bread onto the floor.

After news was shared, Thomas, Hannah and I were soon sitting on the paving stones of the courtyard, in the cooler shadow cast by one its walls. We were all within reach of small bowls containing olives, shelled almonds and some small fish, with a plate of warm flatbread to share. We chattered happily together as we ate, sharing sights seen, tales heard or deeds done, whilst Jude settled down on a patterned mat for an afternoon sleep in the shade. However, after a subsequent plate of halved, fresh figs, and a hurried farewell, the three of us were soon scurrying eagerly back down into the Lower City and to the family workshop.

'The wanderers return!' My uncle unfolded his arms

and straightened himself up from where he had been leaning back against the work-bench, and then turned to retrieve something.

My father smiled. 'And my niece is taller every time I see her. I swear she's catching you up, Martha.' He laid a playful hand on each of our heads, as if sizing us up against each other, and then put on a voice of mock seriousness as he turned to my cousin. 'No, Hannah – you're not there yet. You'll just have to eat more of your mother's cooking.'

'But Martha won't stop growing, Uncle Heli!'

My father leaned down and whispered something in her ear that made her giggle. But before I could find out what had been said, my uncle turned back to face us with a small but weighty leather bag in his hands. 'Ready?'

Chapter 6

The courts of the LORD

'My soul yearns, even faints, for the courts of the LORD.'
(Psalm 84:2)

AD 14

Hannah and I stood together, poised for action. We were both looking to our right, to where Thomas was standing a little distance away, and waiting for his signal to start our dignified race. The three of us had left the family workshop and worked our way back up the Tyropoean Valley, passing, as we did, the sizeable complex of ritual baths – mikvehs – to the south of the Temple Mount. As usual, a number of pilgrims were waiting to go down into the cleansing waters, so they could take part in temple worship. We were taught (even from an early age) that certain things made us unclean before our holy God. A woman's monthly bleeding, childbirth, and contact with the bodies of the dead. These all required ritual bathing and sacrifices for us to be made clean again before we could worship Him. But those considerations were far from our minds that day. As we'd approached the towering walls of the temple, we had turned right and ascended a number of steps onto the wide pavement that ran along the southern wall of the temple.

'Remember, don't run,' whispered Hannah to me as we prepared to race Thomas up the parallel tunnels that sloped up into the temple courts above. The two Huldah gates, through which the three of us were about to go, made a magnificent entrance to the temple from the south side. My father had once explained that they were named after a prophetess who lived hundreds of years earlier, at the time of King Josiah. She had told Josiah that the book that had been found in the temple was the Word of God (although I couldn't for the life of me imagine how God's people could ever have lost it in the first place). Standing there that afternoon, I thought, *How wonderful to be a woman immortalised in Scripture for faith in God!* But Huldah was soon forgotten as Thomas gave the signal.

'Now!' exclaimed Hannah, and we plunged from the sunshine of early afternoon into the darkness of our tunnel.

Hannah giggled beside me as we attempted to walk up the slope as fast as we could without breaking into a run. We wove our way around those making their way downwards to leave the temple, also managing to pass a number of pilgrims ascending at a more respectable pace. We did not dare go too fast and risk disapproving stares from the adults around us. But we also desperately wanted to be the first ones to emerge into the bright daylight of the temple courts.

We were panting by the time we ascended the flight of stairs at the end of our tunnel, but were disappointed to see Thomas already standing grinning at the top of his. 'He's got longer legs' complained my cousin as we wandered over to meet him.

He simply called to us with an impish grin, 'What took you so long?'

We were soon standing together in the middle of the wide open area of the Court of the Gentiles, so-called because any could enter (not just those of us who were Jews). For a few moments we breathed deeply as our beating hearts slowed down again, looking around us and taking in the sights and sounds of the temple courts. People were milling around everywhere. Those who had come for the evening sacrifice were beginning to drift towards the temple itself. It rose majestically in the middle of the court, with smoke from earlier sacrifices curling upwards slowly from its centre. Behind the temple, at the north end of the huge enclosure that made up the temple courts, I could see, however, the towers of the Antonia Fortress overlooking the whole area. It was an unwelcome but ever-present reminder of our Roman overlords, who knew that if there were ever to be trouble from the unruly Jews, it would most likely start at the temple.

I tore my gaze away from the stone towers and back to the court around us. To our left and our right were covered porticos, lined with pillars, which ran the length of the east and west sides of the temple courts. Here and there small groups were clustered in the shade – young men sitting at the feet of various rabbis to be taught by them and gain their wisdom.

'Look over there,' said Thomas, directing us towards the grand portico behind us known as the Royal Stoa. The tunnels we had just ascended ran under it, and it stretched across the whole of the south side of the Temple Mount. I turned to face its magnificent two storeys and pitched roof, and the majestic row of tall columns running along its entire length. I had once also counted these. There were forty (the further three rows of forty behind them being far beyond the highest number to which I could, at that stage, count).

This area was also the source of much of the noise assaulting our ears. Above the general hubbub of conversations, there were the calls of the money-changers, whose stalls were mainly set out in the Stoa. They exchanged the Roman coins used in everyday life into ones that were acceptable in the temple. And there was also the bleating and cooing of assorted animals: the tethered sheep and goats, the caged pigeons and turtle-doves, whose short lives would soon be ended for the most noble of causes.

'What is it?' asked Hannah.

Thomas nodded towards the mass of stalls. 'Father says that they charge the pilgrims far too much,' lowering his voice so as not to be overheard. 'He says that if you bring your own animal to sacrifice, you have to pay the priests a large amount of money to examine it, to find out if it's good enough. But if you buy an animal here, then you're charged far more than it's worth.'

I was puzzled by what Thomas had said. Although I did not question either my cousin's truthfulness or my uncle's judgment, I couldn't imagine why priests would do such a thing in God's House. The word *corruption* was not yet in my vocabulary. I did, however, immediately feel the need to defend the one priest that I *did* know. 'I'm sure Matthias would *never* do that!' Thomas shrugged his shoulders, but it did lead me on to a happier matter. 'I wonder if we'll see him here today…'

Thomas jerked his head towards the temple, indicating

we should move in that direction. As we began to follow him through the crowds, he proceeded to address the question to which I hadn't expected an answer. 'Probably not. Apart from the festivals, each division of priests only serves here for two separate weeks of the year. Which division is he in?' I marvelled at the extent of Thomas's knowledge after only five years or so of being taught at synagogue. That all priests were divided (according to families) into twenty four separate divisions, was something of which I was only vaguely aware, and so I had to confess ignorance. It didn't, however, stop me looking eagerly at each priest we came across, in case I saw Matthias' familiar face smiling back.

As we walked across the Court of the Gentiles, we soon came to the low marble wall known as the Soreg. We stopped by one of the gaps in the wall, beside which was a large sign. Hannah looked up at her brother. 'What does it say?'

Thomas's brow became furrowed. 'It's written in Greek.' His mouth began to move as he followed the characters with which he was less familiar, and began to spell out the words for himself: '*No foreigner… is to enter… the…*'

The silence that ensued as he struggled with the next word was filled, however, by the voice of a stranger behind us. '*The barriers surrounding the Sanctuary.*'

We all turned around to see a priest standing behind us, dressed in his long, plain linen tunic. Whilst it wasn't the familiar face of Matthias, it was nevertheless smiling, and the young priest went on to finish the translation. '*He who is caught will have himself to blame for his death which will follow.* It's written on other signs in Latin, too. No Gentile could ever claim he was entering the temple by mistake.'

He smiled at Thomas. 'I think your Greek is better than mine was at your age. Although even then I did at least know the meaning of the word *Christos*.'

'The Anointed One – the Messiah,' said Thomas.

'Right again, my young friend.'

Thomas's face flushed slightly at the praise from the priest, and decided that he might as well make use of his new acquaintance. 'Do you know where I'll find Zephaniah the Levite?'

The young man, whose name was unknown to us, smiled again. 'The place I'd look first is in the Chamber of the House of Oil.' He must have seen the uncertain looks on our faces, for he went on: 'I'll take you there.' We followed him through the Soreg, and up the twelve steps onto the platform that ran around the temple. He glanced back at us. 'What brings you to the temple and to Zephaniah?'

Both Hannah and I left Thomas to do all the talking. 'My father and uncle provide the materials for the incense for the temple,' he answered. He then lifted up the small leather pouch that he had been holding tightly from the moment my uncle had put it in his hands. 'I'm here to deliver a little of the frankincense we've just prepared.'

'To make sure that it is sufficiently fine and pure?'

'That's right,' answered Thomas. But then his curiosity got the better of him. 'Have *you* ever burned incense in the temple?'

The priest laughed. 'I've only been serving in the Sanctuary for a short while. I would be fortunate indeed if I had already been chosen for *that* honour!'

'Is it true that you are only allowed to offer incense on the golden altar once in your lifetime?'

'If that – there are some who minister as priests for their entire lives without their lot ever being chosen.'

We had, by this time, covered the short distance to an entrance into the first court – the Court of the Women – and walked through a short corridor leading into the large square beyond. On Hannah's face was a look of awe which mirrored my own. Although I had been taken into the Court of the Women as an infant, I could count on the fingers of one hand the times I remembered being there. And each time it had felt as though I were on holy ground. It was as close to the Sanctuary as Hannah and I were allowed to go – not because we were children, but because we weren't male.

Our friendly priest pointed over to a doorway in a corner of the court, directly to our left. 'The Chamber of the House of Oil is through there. That's where they keep the stores of oil and wine for the offerings, and that's where you're most likely to find Zephaniah.'

Thomas thanked the priest, who then left for one of the other chambers in the four corners. 'Are you coming with me?' Thomas asked.

Hannah grinned at me, and didn't need to ask what I was thinking. 'We'll stay here,' she said.

'Very well. I'll be back soon,' said Thomas, and went off in search of the Levite.

I knew that Levites assisted the priests and took care of many of the more practical tasks in the temple. Part of me was curious to go somewhere I hadn't been before. However, the rarity of my trips into the Court of the Women meant I was eager to spend our limited time in the glorious open area, where women were permitted to worship. Not listening to a conversation in a store-room.

An upper gallery ran around three sides of the court, supported by lines of elegant columns. Hannah and I walked slowly and silently behind these columns, in the cool of the shade under the gallery. As we walked around the edge of the court, we watched (between the pillars) the worshippers coming and going. Some went to one of the thirteen large chests against the walls under the gallery. There they could leave their gifts of money: for the temple, for the sacrificial offerings or for the poor. It was little wonder that this court was also called the Treasury. But our eyes were also drawn upwards, and we gazed in wonder at the four huge lampstands rising like tall tree trunks within the court.

I whispered to Hannah (for only hushed tones seemed appropriate), 'Have you ever seen them lit?'

She shook her head. 'I think they only light them at the Feast of Tabernacles. Father says he may take us this year.' The mention of the week-long autumn festival stirred a great longing to be part of one of the great annual celebrations, and I resolved to ask my own father to take me too.

Without a word, we both came to a halt by the large gate on the east side of the court, which was the main entrance for the Court of the Women. But it wasn't that gate, impressive as it was, that had our attention. For we were both looking across the court at the wall directly opposite – and at the impressive Nicanor Gate leading into the inner courts, where only men and priests were permitted to go.

We watched as men ascended the fifteen graceful semi-circular steps leading up to the entrance into the Court of Israel. Almost as soon as I had begun to learn about the temple, I had heard of the famous gate, named after a man called Nicanor, whose money had paid for its stunning bronze doors. I also heard that, in the morning, the east-facing gate shone brightly. But standing there that day, brighter still was the Sanctuary itself, which rose high above the gate and the opposite wall. Even without the sun shining directly on it, its four white pillars and gold façade were dazzling. But even that glorious sight was not, however, where our eyes finally came to rest. Our gaze was drawn to the opening between the bronze gates – and what lay beyond.

I could see part of the huge square stone altar on which the offerings were made. The ramp that the priests walked up to reach the top of it was, however, just out of sight. 'Can you see the priest preparing the fire?' whispered Hannah, as a man in robes arranged wood upon the stone.

'Yes, it must be for the evening sacrifice,' I whispered back. Other fires were still burning there, presumably from earlier offerings. The sight brought to my mind the last time I had stood in the Court of the Women. It had been the previous year, eighty days after Mary was born, when our little family had travelled to the temple, to make the sacrifices required for my mother's ceremonial purification following childbirth. Before we'd left, she bathed in the small ritual bath that we had at home. Then, at the temple, I'd stood at the base of the semi-circular steps with her, as she held Mary in her arms. My father took her offerings through the bronze gates and into the narrow Court of Israel. And he watched as the priests sacrificed my mother's sin offering of a young dove and burnt offering of a year-old lamb. I had followed the smoke as it drifted upwards, and as I stared into the clear blue sky, I'd offered a silent, simple prayer. I thanked God for keeping my mother safe through childbirth, and for giving me a little baby sister.

Gazing now through the Nicanor Gate, we could also see, beyond the altar, more steps. At the top of these were the doors that led into the Sanctuary. We could just make out the solid gold vine that surrounded the entrance. No doorway was so beautifully adorned in all of Israel. This, after all, was the doorway into the Holy Place, beyond which (behind the massive veil) was the Holy of Holies – and the very presence of God Himself. The awe-inspiring vista was almost too much for two young girls to take in. We stood – transfixed – in silence, drinking it all in, until a voice beside us tore our eyes away from the bronze gate and what lay beyond.

'All is well,' announced Thomas briefly and cheerfully. He had emerged just in time. There was a real danger that he would not have found us had he left it much longer, as numerous worshippers were already flowing through every entrance into the Court of Women.

'Can we stay a bit longer?' asked Hannah quickly, mindful that her older brother was in charge of our little expedition.

Fortunately for us, a trumpet blast decided the matter. The temple trumpets were used for announcing many things, not just the commencement of the Sabbath. Hearing the signal for the approach of the evening sacrifice, the three of us moved inwards a little towards the centre of the square. We craned our necks, trying to see as much as we could of what was going on. A hush fell over the Court of the Women, as people stood quietly praying, many of them with their hands raised to heaven. Then, as the smoke of the burnt offering began to rise towards God, the Levites standing near the altar started singing the psalms for that day. No one spoke as they praised the God of Israel in words and beautiful harmonies that had been used for centuries. I felt part of something ageless, stretching back to ancient times and far greater than even the people of God. This was the place, I thought, where heaven touched earth, and where the Almighty came closest to mortal men and women.

I looked up to the sky, and tried to imagine the God who had made everything somehow squeezing Himself into the Sanctuary. But then I worried it might be a sin to imagine the God of all creation in dimensions a small girl could cope with. I then puzzled (yet again) about something that I'd heard in synagogue the previous Sabbath, about Moses speaking to God face to face. *How could that be possible when God was unseen, vast and holy?* Another question to ask my father.

Just after the final trumpet sounded, Thomas spoke again. 'Come on. We'd better get back, or they'll be wondering where we've got to.'

We reluctantly made our way out through the eastern gate, and began making our way diagonally across the Court of the Gentiles towards the staircase that my father and I had descended that morning with Simon. But Thomas suddenly interrupted our chatter, whispering 'Look!' He threw out an arm, quickly bringing us to a halt. We followed the direction of his gaze towards a group who had emerged from the other end of the temple. They were also crossing the Court of the Gentiles ahead of us, making their way towards the Royal Stoa. I could tell that many were priests, and important ones at that.

'That's Annas!' hissed Thomas, his voice lowered so that only we could hear. Although I had never seen the high priest before, I had no difficulty identifying him in the cluster of men. Even without his ceremonial robes, Annas was an imposing figure – not so much because of his stature, but because of the way he bore himself at the head of the group. Even as I stared at him in awe, I felt Thomas's hand on my shoulder. He drew his sister and me back, until we were a respectful distance away.

I would later learn that all high priests were meant to be descended from Zadok, the priest who served King David, and anointed his son Solomon to be king after him. But I already knew that the high priest had a special place before our holy God, and could draw nearer to Him than any other mortal. And yet as Annas swept past, what I sensed was not so much a man of holiness, as a man of immense power, as if the temple belonged to him. And if I had been older on our visit to the temple that afternoon, I might have understood the looks on the faces of some who stood nearby – looks not of respect, but of suspicion and mistrust. And in time I would understand why.

Chapter 7

Change and constancy

'Three times a year all your men must appear before the
Lord your God at the place he will choose:
at the Festival of Unleavened Bread, the Festival
of Weeks and the Festival of Tabernacles.'
(Deuteronomy 16:16)

AD 14

In early September, as the hot, dry summer was coming to
an end, and ripe dates and figs were being picked from the
trees, Abigail and I sat in the shade playing with Mary. We
were doing our best to entertain her with the small baked
clay animals we had made earlier in the week. Once again,
we were at Judas's workshop on the edge of the village,
and could hear the regular sound of the spinning of the
potter's wheel in the background, as Judas worked nearby.
We were too absorbed in our game to notice the approach
of Simon and my father as they walked down the hill,
returning from a day's work in Jerusalem. The first we
became aware of them was when they hailed Judas. The
sound of my father's voice brought a huge smile to my
sister's face. Moments later she was waddling over to him,
arms outstretched. He swung her up into the air and she
screamed with delight.

The wheel came to a stop. Judas rose to his feet, wiping his clay-covered hands on his apron. 'Shalom, friends. What news?'

My father turned his attention away from Mary, now being carried by him, and towards the potter. He raised his eyebrows. 'News indeed, Judas!'

'Rome, it seems, has a new emperor,' Simon continued. 'Jerusalem has spoken of little else today.'

Young as I was, I still knew that a change of emperor was a momentous event in the world in which we lived. Judas joined the little group that had formed where we had been playing, the men towering like giants over our small clay figures. 'What of Caesar Augustus?'

My father replied in a matter of fact tone, 'Died two or three weeks ago – of natural causes, it seems. He was seventy-five, after all.'

Abigail was clearly as excited as I was. This was the most important event ever to have happened in our short lives, and it felt as if history was unfolding before our very eyes. 'How long was he emperor?'

Judas put a hand, which was now wiped almost completely clean of clay, on his daughter's shoulder. 'Longer than I have been alive – '

'Longer than any of us.' added Simon.

My father was thirty-six years old, and before the question was out of my mouth, he had answered it. 'Forty years to be precise – as long as our own King David ruled.'

'And the new emperor?' asked Judas, looking expectantly at the others.

'His step-son, Tiberius,' my father answered, 'as we had always thought it would be when the time came. After all, it was never going to be his own flesh and blood.'

Mary had started playing with my father's dark hair, twisting it around one of her fingers, wonderfully oblivious of the enormity of the matters being discussed around her. I, however, looked up at my father, my brow characteristically furrowed, but confident of his ability – as ever – to answer the question that was now puzzling me. 'Why is that, Abba?'

He gently took Mary's little hand in his own, to put a swift end to the tugging on his hair that had just begun. 'Augustus only had a daughter of his own. One of his wives had a son by a previous marriage, though, and Augustus adopted him. Tiberius is already well over fifty though.'

A little more discussion followed concerning the nature of the new emperor, and whether his reign would be significantly different to that of his step-father. My own father then declared that his hunger could be denied no longer. It was therefore time for the three of us to make our way back to our home – and to my mother's cooking. He continued to carry Mary as we walked through the village, with my hand clasping his free one. So many questions were beginning to flood my mind about the future, but they were soon put to one side as my father asked the question that was uppermost in his. 'So, tell me Martha, what has your mother been cooking for us to eat this evening?'

'Lentil and chick-pea stew,' I said, immediately feeling the need to add, 'I helped too!'

My father laughed. 'I'm sure you did, Martha – I'm sure you did.'

And as we walked along, I chattered happily about the meal. I'd ground the cumin seeds that would give flavour to the stew, and picked and washed the fresh coriander that would be chopped and scattered over the finished dish. I'd also mixed the olive oil, salt and thyme into which the bread that accompanied the meal could be dipped. But as our little family enjoyed the food that evening, my mind kept returning to the report of the new emperor, wondering how our lives would change. Little did we know then that all our lives *would* be shaken, as would history itself. But not by the one considered to be the most powerful man on earth. They would be shaken by a humble carpenter, next to whose power that of a Roman emperor paled into insignificance.

In those days, when the world was changing around us in ways we were powerless to influence, we found, as always, a quiet comfort in the regularity of the land and the rhythm of our year. The cycles of work and worship were woven into our nation, together with the slower cycles of birth, marriage and death that were part of every life. In late September, soon after I had turned eight and Tiberius had had the crown of oak and laurel leaves placed upon his head, confirming him as emperor, we celebrated again the Day of Atonement. The ancient ritual was performed regardless of who was ruling the land. It was the most solemn and holy day of the year. It acknowledged that we had broken the commands of the One higher than any human ruler, and that we needed His forgiveness. The sombre day of fasting and confession was spent mainly in the synagogue – and, even at my recently increased age, it was not an easy day for the young.

The evening before, my father explained again the special sacrifices that would occur. These would atone for, or cover over, our sin, so that we could be reconciled to God. But it was the two goats that he spoke of that fascinated me. 'Are both sacrificed to God, Abba?'

'No, Martha.'

My mother smiled at the exchange between us. She held a very tired eighteen-month-old Mary to her breast. My father picked up two small left-over pieces of bread from the meal we had eaten before sundown. He would not eat again until the following evening when we were to share a meal at the house of my uncle and aunt in Bethany. He held a piece of bread in each hand, as if to illustrate what he was explaining. 'The high priest draws two lots to show which of the goats is to be for the Lord and which is to be the scapegoat.'

'The scapegoat?'

'That's the one that will be sent out into the wilderness.'

'Why?'

'Because it carries the sins of the people.' My father moved one of the pieces of bread slightly. 'The high priest lays his hands on the goat's head to symbolise our sins being transferred to the animal. It's then led out of the temple and over the Mount of Olives – not far from here – and then out into the wilderness.' The piece of bread then hopped to the edge of the table.

'Is it killed there, then?'

My father gave a little shrug of his shoulders. 'According to the Law, the goat should be released far away into the wilderness. The Scriptures tell us that, *as far as the east is from the west, so far has he removed our transgressions from us*.' My father paused. 'But…'

'But what?'

'The rabbis have thought it best that the goat be pushed to its death from a rock in the wilderness.' The bread disappeared over the table's edge.

I grimaced, but Mary let out a small sigh of contentment as she slipped into sleep against my mother's breast. My mother kissed her gently on the forehead, and then said, 'Maybe they want to be sure that the goat bearing our sin never wanders back, by chance, into our midst.'

My father leaned over, put an arm around me, and pulled me close into his embrace. 'Maybe so…'

I pondered for a moment the fate of a goat that could carry so much sin in such a small body. The next question then formed in my mind. 'And what of the other goat?'

'It is sacrificed,' – he laid the second piece of bread down on the table – 'and its blood cleanses the temple and the people from sin.'

'How?' I asked.

'Its blood is sprinkled before the very presence of the Lord, and the Lord accepts it as atonement for our sin. The high priest, Annas, will do that tomorrow. It is the only day of the year when he may enter the Holy of Holies, and he is the only one who may do so.'

I leaned back against my father, and stared at the motionless scrap of bread. I pictured in my mind the man I had seen in the temple courts some weeks earlier. I tried to imagine him dressed in a white robe, walking around the edge of the huge curtain – the veil of the temple – that hung within the Sanctuary, and into the Holy of Holies. 'Are there any windows there?' I suddenly asked.

My mother smiled at my father, and I guessed he must also have been smiling. I felt him stroking my head. 'You do ask such questions, my little one.'

'But *are* there, Abba, because it must be very dark if there aren't?'

'I do not believe so – but I will ask our friend Matthias when I see him tomorrow.'

And as I went to sleep that night I wondered again about Annas, the high priest. I wondered whether he would walk into the presence of God with the same confidence I had seen in him as he strode across the Court of the Gentiles. Or whether he would fear to enter the presence of the Most High – especially if it were dark.

The solemnity of the Day of Atonement soon gave way to shouts of joy. As the days grew shorter, and as clouds in the sky signalled that the early rains were not far away, one of the happiest times of the year arrived. Only four days after the sombre day of fasting and contrition, the Feast of Tabernacles began. It was celebrated at the completion of the grape harvest, reminding us that – even in the Promised Land – we were still dependent upon God for the harvest and for life-giving rain. The population of Bethany suddenly increased, as an influx of relatives from Galilee poured into many of the homes in our village. The streets were filled with men carrying armfuls of branches taken from palm trees, myrtles, and any others that could easily be reached. These were to be woven into makeshift shelters – the tents (or *tabernacles*) in which we would spend the next week. It reminded us of the forty years that our Israelite ancestors had spent camping in the desert, as God led them from Egypt to the Promised Land.

Little booths made from branches sprang up all over Bethany. Many of them were on the flat roofs of our houses, often used for drying (both clothes and produce) or weaving. However, that week everything was cleared from roofs, as men (of whatever trade) applied themselves to the building of booths for their families.

'The least breath of wind would demolish that shelter, Heli son of Saul!'

The familiar woman's voice calling out from below, and the equally familiar peal of laughter, announced the arrival of my aunt Tabitha, late one afternoon. I leaped up from where I had been sitting on the roof, having been given a break from the kitchen to watch my father as he worked on our booth. I careered down the outside staircase into the courtyard where my aunt, uncle and cousins were now standing. I threw my arms around my aunt's ample waist. My uncle Reuben shouted out, 'Well, what do you expect from a perfumer? You need a mason to build anything that will stand!'

My mother emerged from the kitchen, wiping her hands clean of flour. My aunt disentangled herself from my embrace, and held me at arm's length. 'My! How you have grown since I last saw you, Martha.' She then caught sight of my sister, who had toddled out of the kitchen, following my mother. 'And Mary! What have you been feeding your children, Sister?'

My mother and aunt kissed each other and embraced, both laughing. 'Only the good food that I have always fed them.'

My uncle Reuben and his eldest son, Simeon, had stayed with John and Elizabeth at Passover earlier in the year. They had travelled from Japhia, to fulfil the Law's requirement that all men should appear before the Lord at the three main festivals. I hadn't, however, seen my aunt since Tabernacles the previous year, when she and their youngest, Joseph, had also made the seventy mile journey south.

My mother went back into the kitchen whilst my father, who had descended the staircase in a more dignified fashion, greeted my uncle and aunt and his nephews warmly. 'Good journey?'

'The Lord blessed us with fine weather,' said my uncle. 'And whatever else you may say about the Romans, they make fine roads.'

'Did you come by the usual route, then?'

'Yes. Across to Scythopolis and then up towards Jerusalem through Jericho – nearer to three days than four.'

My mother re-emerged with a large bowl in which a stone pitcher was resting on a towel. She placed it on the ground, and picked up the pitcher. 'Martha – fetch the stools and some cushions, please, whilst I get water for our guests to wash themselves.'

My mother went through a door off the courtyard, and down some steps to the water cistern that was dug out beneath our house. By the time she returned, there was a flurry of activity. My father, uncle and cousins were unloading their supplies from their donkey and cart, while my aunt Tabitha was busying herself with amusing Mary. Just looking at my mother and aunt, it was hard at times to believe that they were sisters, even allowing for the fifteen years between them. Whilst my mother was tall and graceful, her older sister was somewhat shorter but carried far more weight. My mother tended to be gentle and reserved, whereas my aunt was never at a loss for something to say. However, where they were alike was in the warmth and love that flowed from both of them in different ways.

After bread, olives and cakes of raisins were served to our guests, the next two or three hours were filled with laughter and activity. Both increased greatly when my uncle John and his family also arrived from across Bethany. With five male cousins and three men working on the roof, it was left to the three women and me to work on the evening meal. The kitchen and the courtyard began to fill with wonderful smells. The lamb, which my mother had cut into cubes and speared onto pomegranate sticks, was roasting over the open fire, having first been brushed in olive oil that I'd mixed with chopped mint and salt. A huge quantity of flat bread to feed thirteen mouths (if Mary's was included) was being produced by my aunt Elizabeth. Meanwhile, with occasional help from the women who were constantly moving between the kitchen and the courtyard, I did my best to grind together garlic, sesame seeds, salt and olive oil. When they had become a smooth paste, I added the mixture to crushed chickpeas, to make a dip for the bread. It was also my job to keep an eye on my sister, who was thankfully and almost miraculously sleeping through all the hubbub. My aunt Tabitha diced cucumber and onions finely for another dip, adding them to yoghurt made from milk from our goat. She then sliced more onions thinly for the salad she was making with bulgur wheat, parsley and mint. My mother halved and stoned apricots, chopped pomegranates and sliced melons. These would be eaten after our main meal, with the honey and cinnamon dip she had already prepared.

And as the sun began to set, a small procession carefully made its way up the steps and onto the roof, where a passable shelter was finally in place. My father said the blessing over the meal. Then, by the light of numerous small oil lamps scattered around, we shared the freshly-prepared food, together with the ever present olives in brine and the bowls of roasted grain, coated lightly with olive oil and salt. We consumed the feast with relish, and the wine flowed – as did the conversation. Reports from Galilee were exchanged with local news, often with much laughter, and it felt (with stars peeking through the gaps in our leafy roof) as if we were somehow closer to heaven. Although my cousins were all boys, and their chatter was largely amongst themselves, I was content simply to watch and enjoy the family that was gathered around me, listening to all that was being said.

As we moved onto the fruit and honey dip (with a look from my mother that told me not to over-indulge), the conversation widened beyond that of family matters. My uncle John turned to his Galilean brother-in-law, and asked: 'So Reuben – what of Antipas? You've had him ruling over Galilee for, what, almost eighteen years now?'

My uncle nodded. 'Well, for a start, I'm not sure he's any less Roman than your prefect.'

My father leaned over to the honey that my mother had thinned with a little wine, and dipped the slice of melon into it. 'What do you expect of a son of Herod, who was never a Jew in the first place?'

My aunt Tabitha turned to her husband, and said, 'Ah, but at least he keeps you in work. Sometimes I hardly ever see you and Simeon, you spend so much time in Sepphoris.'

'Sepphoris?' I echoed, unashamed to admit my ignorance, and my uncle Reuben was happy to enlighten me.

'It was the capital of Galilee at the time of Herod, until Rome decided to burn it down in the rebellions after his death. Anyway, Antipas decided to rebuild it. I think he was keen to prove he could build a city as fine as any of his father's – '

'And as Roman,' added my aunt Tabitha. 'Theatres and baths and a stadium! But it does keep most of the craftsmen in the area in business. I think half the masons, builders and carpenters from Japhia and Nazareth work there, not to mention those that come from Cana! And I hear that my son is becoming a fine stoneworker.'

Even in the limited light of the lamps I could tell that my cousin Simeon was blushing slightly, and Reuben leaned over and clapped his eldest on the shoulder. 'He is that – and a better builder of a Tabernacle booth than his uncle Heli!'

After the laughter had died down, our roof-top gathering soon moved on to the telling of stories and the singing of songs. To my mystification, Mary quickly fell asleep, oblivious of the music being made around her. It wasn't long, however, before I, too, was feeling drowsy. I wriggled down on one of the rugs that had been set out for our feast, resting my head on the cushion on which I had been sitting. I felt my mother gently pull a woollen blanket over me, just before I dropped off to sleep.

I never heard the sounds of my uncle John and aunt Elizabeth leaving with their boys some time later, or of my mother and her sister clearing away the dishes from our feast. They then, with the other remaining family members, also lay down with blankets and cushions beneath our Tabernacle shelter.

My father was busy with my uncle Jacob all week, with business brisk as Jerusalem heaved with all the pilgrims.

But every evening, after sundown, the pattern of rooftop meals and nights under the stars continued, with different friends joining us, or our family being invited elsewhere. And as the week of the festival slipped by in a flurry of cooking and feasting and joyful celebration, my excitement increased. My father had agreed that I could go with the family to the temple, for the last and greatest day of the Feast.

When the day finally arrived, my mother stayed behind with Mary. We left early, to be in Jerusalem for the special ceremony that happened every morning during the Feast, equipped with what every pilgrim carried – our lulab. My mother had helped me the previous day to construct the strange little posy that we waved, made by inserting a small palm branch, together with myrtle and willow, into a citron fruit.

My aunt Tabitha proved to be wonderful company as we made our way into Jerusalem with my uncle and cousins. 'How about an almond and honey cake, Martha?' she asked, as we stopped at a stall laden with sticky treats. 'They look good, don't they?' My eyes widened in anticipation. All manner of tempting smells were beckoning to me. Raisins and apricots, figs and cinnamon. 'Would you like a cup of pomegranate juice too?' I didn't really need to be asked. Not having a daughter of her own, my aunt delighted in indulging me whenever the occasion allowed. And cakes and sweet breads, both laden with honey and fruit, were purchased more than once that day, from the myriad stalls that had sprung up around Jerusalem.

We arrived at the temple precincts, lulabs in hand, just in time to join other pilgrims in the procession that was joyfully making its way down the Tyropoean Valley. 'Can you see the high priest, Martha?' my uncle asked. 'He's the one at the front.'

'Yes, I've seen Annas before,' I replied, keen to demonstrate to my older cousins that I not only recognised the high priest, but also knew his name.

He deftly raised me up onto his shoulders to give me a better view. 'See that gold pitcher he's carrying? He's going to fill that with water from the Pool of Siloam, down near the city walls.' We went with the crowd down the street, lined with stalls and booths, to the brick structure which housed the pool. We then stood watching as Annas disappeared inside, re-emerging a short while later with a full pitcher. The procession then made its way back up the valley and into the temple courts. It moved through the Court of the Women (where my aunt and I had to remain) and into the Court of the Priests, where the stone altar had been decorated with willow branches for the festival.

'On every other day of the Feast,' explained my aunt, 'the priests parade around the altar once. But today they're doing it seven times, waving willow branches as they go.' The ram's horn sounded, blown by one of the Levites, and we and the other worshippers waved our lulabs and sang words from the Psalms, the songbook of the Scriptures. *O give thanks to the Lord, for he is good; his steadfast love endures forever!* There was then another blast of the ram's horn. 'That means the high priest has now reached the top of the altar,' continued my aunt. 'He's about to pour out the water from the golden pitcher.' She looked down at me. 'It's like a prayer asking God for rain. If He does not send rain, our crops will not grow, and if they don't grow, we won't have a harvest.'

A chant began to reverberate around the court: 'Lift up your hand, lift up your hand!' And we joined in. We all wanted to see the water being poured out, although being small and not having my uncle Reuben's shoulders to sit on, all that I saw was the backs of other pilgrims. However, as I stood there, my lulab in one hand and the hand of my aunt in the other, my heart was almost bursting with joy. But I also knew that the greatest treat of all was still to come.

We spent a happy morning in the temple, watching and listening as the Levite choir sang on the semi-circular steps in front to the Nicanor Gate, as they often did at special times. As sacrifices continued to be offered on the specially decorated altar, my aunt, uncle, cousins and I wound our way slowly down from the temple through the crowds, struggling to stay together in the constantly moving sea of people. We then followed the streets upwards again to the Upper City, to where Jacob and Ruth lived. My lulab had, by this time, lost most of its myrtle and was looking somewhat the worse for wear. My aunt Tabitha and I joined Hannah and her mother in preparing the meal for that evening, whilst my uncle Reuben took his sons through the Upper City to see the Tomb of David.

Thomas was with my father and uncle at the workshop, helping as they sold their wares to the pilgrims, who were in a mood, not only to celebrate, but also to spend their money. The three of them were back early, however, and that evening's meal was not a long, lingering one, as it had been on every other night of the festival – for that evening we were returning to the temple. After the food had been consumed, my aunt Ruth sent us on our way, as she stayed behind with my young cousin Jude and the clearing up.

The nine of us made our way back to the temple and to the Court of the Women, almost carried along by the throng of people heading in the same direction. This time, however, my aunt Tabitha took Hannah and me up the stairs to the gallery – the only area that was permitted for women on that evening. Somehow we wormed our way to the front, and to a place where Hannah and I (and my short aunt) could watch the proceedings. 'Look girls!' My aunt pointed to some youngsters climbing ladders up the four huge lampstands in the court. I held my breath, marvelling at their courage. 'Those boys are all from priestly families,' she explained. 'They're going to fill the bowls at the top with oil, and then light the wicks. But they're not like the lamps we have at home. They have enormous wicks. Can you guess what they're made from?'

'String?' I replied.

My aunt shook her head. 'Rope!' exclaimed Hannah.

'Wrong again. They're made from the old robes and girdles of priests. How about that?'

I watched, transfixed, as the boys continued their precarious task. And soon, the huge lamps were flooding the court beneath us with light. 'They can be seen throughout much of Jerusalem,' added a woman standing next to my aunt.

As the light fell on the crowd below, Hannah cried excitedly, 'Look, there's Thomas… and Simeon and Joseph!' She pointed to my cousins who appeared to have become separated from the adults.

'With their fathers nowhere to be seen,' added my

aunt, in a voice heavy with good-natured indignation. 'I swear, if those men weren't talking so much, they might take better care of their sons!' – a comment that evoked almost equal amounts of sympathy and laughter from the women nearby. But no one seemed unduly perturbed. The only real danger for the boys was of ending up with a lengthy search to find their fathers when it finally came time to return home.

I soon lost the heads of my cousins in the teeming mass of people around the edges of the square, but almost immediately lost any interest in trying to find them again, when the entertainment started below. Acrobats, dancers and jugglers performed in the light from the gigantic lampstands. We gasped as one (apparently) famous rabbi juggled with eight flaming torches – the audience making sure that they kept a suitable distance away. Music flooded the area as well as light. The Levites played flutes, harps and trumpets, and beat out the rhythms on drums and cymbals whilst men danced, again with flaming torches in their hands. I had never seen anything like it. My eyes drank in every sight and every sound of the revelry, as God's people rejoiced in celebration of His bounty.

Although the music and dancing always continued throughout the night, to mark the end of Tabernacles, my aunt tore Hannah and me away whilst the festivities were still in full flow. Although we both protested and claimed we were not tired, she'd seen the stifled yawns that had slipped out, despite our excitement. All the way back to Hannah's house we chattered about everything we had seen, and were desperate to describe it all in detail to her mother on our return. We found my aunt Ruth sitting quietly in the courtyard under the stars, with Jude fast asleep on her lap.

'What have you done with the men and the boys?' she asked, smiling.

'The Almighty is the only one who knows where they are in that crowd,' laughed my aunt Tabitha in reply.

My other aunt rose to her feet, Jude still in her arms. 'Well, we will leave them to find their own bedding when they finally return – if they do so before dawn.' I stifled another yawn. 'Would you girls like a drink of milk before you go to bed?' We both nodded, somewhat sleepily, and – despite our previous desire to tell Ruth all we had seen – our beds on the roof of the house suddenly seemed more inviting.

I never heard the men or my cousins return, although I woke in the morning to the snores of both of my uncles. But before finally giving in to sleep that night, I took one last look in the darkness at the tops of the huge lampstands, which could just be seen from the roof through the leaves of the booth. And as the joy of the festival filled my heart a final time, I believed once again that we were truly a people blessed by God. In my young mind that also meant that no misfortune could possibly befall us.

I was wrong.

Chapter 8

A dark shadow

*'Even though I walk through the valley of the shadow of
death, I will fear no evil, for you are with me.'*
(Psalm 23:4)

AD 16/17

Before I became aware of the swelling of my mother's
belly, I noticed that she had stopped her regular bathing in
our mikveh to cleanse herself after her monthly bleeding.
It was summer again, and almost two years had passed
since our glorious trip to Jerusalem during Tabernacles.
Mary had passed her third birthday some months earlier,
and I was soon to be ten years old. Learning that I was to
have a new brother or sister the following January filled
me with a joy that I could also see shining in my mother's
eyes. My sister was, of course, largely in a state of oblivion
about the changes that were soon to happen to our family.
Although she had found almost a year earlier that her
voice could be used to produce words, her vocabulary was
still limited, and certainly did not include words such as
pregnancy or *childbirth*. But I delighted in seeing once again
my mother's stomach begin to swell with the signs of new
life.

But our joy was mingled with sadness as summer

began to melt into autumn, although it was a sadness that arose from the misfortune of others, rather than our own.

I could tell something was wrong the moment my father walked into the courtyard one evening. His usual cheerful disposition was replaced by an expression of deep concern. My mother immediately asked, as she glanced up from her mending, 'What's the matter, Heli?' I stopped feeding the chickens that were strutting around my ankles, pecking at the grain that I had already scattered on the stones of the courtyard. My mother rested her needle and thread in her lap. And we both waited for him to speak.

My father didn't respond straight away. Instead, he sat down on a stool, pulling Mary (who was clutching a small wooden bowl in her little hands) up onto his lap as he did so. He sighed deeply as he started stroking Mary's hair, and then looked up.

'It's Simon. He went to see Matthias today. He confirmed what Simon had feared: he's got leprosy.'

My mother's hand immediately went to cover her mouth, as she drew in a sharp breath. 'No! Are they sure?' My father looked down again at Mary's head, which he continued to stroke, and gave a little nod.

My eyes darted back and forth between my parents. This was terrible news for Simon's family, for leprosy was one of the diseases that people dreaded most. I was puzzled, however. 'Why didn't Simon go to Jonathan if he's ill? He's the doctor, not Matthias.'

'He did go to Jonathan first,' explained my father, 'but the Law says that it has to be the priest who pronounces a person unclean – or clean if they are healed.'

'And *will* he get better, Abba?'

'Only God Himself knows, Martha. Sometimes the disease goes after a while, and the person is well again, but other times…' My father's voice trailed off. The awful truth was that sometimes it was more like a death sentence. In the end, he simply added, 'it doesn't.'

I had only ever seen lepers from afar. Because whatever form the skin disease took, there was always one terrible consequence: it drove its sufferers away from their families and out of their communities. They were, according to God's Law, unclean, and no amount of washing in any mikvehs could change that. And so they were required to live apart from the rest of the community, for as long as the dreaded disease persisted.

My mother's eyes welled up with tears. 'How dreadful – poor Simon – and poor Rachel! What will they do?'

My father sighed again. 'I spoke with Simon briefly. He knows he will have to depart immediately for a leper house. I suppose his only good fortune – if you can call it that – is that there is one so close by.'

'But what of Rachel and James – how will they live?' asked my mother, with anguish on her face as well as in her voice.

My father shrugged his shoulders. 'They have family with the means to help them – and there is no reason for them to leave their house. One of the other silversmiths will continue training James – he's sixteen now, and knows much already. He should be able to take on the business and, even if he won't be able to bring in as much money as he and his father did together, it should still be enough to live on.'

His answer appeared to do little to assuage my mother's fears. Her next question was one that, if anything, was even more anguished. 'But why has God allowed this to happen? Simon is a *good* man.'

I waited expectantly for my father to answer. If my mother hadn't asked the question, then I would have done so. I'd known Simon all my life, and it seemed almost inconceivable that a man who loved and obeyed God as Simon did, should be punished with such a terrible disease – and my longing to have a question answered had never been greater.

Silence filled the air, as my father gazed up into a sky that was beginning to fill with the oranges and pinks of a glorious sunset. After a few seconds that felt like an age, he finally lowered his eyes to look at my mother once more, and took in a deep breath to respond. But I never got to hear his answer – at least, not at that moment anyway – for it was not his voice that broke the silence.

'More grapes!' Bored of an adult conversation well beyond her years, Mary interrupted our sadness with another of her sunny smiles, framed by the dark curls around her pretty face. The season that brought an abundance of grapes was upon us, and there seemed to be no end to my sister's appetite for the sweet, plump fruit of the vine, which grew in abundance on the Judean hillsides. The question was left hanging.

As my mother went inside to re-fill Mary's small olive-wood bowl with more of the deep purple grapes, I went over and sat at my father's feet. I rested my forearms on his unoccupied knee, and then rested my chin on my arms. Leprosy filled me – as it did others – with a deep dread. 'Will we ever be able to be with Simon again?' I asked.

My father had never taken the easy way out of

responding to a child's difficult question, with answers that were at best evasive or, at worst, untrue. 'No one knows, Martha. We will have to wait and trust in the Almighty.' He became quiet again, and I couldn't tell what thoughts were going through his head, other than they were troubled ones.

I voiced another question that had arisen in my mind: 'When the Messiah comes, will he be able to stop all the diseases?'

My father smiled wearily. 'Only God can do that. But He has spoken through the prophets of a time when the blind will see, the deaf will hear and the lame will leap like deer – so who knows, Martha? The Almighty will one day put all things right, but we do not know the times of His choosing.'

I was still pondering my father's wisdom when my mother returned with the grapes. They immediately diverted Mary's attention away from the tassel on my tunic's drawstring that had become her latest plaything. My mother placed the bowl into the small hands that were stretched out towards her. 'The Essenes are good people. They will care for Simon well.'

Before I could voice it, my father was answering my next question. 'The Essenes, Martha, are godly men and women. They believe that to remain pure before God, they must separate themselves so that they can live holy lives, studying God's laws, doing good and living at peace with one another in their communities. And the small community that lives near us runs a house where lepers can be cared for.'

'It's strange,' my mother interjected, 'that although they want to remain pure before God, they are willing to care for those who are unclean.'

I looked quizzically at my father again. He rubbed my head affectionately, and said simply, 'They are, as your mother says, good people.'

The sombre mood persisted in our home for several days. Rachel and James became regular guests at our meal-table, and although we laughed at times as we shared food together, there was an unspoken sadness at the empty place at our table.

But life went on, despite Simon's absence – and the time of ploughing and sowing went by, as it always did in late autumn, before the heavier winter rains of December came. The Feast of Dedication in that month, with its joyful lighting of lamps, also came and went; and all the while, the arrival of the new member of our family drew closer and closer.

Eventually the day came when Miriam again came to our house, accompanied, as before, by my aunt Elizabeth. I did not, however, have the comforting presence of my grandmother Anna with me this time. Her advanced years were making even the short journey between Jerusalem and Bethany increasingly difficult. And at the age of ten, I was deemed to be perfectly capable of looking after my sister, and running the household for the short time that my mother would be in labour and giving birth. I was assured that as soon as the baby was born, I would be able to go in to my mother. I would watch the tasks that followed childbirth that all women needed to learn: how the new-born was washed and rubbed with salt to cleanse it after the birth, and then wrapped for the first time in swaddling bands.

I was, however, never taken into my mother after the birth. The short time that I was meant to be in charge turned out to be much longer than any of us had anticipated. It began as I was starting on the first bread of the morning, and turned into more than a full day. My father went into Jerusalem with James as usual, as my mother's labour progressed. But even when he returned to find Rachel and me preparing that evening's meal together, there was still no news. The night passed in fitful sleep, as Miriam and Elizabeth continued to attend my mother. Then finally, with the coming of a new day, we heard once again the cry of a baby, and the midwife came in to give my father the news we had been waiting for: 'You have a son.'

My father's look of joy faded, however, as he caught the expression on Miriam's exhausted face. She chose her words carefully: 'It was a difficult birth – you must prepare yourself, Heli.'

And for the first time in my life I saw fear in my father's eyes.

My mother held my baby brother for just under two days, before slipping quietly away into the hands of the Almighty. During those short days, Jonathan – the synagogue ruler, but also our physician and our friend – had been a frequent caller at our house. There were many grave conversations between him and my father, spoken in low voices, so that what passed between them could not be caught by my ears. But whatever treatment Jonathan may have given proved to be futile. During the night, two days before the Sabbath, my mother's life ebbed away, even as the new life she had bestowed on another grew stronger. And so I learned the customs of death rather than birth, as the month of January drew to an end. And the first thing I learned was that, whilst both men and women could prepare the body of a man for the grave, not even a husband was permitted to bind his wife in her burial cloths. So as my sister sat with my father, and my new-born baby brother was taken care of by a hastily found wet-nurse, I was taken some hours after her death into the room in which my mother was laid.

She looked so peaceful, but there was no mistaking the stillness of death. Elizabeth and I were joined by Rachel. But also by my aunt Ruth and my grandmother who, despite her age, had still made the journey from Jerusalem. Our tears, which had been flowing freely, were for a time staunched, as together we worked on the sacred task. We were helped once more by my grandmother's prayers and her gentle words of comfort, and from time to time we sang together the laments that gave expression to our grief. We washed my mother's body, which felt horribly cold and still, and then clothed her in one of her own dresses. It was a pretty one, dyed pale green, with some embroidery around the hems of the sleeves and the neck. A large square cloth was then placed over her face, causing fresh tears to silently roll down my cheeks. *I would never see her beautiful smiling face again.*

My grandmother understood me perfectly, and gently laid a hand on my shoulder, speaking quietly with the wisdom of her years: 'You will see your mother again at the resurrection, Martha. We must leave her in the hands of the Almighty until then.'

We then took the long strips of linen that were used for burial. We slowly and carefully wound them around her body, gently rolling her onto one side and then the other, to allow the cloths to be passed under her back. And as we wrapped her body, the room became filled with the rich smells of the perfumes and spices that I knew so well from my father's workshop. My uncle Jacob had arrived with jars of myrrh and aloes, and we poured those perfumes, together with other spices, between the strips of linen as we went along. Even in our darkest times, the Lord had granted us beautiful fragrances to mask the ugliness of death. And I was grateful for the way the perfume reminded me of all that was lovely about my mother.

Our painful task took until mid-afternoon, and as we laboured away, more and more friends and family arrived. Saul, Jacob and the rest of the family were not the only ones from Jerusalem. Other relatives arrived, as did those whose workshops were close to my father's, and a number of priests known to us through his work. Then, of course, there were our friends, neighbours and family from Bethany. And when the time came for laying my mother to rest, we took off our sandals to walk barefoot to the grave. It was a sign of our mourning, as was the covering that my father and many other men put over their heads.

The procession to the cave just outside Bethany, where my mother's body was to be laid, was not a quiet one. We did not hide our grief, and were unashamed to cry or to groan as we walked through the streets of the village, with many beating their breasts as we made our slow progress towards the grave. Laments were again sung, but this time with the rich, deep voices of the men beneath those of the women. I walked along in a daze. Mary dawdled between my grandmother and me, each of her hands in one of ours, clearly mystified by what was taking place around her, and yet untroubled. Elizabeth walked by my side, cradling my baby brother in her arms. Just ahead of us was my father, who with Jacob, John and our friend Judas, bore the bier on which my mother's body was being carried. From time to time I would catch a hint of the myrrh and aloes in the burial cloths, and the fragrance only deepened my sense of loss. The weeping around me intensified as we left Bethany, and approached the tomb which lay a short distance from our village. Unlike many others in Bethany, our family was sufficiently well-off to have been able to purchase a burial cave, into which had been cut several ledges for the bodies of family members. Both of my mother's parents had been laid there before her, and the large stone that was normally across the entrance of the cave had been rolled back before we arrived. The rituals at the tomb, and the words spoken by Matthias and others as the body was laid to rest, washed over me. As my eyes wandered from one mourner to another, and then beyond the crowd, I suddenly saw a solitary person in the distance watching all that was happening. It took me several moments to realise that it was Simon. And my feeling of desolation had never been greater.

Once the tomb was sealed up again, we returned to the house, and almost immediately a small army of women began to arrive with dishes of food. First among them were Salome and Jonathan's wife, Naomi, carrying large pots of stew from which steam was still rising. Others arrived with further savoury dishes, or wooden platters laden with fresh bread or with salad. The house of a dead person was ritually unclean, so we could not prepare food in our home. But once again the community around us supported us in our time of need.

Although I normally loved my food, I could not enjoy it and only picked at it, although Mary's appetite seemed unabated. 'You must eat, child.' The gentle and kindly tone of my grandmother's voice brought a lump to my throat and fresh tears to my eyes.

'I'm not hungry,' I said in a wavering voice.

She said nothing, but held me close for a while, allowing me to cry once more. When the tears subsided, she disappeared for a short while, only to reappear with a bowl full of yoghurt and fruit, amply laced with the honey that I loved so much. Only a little coaxing was needed to get me to start eating, and when the bowl was empty, she took it from me. She then took my hands in her thin, gnarled fingers. 'Now, Martha, we have some work to do.'

And with that, we went hand in hand in search of my baby brother, still un-named. The rest of the evening, which had long since fallen, was taken up with washing him, changing his swaddling cloth, and then laying him in the little cradle in which Mary and I had previously slept. It was so strange that we were taking care of a tiny bundle of new life, so frail and yet so perfect and vibrant, whilst at the same time mourning the death of his mother. I was glad to be away from the almost constant noise of the gathered mourners, and the company of my grandmother was enough to bring some sort of peace to my wounded soul.

We then took care of a very tired Mary. She was asleep even before I lifted her clumsily (with my grandmother's help) onto her small bed, and pulled a couple of blankets over her against the chill of the ever-advancing night.

It was only then that my grandmother attended to my needs, bringing me a cup of milk, and then sitting quietly with me on the edge of my bed, as I slowly sipped the comforting drink until it was all gone.

'Is Mama with God now?' I suddenly asked. The memory of the cold, stone tomb had brought a sudden fear to my heart, as I imagined my mother's body lying in the pitch black of the sealed cave.

'The arms of the Almighty took her to Himself when she became too tired to go on,' said my grandmother quietly. I didn't respond, and simply handed back the empty cup. 'You must rest now, Martha. Lie down and I will stay with you until you go to sleep.' I obeyed, and felt the coarse wool of the blanket on my cheek, as she pulled it up to cover me. I then felt her kiss my forehead, and went to sleep that night to the sound of her softly singing words from David's psalms.

The next few days were a blur, as friends and relatives visited us through the week of mourning. But one event in that time stood out above all others. On the sixth day after my mother's death, which was the eighth day of my brother's life, our friends and family gathered around us once more, with many other neighbours from Bethany. We crowded around the table that had been set up in the courtyard of our house, and my father picked up a flint knife to circumcise his son, from whom all the swaddling bands had been removed. He lay naked on the table, and I looked away as the soft flesh of the foreskin was cut away, accompanied by the screams of my brother. With the absence of my mother, it was a bitter-sweet occasion, as my father performed the ancient rite, first performed by Abraham on his son Ishmael and all the males of his household. It marked them – and us – out as God's people.

We were all taught, as soon as we were able to understand anything, that this was the sign of God's covenant with Abraham – the solemn and binding agreement, promising that Abraham and his descendants would be God's people, and that He would be their God. And we were taught, ever since that time two thousand years earlier, that every Jewish boy must be circumcised on the eighth day – circumcised *and* named.

Matthias the priest held up my still-crying baby brother, as he began the prayer of blessing. Although (to my greater pain) omitting the reference to the child's mother that usually occurred. 'Our God, and the God of our fathers, raise up this child to his father, and let his name be called in Israel: Lazarus, the son of Heli.' It was the first time I had heard my brother's name.

As soon as the short ceremony was finished, my father carried my baby brother (now wrapped in a simple cloth) over to where Mary and I were standing. He crouched down so that we could touch him, introducing him to us as if for the first time. 'Here is your brother, Lazarus.' My sister patted him with a rather heavy hand, in a clumsy attempt to comfort him in his crying.

All names had meanings, and so I asked my father, 'Why is he called Lazarus – what does it mean?'

My father handed the little bundle over to me. 'The grandfather you don't remember – your mother's father – was called Eleazar. Lazarus is a form of that name.' He paused and then added, 'It means, *God is my help*.'

I looked down at the little screwed-up face, the noise of his screaming still in my ears. I didn't know whether his name had been chosen before my mother's death or not. Either way, it felt like a statement of faith in the midst of the pain and the uncertainty that the future now held.

That evening, as I sat on the floor next to my father, with his arm wrapped around me, I finally heard the answer to the question my mother had asked all those month's before: *Why had God allowed this to happen?* Then, the question had been prompted by Simon's leprosy, but now it was even more troubling and personal. Not that either my father or I voiced the question as such. I simply whispered to him suddenly, 'I don't understand.' And he understood perfectly what was on my heart.

I both felt and heard him sigh, and, after a pause, he began by quoting words of Scripture that were inscribed on his heart. '*As the heavens are higher than the earth, so are my ways higher than your ways,* says the Lord. Martha, there will always be ways in which the Lord works that we do not understand. But we know that the Lord is good, and so we must trust Him – even when we cannot see His purposes in the things that happen. We don't stop trusting Him just because difficulties and pain have come into our lives. When suffering comes, we must learn courage, and how to patiently endure and pray. But most of all, we must learn to trust Him. It has always been that way with God's people.'

And then it suddenly dawned on me. Our friends and neighbours from Bethany had wept with us. But they had also been in the synagogue with us on the Sabbath. We had all still been there nevertheless, worshipping our God.

My father went on, 'You remember the story of Joseph?'

'Yes, Abba.' I well recalled the Sabbath-day story of the dreamer, retold by Judas and Salome. It was also one of the stories that Abigail and I acted out frequently with our friends. Jacob – Abraham's grandson, and also known as Israel – made a favourite of his son Joseph, to whom God had given dreams foretelling the future. Joseph's ten older brothers had turned on him, however, beating him up and then selling him into slavery in Egypt, before God finally fulfilled the dreams many years later.

'Joseph must have wondered many times – when he was taken as a slave to Egypt, or when he was in prison for many years, accused of something he didn't do – if God had forgotten him. He must have asked how God could possibly have any good purposes in what was happening to him. But the Lord did. How did the story end?'

I knew it so well that I barely had to pause before answering. 'He became a great ruler in Egypt, and his brothers came to him there, and they all got back together again.'

'Yes, that's right, Martha. But God also used him to save the lives of many, many people, including the lives of his own family. And Joseph told them at the end of the story that God used all the bad things that had happened for good.'

'But Joseph didn't die,' I blurted out.

My sudden outburst didn't, however, trouble my father. He stroked my head, which was by now resting against his arm, and replied gently, 'You are right, Martha. But we are not the first of God's people to lose those whom we love the most – and we will not be the last. Joseph was eventually able to see many years later how God's hand had been at work. We may never be able to do that, but that doesn't mean we can't trust Him. The Lord has not promised to tell us everything we would like to know, but He has promised that He will help us.'

I wasn't sure if I could trust God in the way that my father did, but I trusted my father. And that was enough. I thought again about the meaning of my brother's name: *God is my help*. And I hoped that He was.

It was hard when the seven days of mourning came to an end, as then my father had to return to his work. My grandparents stayed for a few days longer, to help as our very different family tried to settle into its new daily pattern, with my mother's absence and the frequent presence of a wet nurse instead. Salome and Rachel were often at the house, as was my aunt Elizabeth, and Esther and Naomi, the wives of Matthias and Jonathan. It never occurred to me at the time that God Himself *was* helping us through the kindness and care of His people.

Before my grandmother left, she took me aside one afternoon, and together we sat on the small wooden bench that stood in the sun against one of the courtyard walls. She took my hands in hers, and her eyes – full of wisdom and love – looked deeply into mine. 'Martha, you are now the woman of the household.' It didn't seem to matter to her that I had not even reached my eleventh birthday. 'It will be your job to provide the family with meals and to care for their needs. You will have to be the mother now for your sister and brother until they grow older. Others will help you. But you are a true daughter of Israel, and your mother has taught you and prepared you well. You will do her proud. I know you will.'

Somehow, the confidence that my grandmother

had in me filled me with a strength that lifted me and drove my fears and worries further away. And once again, though I did not recognise it, God was helping.

Chapter 9

Life after death

'And I will dwell in the house of the LORD for ever.'
(Psalm 23:6)

AD 18

The time of mourning for my mother was only fully completed after a year. As was our custom, we stood once again at the tomb on the anniversary of her death, for the simple ritual that I had not yet observed. My heart jolted as the stone was once again rolled back from the opening of the cave. My father turned towards me, 'Do you want to come in with us, Martha?' I silently shook my head. I had looked upon death once, and I did not want to do so again.

But a little voice beside me asked, 'Can I come?' At the age of almost five, Mary still had her innocence, and little fear of dark caves or death whilst her hand was in that of her father.

'No, Mary – stay with your sister and your brother. Your aunt and I will be back out soon.'

My uncle John stood with us, as my aunt Elizabeth went in to the tomb with my father, who was carrying an engraved wooden box. Their task was a simple one. They were to take my mother's bones from the grave-cloths and place them in the box – the ossuary. It would then be left on one of the shelves of the tomb, beside the boxes that already held the bones of her parents. Mary's attention was soon diverted from what was happening in the dark cave, as she began to play with my brother. He had become far more interesting to her since he had learned to waddle around on his little feet. The happy screams of my brother and sister, and the sunshine of the bright February day, did little to lift the ache that was still in my heart. I was glad when the simple ceremony was quickly finished so we could begin our unhurried walk back to the house. My father and aunt would both bathe in the mikveh, to ritually cleanse themselves from the contact with the dead.

Although Lazarus could walk, my uncle carried him, as our progress would otherwise have been excessively slow, despite our unhurried pace. My sister suddenly looked up at my father. 'What has happened to Mama?' Her question came without warning, and was asked in a matter of fact voice, as if she was asking why the sky was blue or what I had cooked for supper.

'She is resting with Abraham, Isaac and Jacob, and all of our people. The Lord will raise her to life again, with all those who belong to him, on the last day.'

Mary appeared to accept what he said with little trouble, and only had one more question on the matter: 'When's the last day?'

My father laughed, 'When the Lord chooses, Mary.'

My sister beamed at him, happy that something she had said had been deemed funny, and then turned her smiling face towards me. 'Can I have a raisin cake when we get back, Martha?'

In the year since my mother's death, I had become the provider of food for the family. I would be twelve years old later in the year, an age at which some Jewish girls were beginning to marry, although for boys it was thirteen. My mother had married my father when she was sixteen and my father eighteen, so I had no expectation of being wed for several more years – and was glad of that. But I was, by now, the one responsible for running much of the household and, after my mother's death, Salome and Elizabeth in particular had hastily supplemented all that she had already taught me. And so my skills now ranged from milking the goats we owned to making cheese from the milk that they produced, from sewing clothes for my brother and sister to washing them when they became dirty. Which they frequently did. I became more expert at tending the vegetables in the walled garden adjacent to our house. And I now knew how to turn the hard, bitter olives that fell from our tree into the soft, brined variety that were so often eaten with our meals.

Mary had obviously decided that it was a day for asking questions. As I brought in for our evening meal the stew that I'd flavoured with cumin and mustard seeds, she asked another. 'Why don't we eat rabbits?' The talk in the synagogue the previous Sabbath had been about the food laws, and two young rabbits, bolting from our path as we'd returned from the tomb, had evidently prompted a memory of something said.

My father said simply, 'The Lord has told us what is fit to eat and what is not. And He has told us that we must not eat rabbits.' I think he could see that Mary was about to ask another question, so decided to start our meal before any further explanations were required. 'But the

Lord *has* allowed us to eat' – my father leaned over so that he could see what was in the dish that I had just put at the centre of the table – 'chick-peas and onions. And so we will give thanks for the good food that He has provided and that Martha has cooked for us.'

But almost as soon as the blessing had been said, Mary continued, 'Are rabbits poisonous?'

'No, child.'

It was my turn then to ask a question that had perplexed me for a long time: 'Gentiles don't die if they eat food that is unclean, do they?'

'No, Martha.' My father quickly scooped up some of the stew with a piece of bread, presumably conscious that another question was coming, and that his hunger could wait no longer.

'So why is it unfit for us to eat?'

My father shook his head in some amusement as he ate, and when his mouth was empty, he said with a smile on his face, 'You girls ask so many questions!'

I grinned at him. 'You know so many things, Abba.'

'But I don't know everything – far from it. We don't eat rabbit because they don't have hooves, and we don't eat pig because they don't chew the cud, but we can eat cows and goats and sheep because they do both. But why the Lord has made those rules, we do not fully understand. But He knows all things and He knows best, and so we trust His wisdom and obey, even when we cannot see why He asks one thing of us and not another.' A look of sadness passed briefly across his face, and I guessed he was not only referring to the food that we ate. But it was quickly gone. He reached over to dip another piece of bread in the stew before continuing: 'The laws about food remind us each mealtime, however, that we are God's special people, called to live differently in His world. We are to be a light to the nations, showing them the greatness and wisdom of our God.'

And that was enough for my sister and me, at least for the moment. It was not, after all, in Mary's nature to be troubled by much, and she once more graced us with the smile that lit up her whole face – and our lives.

If Mary was the sunshine in our lives, then Lazarus was the whirlwind. Having a sister as placid as Mary did nothing to prepare me for the chaos that could be caused by my young brother, particularly after he had learned to move around on his own two feet. I soon learned to move any bowls away from the edge of the table in the kitchen, after a bowl of eggs (fortunately hard-boiled) and then a plate of cheese (less fortunate) found themselves pulled off the table. They crashed down to the floor, neither the pottery nor the cheese surviving the experience. And so a large part of running the household seemingly involved running around after my brother, in an attempt to keep him out of mischief, out of danger and under control. Or at least a pale imitation of that. Games played with Abigail were a distant memory, although she often found herself being sent by her mother to our house to help. It was a joy to work together in the kitchen, or out in the courtyard or garden. Whenever, that is, we weren't having to answer my sister's call for help, when her attempts at keeping an eye on her younger brother were proving less than successful.

Although my childhood had ended abruptly, I did not begrudge the responsibilities that had been thrust upon my young shoulders. We girls did not have an age, as the boys did, when we were formally recognised as adults. But that was what I felt I'd become, as if I'd found my place in the world. It was, however, always a welcome break whenever we were invited to the houses of friends or family to eat, particularly the special weekly meal eaten after sundown at the start of the Sabbath. It was on one such occasion that we were invited to the house of Matthias and Esther to share their Sabbath meal. In addition to Levi and Tamar, they also had two younger children: Ananias and Rebekah, the first of whom was ten years old, and the second the same age as Mary.

I found myself suddenly and unexpectedly aware that Levi (who had once so unfairly derided me for being a girl) had transformed into a sensible young man of almost fourteen, in whose presence I felt strangely shy. Jonathan and Naomi were also invited that evening with their three children. Jonathan was one of the highly respected group, the Pharisees, which numbered several thousand. I was impressed by how they had all taken a pledge to live a pure life, and attended regular meetings to learn more of how God's Law was understood in our traditions.

Although we were guests that evening, I arrived with some cheese I'd made, and with salad picked earlier in the day from our garden. Naomi also arrived with a dish of spicy vegetables. Although our meal that evening was a Sabbath feast in every sense of those words, what brought me the greatest delight was sitting and listening to the men as they talked, particularly of affairs in Jerusalem and its temple.

'This Caiaphas – the new high priest – what's he like

then?' my father asked Matthias, who, as a priest, was best placed to provide an answer.

I had heard of Caiaphas, a priest who had married the daughter of Annas. My memory flitted back to the day I had first seen Annas in the temple, and I listened eagerly. Matthias shrugged his shoulders. 'What can I say? He's a son of his father-in-law.'

My father quickly interjected: 'You tell me nothing, and yet tell me everything I need to know.'

Jonathan took several olives from a wooden bowl near him, but before putting them in his mouth he turned to Matthias. 'From what I hear, Annas may not be high priest any longer but he still holds the real power at the temple.'

Ananias looked at his father, puzzled. 'If Annas isn't dead, Abba, why isn't he still the high priest?'

His mother laughed as she passed the platter of flatbread around the table. 'It *is* a good question for the son of a priest to know the answer to.'

Matthias glanced over to Jonathan at the same time as pointing to his own mouth (which was full of spicy vegetables), inviting him to answer instead. The synagogue ruler smiled and turned to Ananias. 'Have you heard of Gratus?'

'Everyone's heard of Gratus!' replied Ananias, sounding slightly indignant at the mere suggestion that he might not have heard of the latest Roman prefect to govern Judea.

Jonathan continued, 'When Gratus was appointed three years ago, it appears that – for whatever reason – he took a dislike to Annas. It seems that he didn't want him holding the power that goes with being high priest, and so replaced him with his son Eleazar, whom he's now replaced with Caiaphas.'

Ananias was clearly, however, in a mood for indignation. 'Why should the Romans decide who's high priest anyway? They're not even allowed in most of the temple!'

'Rome decides many things for us that we would rather decide for ourselves,' replied his father. 'But if them appointing the high priest – and keeping the high priest's robes in their *safe-keeping* – is the price we have to pay for still being able to worship God in the temple, then so be it.'

'When the Messiah comes – ' began my father.

Jonathan laughed, 'Yes, Heli, we know. He will put right all these matters, and be our rightful ruler. But I'm not sure how our friend Caiaphas would feel about having to yield to another the power he and Annas have over the temple and Sanhedrin. I suspect that is why you never hear of them speaking of the Messiah.'

My mind wandered briefly to an occasion when I'd heard Judas call the Sanhedrin *a huddle of serious old men.* He'd been quickly chided by Salome, who had warned him to give Benjamin a more sensible description of the Jewish ruling council, before he shamed his father by repeating the words at synagogue.

I was suddenly brought back to the present by Naomi speaking. 'But not all who serve at the temple are like the family of Annas.' She doubtless felt the need to remind her husband of the occupation of their host, given his criticism of the current high priesthood.

It was Matthias' turn to laugh. 'Fear not, Naomi. Your husband has not offended me – I know his contention is not with priests.' He turned to Jonathan, exclaiming with another laugh: 'You Pharisees are all the same, always looking for a chance to disparage anyone who happens to be a Sadducee!'

'You do me wrong, Matthias. I don't disparage any Sadducee – only what they believe.'

The good-natured banter was interrupted by our hostess rising to her feet. Esther picked up an empty platter with one hand and rested the other on her daughter's shoulder. 'Come, Tamar,' she said. 'Their conversation has made these men even more hungry than usual. Bring the other platter and we will make sure they have enough bread to sustain their talk.' And with that they left the room briefly.

It was soon clear that the discussion was far from over. Ananias asked another question, this time about the elite group to which many of the chief priests belonged. 'So what *do* Sadducees believe, Abba?'

But Jonathan cut in before Matthias had time to respond. '*What* do *they believe?* You would do better to ask what they *don't* believe.'

Levi set down his cup and asked, 'Is it true that Sadducees do not believe in the resurrection, Father?' I suddenly sat up. The memory of the tomb in which my mother lay was far too fresh for Levi's question to be anything other than troubling.

'They believe neither in the human soul nor in the resurrection of the body,' answered Matthias, 'let alone any reward or punishment that follows.'

'Why is that?' responded Levi.

I was glad that he'd asked the question, for it was the one burning in my heart. My grandmother had assured me that I would see my mother's face again. And yet now I was being told that some of our people – and ones in high position – denied that. I looked anxiously at the priest for his response, but it was Jonathan who replied with disdain in his voice.

'*Why don't they believe in the resurrection?* Because they don't need to!' he exclaimed. 'They have all that they desire now. They have more wealth and power than any others in Jerusalem – you can see that from the houses they build for themselves. They lavish upon themselves the best Roman luxuries that money can buy, and all the while they know little of the hardships that most of our people face. Then they have the temerity to suggest that the struggles of the poor and oppressed, who live outside their little world, are in some way their own fault. And if that isn't bad enough,' he continued, 'they deny the resurrection, the very thing that brings hope to ordinary men and women. Hope that one day there will be something better!'

My father clearly decided that Jonathan's outburst needed a more moderate response, and chided him light-heartedly. 'So, this is you *not* disparaging the Sadducees is it, my friend? Still, it explains why you Pharisees are the ones who will always have the ears of the people.'

Jonathan's hard expression softened a little. 'Well, they are a contradiction, aren't they? They reject the tradition of the elders, and all the wisdom that God has given to his people over the years, claiming to be pure, because they only follow what can be proved from the Law. Yet they live like Romans and seem happy to run after their power and influence. And Caiaphas is no different.'

The conversation was momentarily interrupted once

more by the return of Esther and Tamar, bearing not only more bread, but fruit and yoghurt and the goat's cheese that I had made earlier. Although Levi's question may not have been answered as fully as I would have liked, I was content that the men in the room that evening held a strong belief that death was not the end. And, once again, that was enough for me.

My gaze drifted around the room, resting briefly once again on Levi. He chose that moment to glance up, however. I swiftly looked away, aware of colour rising in my cheeks. It was safer, I decided, to look in the direction of my father. But as I did so, I caught an unspoken understanding passing between him and Matthias. It intrigued me as I didn't know its meaning. It would be almost four more years until I did.

Chapter 10

Betrothed

'…a man leaves his father and mother and is united to his wife, and they become one flesh.' (Genesis 2:24)

AD 22

The world was changing around me – at least, that is, the world of my childhood, populated by the friends who had been so much a part of growing up in Bethany. Benjamin and Abigail were married within a year of each other, Benjamin when he was sixteen and Abigail when she was fourteen. All three sons of John and Elizabeth were also married, and in Jerusalem, Thomas had married a cousin on his mother's side, and Hannah, a more distant relative in Jericho. It had, however, been necessary for me to help at home in the absence of my mother, otherwise I might already have been married. But however much I loved my family and our home, change was inevitable. A time would soon come when my father would draw me aside to tell me of the choice that he had made for me. In the event, the conversation happened one January evening. I had settled Lazarus down for the night and Mary (who was almost nine) was still happily munching her way through a bowl of dried figs that had finished off our evening meal.

'Come into the courtyard with me for a while, Martha,' said my father softly. As he rose from the low table around which we had been seated, the light from the lamp on the table cast a big shadow of him on the walls behind. Mary's attention was briefly diverted from the figs, as she glanced up at him. 'We won't be long, Mary. You stay here.'

I quickly picked up my shawl as we went out into the courtyard, wrapping it around me against the chill of the night air. 'Come and sit with me here,' said my father, patting the wood of the bench on which he'd sat down. I took my seat beside him. We sat in silence together under the stars for some time, listening to the sounds of Bethany that, from time to time, punctuated the quiet of a winter's evening. Distant laughter as a family shared a meal, two dogs barking at each other on the edge of the village, the cry of a baby nearby. I knew before he even began to speak what the nature of our conversation would be. I felt my heart beginning to beat faster, knowing that my future had been decided and that I was about to discover one of its most important details.

'Martha, you are fifteen years old now and later this year you will be sixteen. Like any father, I wish to provide for my daughter. And the greatest provision I can ever make is to find you a suitable husband.'

'But who will care for you, Abba?' I blurted out. 'Mary is still so young!'

'Do not worry, Martha. These things have been considered.'

He paused, and I said nothing, fixing my gaze on the smoke that was still slowly rising from the open fire in the courtyard, over which I had grilled the fish for the evening meal. The night air was briefly pierced by the faraway cry of one of the foxes that occasionally roamed near Bethany. My father took my hand in his, and I tore my eyes away from the fire to face him – only to find a smile rather than a serious expression on his face. My heart calmed as I told myself that all would be well, and my father continued. 'I have not started thinking about this only recently – it has been on my mind for a number of years. And that is only right when it is a decision that will affect the rest of your life – and when I want only the best for my daughter.' He paused again before continuing: 'I have been speaking to Matthias…'

And with those six words I knew the decision that had been made.

My betrothal to Levi was arranged for shortly after my sister's ninth birthday. Although it was more common for priests to marry within priestly families, it was certainly not unheard of for them to marry someone other than a descendant of Aaron, the first high priest chosen by God. I did not question my father's choice for me. Matthias was a trusted friend, and Levi had become a fine young man, who would not only serve at the temple in Jerusalem, but who would also work locally in Bethany. I considered myself fortunate to face betrothal to a man who would not be difficult to grow to love, and I hoped that God would grant me a marriage as loving and as happy as that of my parents.

Not that I was indifferent to his choice! Betrothals were always a constant source of conversation between girls of my age. Although we accepted the decisions of our parents, it did not stop us admiring or thinking about – or talking about – the eligible boys of Bethany, and much giggling and laughter accompanied our speculation. Levi had certainly been amongst those who had caught my eye over the years. Although he may not have had the fine looks of James or Benjamin, there was more than enough about him for me to find attractive. And I certainly considered it a great honour to be chosen as the wife for a priest.

As usual, the betrothal would last a year. We would then be wed when my brother was six, the age at which he would start school at the synagogue, reducing the amount of care and supervision that he would need at home. My sister would also have turned ten, and be more able to run the household – though still with my help. It had been agreed that although I would live at Levi's home, I would return each day to help my father, sister and brother. The wedding would also fall just after Passover, when relatives from Galilee who'd come for the festival would still be with us, and the extra duties at the temple for Matthias and Levi would be over.

The betrothal feast kept Mary and me busy for many days. We were also aided by Elizabeth and those who were as close to us as family – Salome, Abigail and Rachel, not to mention Esther and Levi's sister Tamar, who would be our family after the wedding. And shortly after my sister turned nine the betrothal finally took place.

Matthias and Levi arrived at the house, dressed in new linen tunics and fine leather sandals. They had both obviously taken far more care of their appearance than usual (although the same could also be said of me and our small family). My father greeted them and showed them inside. Mary and I then served refreshments to the three of them, before leaving them to make the betrothal covenant. The bridal price would also be paid to my father, a sum that reflected his loss of a daughter.

I waited out in the courtyard nervously, constantly adjusting my lace-edged head-covering and the pale peach coloured tunic that almost reached down to my ankles. I had recently made it, and had laboured for many hours embroidering it with blue and green thread. 'You look beautiful,' said Mary, grinning at me, which eased my nervousness and put a smile on my face. My sister, who had spent so many years as my little shadow, following me around wherever I went, still adored me and I her. She looked pretty in the little cream tunic that I had made for her.

I gave her a mischievous smile. 'This will be you, one day, little sister!'

'I'm not so little now,' she protested.

'Maybe you'll be betrothed to your cousin Jude,' I teased.

'Don't be silly, Martha! He's younger than me…'

'Well, what about cousin Joseph in Galilee? He isn't married yet.'

'He's ancient,' giggled Mary.

'He's only a year older than me. I think he would make you a fine husband, Mary daughter of Heli.'

The teasing of my sister came to an abrupt end, however, when the curtain that hung over the doorway on the other side of the courtyard was pulled aside. The nervousness that had been briefly banished from my heart quickly returned. My father smiled at me. 'Martha, please come in and join us.'

Although I had known the two other men for the whole of my life, I found myself self-conscious in their presence, and cast my gaze respectfully to the ground. I could sense, however, that Levi was as nervous as I was, and under the watchful eyes of both of our fathers, he stood before me and asked for my hand in marriage. There was no question, of course, that I would refuse the request, but Levi nevertheless looked relieved when I accepted. He then took out of a little pouch that hung on his waist two beautiful gold bracelets, which he placed with a shy smile on my wrists as a betrothal gift. My father, beaming proudly, then placed on my head the band with ten silver coins, a traditional part of the dowry that I would bring to the marriage. The covenant was then sealed by Levi, myself and our fathers, by sharing a cup of wine together. My betrothal was as binding and solemn as our marriage would be, and could only be broken by divorce. It felt strange that the act uniting the two of us, for as long as we both drew breath, should be over so quickly.

The betrothal feast, however, was another matter. Our home was filled for the rest of the day with friends and neighbours and with much joy. Though I caught a fleeting expression on my father's face that I understood – a sadness that my mother was not there to share the day with us. And I imagined that Rachel knew how we felt. In one of the marginally quieter moments of the day, she pulled me aside.

'Simon wants you to know that he is very happy for you, and is proud of you on this day.' Despite her smile, there was sadness in her eyes. My mind flitted back two years to the day of James's wedding, which Simon again had only been able to observe from a distance. It had pained me to see my own sister and brother talking in whispers, as they warily regarded the watching figure.

Maybe because I knew the pain of grief myself, my young heart went out to her in her sorrow – and Rachel must have seen this, for she quickly lowered her eyes. 'I should not have brought you sadness this day. I'm sorry.'

'Don't be!' I grasped her hands in mine, the new bracelets jangling on my wrists as I did so. My new status made me feel as if I was now fully in the world of adults, with Rachel no longer simply a friend of my parents. 'Rachel – please thank Simon for his good wishes. They are another beautiful gift to me today.'

She looked up, relieved and comforted that she had not spoken out of turn.

'How is Simon?' I asked. She helped regularly at the house of lepers run by the Essenes, and was at least able to see her husband when she was there.

Rachel sighed. 'There is no sign of any improvement – his skin looks worse if anything.'

'I'm so sorry, Rachel,' I replied. 'We do miss him.'

A little smile returned to her face. 'Thank you, my dear Martha.' She paused, and I didn't know what more to say. 'But this is not a day for speaking of sad things,' she quickly continued. 'It is enough that you have asked after him and think fondly of him.' And her smile broadened.

A crash, and then a shriek of laughter from my sister, reminded me that, even at the age of five, my brother could still wreak havoc on an unattended table. I hastily excused myself, and our brief conversation about Simon came to an end.

It was only when each and every guest had eventually left, and the clearing up had been finished, that my father and I finally sat down together. By this time, both Lazarus and

Mary were curled up and fast asleep on cushions and rugs on the floor, with patterned covers drawn over them. My headband was somehow miraculously still in place, and my father carefully lifted it off, and I removed the veil beneath it. 'Martha – I have one more gift to give to you today. Wait here.' He briefly disappeared from the room, and when he reappeared he was carrying an alabaster jar. 'This, Martha, is your dowry.'

Dowries were often bestowed in the form of items that could be kept and later sold, such as jewellery. But I recognised the jar as being of the type used for my father's most expensive perfumes. I looked at him questioningly, and he continued with a smile on his face. 'Do you remember, Martha, how I put two different perfumes on your wrist many years ago?'

I nodded and smiled at the memory. 'Myrrh and nard.'

'I asked you which you preferred. Do you remember what your answer was?'

'Myrrh.'

My father held out the jar to me. 'This myrrh is worth a year's wages. You can sell it when you are ready, to help you set up your home with Levi. It will buy all you need and hopefully more.'

The generosity of my father stunned me and brought tears to my eyes. I set the jar carefully down on the floor, before flinging my arms around his neck. 'I love you, Abba, and I don't want to have to leave you!'

My father held me in his embrace for a while, neither of us speaking. He then kissed me on the head before untangling himself from my arms, and he took my hands in his as he had done several weeks before. 'I will still see you every day, Martha – you will not be leaving me.

Matthias and Levi both agree that it is the right thing for you to continue helping with Mary and Lazarus here, until they do not require your help any longer, or until your own children arrive. Our lives constantly change in this world, Martha – that is the way that the Lord has ordained life to be. And all our lives will change when you marry Levi and start your own family. But that is right and good. And, speaking of your wedding – ' My father broke off, and put his hand into a pocket in the large, loose over-garment that he was wearing. 'I was wrong. I have *two* gifts to give you.' He pulled out a small ornate bottle, and put it in my hands. 'A gift for my daughter for the day of her wedding.'

I carefully pulled out its stopper, although I suspected that I already knew its contents. I put my nose to the open bottle and laughed. 'Myrrh again!'

'Ah yes, but that is perfume just for you, to make you even more beautiful for your husband on your wedding day.'

'Thank you, Abba.' And in the pause after my words, I heard my brother stirring, letting out a little sigh in his sleep. Before I was married, I still had plenty of work to do in the house in which I had grown up.

The next few months were busy ones – and not only for me. Levi busied himself extending his father's house, so that he and I would have rooms to call our own. And whilst he worked outside, I tried to keep out of the sun as much as possible, in an effort to keep my complexion as pale (and therefore as beautiful) as possible for my wedding day. As I continued looking after the needs of the family, I was also preparing to take my place in a new one. I prepared exquisite embroidered garments for my wedding day, and other clothes I would wear as a married woman. That was not, however, my only preparation for becoming Levi's wife. I was also to become the wife of a priest, and I did everything I could to learn about the life that Levi would lead.

I learned that he was from the priestly division of Harim, one of the twenty-four groups, each of around three hundred, into which the priestly families were divided. During the two separate weeks of the year when his division was on duty in the temple, he would sleep there. I already knew that much of the practical work in the temple was carried out by the Levites – the descendants of Levi, one of Jacob's twelve sons, after whom my future husband was named. But I also knew that only the priests – those descended from Aaron within that tribe – could carry out the maintenance work within the Sanctuary itself. The greatest tasks carried out by priests, however, were making the sacrificial offerings which the Law required.

From the earliest days of creation, when the sons of Adam had presented their offerings to God, our worship had involved sacrifice. Although our pagan neighbours, most notably the Romans and the Greeks, also performed sacrifices at their temples, unlike them, we did not sacrifice animals to placate or appease capricious gods. Neither did we bring them offerings of food in an attempt to obtain their favour. We made our offerings in gratitude to the God of all creation, to whom all things belong, and to express our worship of him. But even more importantly, we offered sacrifices for the sins that offended a holy and righteous God. In his mercy, he had provided for us a means of forgiveness: an innocent creature to bear the guilt of His people, its blood shed to cover our sin…

'Does blood go everywhere when you kill the animals?'

I cringed inwardly at my brother's blunt question. It was the day on which the second son of my cousin Thomas was to be circumcised. Mary, Lazarus and I were accompanying our father on his daily walk into Jerusalem, so that we could all be present at the ceremony later that day. But we were also accompanied by Levi. It was late in the year, and almost eight months had passed since the betrothal. In preparation for Lazarus starting school at the synagogue, Levi had offered to show him around the temple, and my father had gladly agreed. Except Lazarus clearly felt it was now incumbent upon him to amass as much detail as possible about the work of priests at the temple, so he could display his superior knowledge when he finally started at school.

'Lazarus!'

Levi smiled at my reprimand. 'It's alright, Martha. I remember asking my father similar questions when I was your brother's age.' He must have seen the look of slight revulsion on my face, and he grinned. 'Boys are fascinated by different things.'

Mary, as usual, took it all in her stride. 'I think it's interesting too!' My father just smiled in amusement at our exchanges.

Levi, however, then turned back to Lazarus to answer his question. 'I haven't killed any animals yet – I'm still being trained as a priest. I won't begin to offer the sacrifices in the temple until I am twenty years old – and even then, I'll only offer the daily sacrifices if I'm chosen by lot.'

'Who's Lot?' asked Lazarus.

Levi laughed, though not unkindly, at my brother's mistake. After all, Abraham did have a nephew with that as a name. 'I should have explained better, my young friend. I'm not talking about a person. *By lot* means we allow God to choose the particular people who will carry out the four most important tasks each day. Cleansing and preparing the altar, making the animal sacrifice, offering the incense, and burning the pieces of the sacrifice on the altar. Four lots for four daily tasks – and God decides each one.'

'How does He do that?' asked Lazarus.

'It's very clever,' answered Levi with a grin – and I was immediately intrigued. 'The priests all stand in a circle around the person responsible for casting the lots. He then takes off the hat of one of the priests – '

'Which one?' asked Mary.

'It doesn't matter – he just chooses anyone. It simply shows where he's going to begin counting.' Levi was breathing slightly more heavily, as he continued his explanation whilst walking up the steepest part of the path leading to the top of the Mount of Olives. The ground beneath us was still slightly muddy following an earlier shower, and the clouds were still looking heavy and threatening in the winter sky. He continued, 'On a signal, every priest holds up a number of fingers. It's their choice how many – one, two or maybe more. And at the same time, the person in the middle says a number they have chosen. Again, it doesn't matter what the number is, but let's say he chooses the number seventy. He then starts counting, starting with the man without the hat. But the Lord does not permit us to count people, so he counts the fingers that are held up.'

'What's wrong with counting people?' I asked. 'After all, I do it every time we have a house full of people who need to be fed!'

Levi shrugged his shoulders and laughed. 'You have me there, Martha,' and he looked to my father for any wisdom that he might have on the matter. I found my heart once again drawn towards my future husband, pleased that he respected my father's knowledge as I did. And once again my father's grasp of God's Word did not disappoint.

'King David displeased the Lord once, by numbering the men in his army. He should have known better, because it does not matter to the Lord whether there are few or many in His battles. Maybe the priests simply want to avoid any sin of pride or distrust that caused David to number his men.' My father then smiled at Levi. 'Now enlighten us further.'

Levi had a look of pleasure on his face at my father's approval that he couldn't altogether hide. A slight breeze picked up and, glancing upwards, I was glad that the heavy clouds were moving away, rather than towards us. As I looked down again, I caught Levi stealing a glance at me – causing me to smile shyly – as he proceeded to finish his explanation.

'When the person counting reaches seventy, then the priest whose finger is the seventieth to be counted is the one on whom the lot has fallen. And therefore the one whom the Lord has chosen that day.'

Lazarus' brow furrowed. It was a great deal of

information for a child who hadn't quite reached the age of six, and for whom the number seventy was probably larger than he could imagine. But whilst he continued to puzzle it out, Mary asked what seemed to be a perfectly reasonable question: 'Why can't they just take it in turns?'

We had finally reached the brow of the hill, and as we paused to both admire the view and catch our breath, Levi attempted to answer my sister's question. 'Offering a sacrifice to the Lord in His Sanctuary is the most solemn and holy duty that we ever carry out. Only the Lord Himself sees the hearts of those who minister to Him, and so it is right that He should choose the men who are to perform the most holy acts of service.'

'And nobody could make the lot fall on a particular person...' I offered.

'Not when each person makes their own decision as to how many fingers to hold up,' said Levi, 'or what number to count to.'

My father tore his gaze away from the view of Jerusalem and turned to face us, quoting from the Scriptures as he did. '*The lot is cast into the lap, but its every decision is from the Lord.* And it is, indeed, the Lord who knows the heart of every man.'

Levi spoke again excitedly. 'Father tells me of one priest chosen to burn incense who had a vision in the Sanctuary!'

A memory stirred in my mind of the same story, passed on to me by my father many years earlier. But if Levi had any more information on that incident to share, we were not to hear it. Lazarus, having found the complexities of the system of lots beyond his ability to fathom, hadn't been listening. He had been staring instead at the holy city, rising majestically across the Kidron Valley. 'How many people live in Jerusalem?'

My father laughed, 'Ask the Romans! They love a census.'

'They are not troubled, as we are, with counting people,' agreed Levi. 'After all, it allows them to keep track of who they can tax.'

'Too true, Levi – too true,' said my father with a sigh, and then looked down as he felt a tug on his outer garment from his son.

'But how many people *are* there?'

'More than you can count, my son.' But he then relented slightly, seeing the slight pout on Lazarus' face at not getting the answer he sought. 'It is said that some tens of thousands live there.'

'And maybe three or four times that number at the festivals,' added Levi. The numbers were certainly far beyond my little brother's ability to comprehend, but he appeared satisfied enough.

We started our descent down the Mount of Olives, and after climbing up again on the other side of the Kidron Valley, Levi explained to Lazarus why the temple stood where it did. 'You know the story of Abraham?' asked Levi, as we passed through the Susa Gate, and began our ascent up the long flight of steps beyond. Lazarus nodded. 'And do you remember the name of Abraham's son – not his first son Ishmael, but the son God miraculously gave to him and Sarah?'

'Of course, I do!' protested my brother. 'It's Isaac.'

'Well, sometime after Isaac had been born, God tested Abraham's faith. He aked him to sacrifice Isaac on an altar he had built on Mount Moriah.'

'But he wasn't killed, was he?' my sister responded.

'You're right, Mary. An angel of God stopped him just as he raised the knife, and God provided a ram for the sacrifice instead. It is said that this temple is built over the place where Abraham offered his son.'

We finally emerged into the Court of the Gentiles. As we walked towards the temple, Levi began to describe the parts of it that none of us – not even my father – had seen: the Holy Place and, beyond it, the Holy of Holies. Lazarus was fascinated by the description of the huge veil, embroidered with lions and eagles, which hung from floor to ceiling between the two parts of the Sanctuary. As we passed through the Soreg his eyes grew wide, as Levi explained how it took three hundred priests to take it down and wash it.

'What do they see when they take it down?' asked Mary curiously.

'Nothing,' answered Levi. 'They're not allowed to look into the Holy of Holies. Even when priests do work on its inside walls, they can only do so from within enclosed cages. They're lowered down from above, so that they see nothing of the Presence of the Lord. In Solomon's temple, the Ark of the Covenant was also there, but now there is only a large stone on which the high priest sprinkles the blood on the Day of Atonement.'

We had entered the Court of the Women, and were approaching the semi-circular steps leading up to the Nicanor Gate – as far as Mary and I could go. 'Where's the Ark now?' asked my sister, but it was my father who responded.

'Ah, my daughter! That is one of the greatest mysteries of our people. If only we knew.'

As we stopped at the bottom of the steps, Lazarus turned hopefully towards Levi. He was clearly eager that our own priest should shed some light on, or give us some clues into, the mystery of the ornate, golden chest. It had been made at the time of Moses and contained the two stone tablets of the Law, given by God on Mount Sinai. 'Some rabbis say,' Levi began, 'that the Babylonians took it, when they destroyed the first temple and took the Jews of the time into exile.' He then crouched down, and whispered to my brother, 'But other rabbis say that it was hidden from them by the Jews, and is still somewhere within this land.' Lazarus' eyes widened again, and Levi continued: 'Maybe we'll find it again one day. That would be exciting, wouldn't it?' Lazarus nodded enthusiastically. 'Maybe it's even buried somewhere below these courts?' He paused, giving time for the tantalising thought to sink in.

And my heart once again warmed to the young priest whom I was to marry. I marvelled at the way that people could change, and at how my heart had done so too. *How could I not love a man that my beloved brother so evidently adored?*

Levi straightened up. 'Did you know that the further you go into the temple, the higher up you go, and that the highest point is the Sanctuary itself?' Lazarus shook his head, awed into silence, and gazed up at the huge bronze Nicanor Gates at the top of the steps. 'Shall we go in?' asked Levi, as he took Lazarus' hand in his, my brother nodding vigorously once again.

'You go on together,' said my father. 'I'll wait here with the girls.'

As the two who would become brothers disappeared into the Court of Israel, the three of us walked over to the centre of the large square. As Mary wandered around happily, I stood with my father, watching the people worshipping, or depositing their offerings of money in the large chests around the Court of the Women. We stood in amiable silence for a while, my father deep in thought.

'I wonder if any of us ever have a faith as great as that of our father Abraham…' he began. I glanced round at him, and there was a faraway look in his eyes, as if he were trying to picture the events that Levi had spoken of earlier. 'I'm not sure I could offer up my only son.'

'But God didn't let him kill Isaac,' I said.

'No, but Abraham didn't know that when he raised his knife.' My father then fell silent again for several moments. 'I can trust the Almighty to take Lazarus when He deems the time right. But to willingly give him up…' My father trailed off again, staring through the bronze gates to where the priests were offering the sacrifices on the altar. '*That* is another thing entirely.'

Chapter 11

Married

'My beloved is mine and I am his.'
(Song of Solomon 2:16)

AD 23

'There are thirty-nine sorts of work we can't do on the Sabbath,' declared my brother loudly, in answer to my grandfather's question. He was keen to display his newly acquired knowledge, having spent several weeks at school under the stern tutelage of Joseph the scribe.

We were in Jerusalem for the Passover, which, according to our traditions, had to be eaten within the city walls. This meant that seemingly every available room in Jerusalem was used for that purpose, especially as its population multiplied, with pilgrims flocking there to share the sacred meal. Jacob and Ruth had invited us to their house in the Upper City, to join their family (including a son- and daughter-in-law) and my grandparents. As we waited for sunset, so we could begin the evening that was the high point of every year, my grandfather Saul had asked Lazarus what he'd learned so far at the synagogue. As my brother made his pronouncement, my cousin Hannah smiled at me across the table, cradling the son born to her a few months earlier, just before the end of her second year of marriage. She looked radiant and happy in the soft, fading light.

Her younger brother Jude was not, however, to be outdone by Lazarus. 'Those were the sorts of work that were done in making the Tabernacle,' he said knowledgeably. 'But each of those sorts of work is described by thirty-nine different activities, giving a total of…' At the age of ten, Jude was struggling to remember the very large resulting number.

'One thousand, five hundred and twenty-one types of work that should not be done on the Sabbath,' finished Hannah's husband as he reached across the table for some olives.

'Most of which are done by women for the other six days of the week!' announced Ruth, as the smell of roasted lamb floated enticingly through the room. A little way across Jerusalem, my aunt Tabitha and her family from Galilee were with John and Elizabeth, celebrating Passover with other relatives. But I was pleased that night to be sharing the joyful and yet solemn meal with my father's family – and my good friend Hannah.

Just after noon, my father and Jacob had left the workshop, and joined those flocking towards the temple to procure the most important part of the feast – the Passover lamb. Having bought, from one of the official stalls, the unblemished male lamb that alone was acceptable, they then waited for the animal to be sacrificed in the Court of the Priests. As did thousands of other pilgrims who had streamed into the city. And after it was finally slaughtered by one of the many priests on duty, they'd watched the ritual of some of its blood being poured out at the altar.

Earlier in the day, Ruth had performed one of the other important tasks of the Feast: that of searching out anything containing yeast and removing it from her house. Mary and I had done the same before leaving for Jerusalem. After the men returned with the lamb, I helped Ruth set up a large spit, on which the carcass would slowly turn for several hours. The fire had soon scorched it enough for the rich smells of roasting lamb to fill the courtyard. More than once, I'd breathed in deeply, savouring the mouth-watering aroma and eagerly awaiting our special feast.

'Oh no you don't!' Ruth cried, when Thomas's son of almost two years had waddled towards the fire. No harm was done, although we had to endure deafening screams until his mother pacified him with her breast.

Apart from his short-lived tears, it had been a happy afternoon, spent chatting and singing, as together we prepared the unleavened bread and other necessities for the Passover meal.

As the sunset finally approached, my aunt went round the room lighting the lamps. My uncle Jacob then prayed the blessing, thanking the Lord for the Passover and for our food. We reclined around the table as appetisers were served, and the first of the traditional four cups of wine was poured. And as the meal commenced, my father nodded to Lazarus. My brother, being the youngest of those who could talk, had the honour of starting the traditional recounting of the Passover story, asking the same question that had been asked by countless generations: 'Why is this night different from all others?'

Jacob, aided by others around the table, told the story of how Moses, under God's direction, led his chosen people out of Egypt. We shared the salty dip Mary had made, reminding us of the bitter tears our ancestors had shed, in the land in which they'd been slaves for four hundred years. We then ate the charoset. I loved making – and eating – it. It was a sweet dish of raisins, almonds, dried apricots and figs, mixed together and flavoured with cinnamon, honey and sweet wine. It reminded us of the mortar used by our forefathers as they built cities for the Egyptians. But at the heart of the meal were the lamb and the unleavened bread.

'Why are we eating roast lamb?' asked Lazarus, enjoying the part he was playing.

'The last of the ten plagues that God brought upon the Egyptians,' started Saul in a dramatic voice, but rapidly bringing it down to a hushed tone, 'was the death of the firstborn. God told his people that each household must kill a lamb and put its blood over their doors. That night, as the angel of death moved throughout Egypt, whenever he saw the blood, he would not enter that house and would spare the firstborn of both man and beast inside. And each family was commanded to eat the lamb they had roasted – and to eat with haste, so as to be ready for their escape.' A silence fell on the room, the flickering lamplight causing our shadows to dance on the walls around us, as we chewed thoughtfully on the succulent lamb.

My father continued, 'And the Lord told us to kill and eat, each year, a Passover lamb, so that we should not forget how he rescued us from death and from slavery in Egypt.'

'But why is this bread different?' asked Lazarus again.

Ruth held up a large piece of the unleavened bread she had baked. She broke off a piece and handed it to

Lazarus, who duly ate as she gave her explanation. 'When Pharaoh, grieving for his son, sent the Jews from the land, our people had to leave in a hurry, with no time for bread to rise, and so that is why we eat our bread flat, without yeast. It is bread that can be made and eaten quickly.'

As the meal continued, we told more of the story of the escape from Egypt, sang psalms, and said blessings. We poured and drank all the cups of wine as we celebrated together the great act of deliverance of our God. It was the evening when we remembered, more than at any other time, what it meant to be God's people. And central to our celebration was the killing of the Passover lambs at the temple. I wondered how Levi had fared there that day – and suddenly realised with a jolt that, in a little over a week, the world that I had known and grown up in would change forever, when the two of us were married.

My wedding day, when it came, was a bright one in mid-April. The rains had ceased, and the flax was being harvested as the dry season began. I had spent much of the day, aided by Abigail and Mary, bathing and applying perfumed oils to both my hair and skin. Over near the window hung the richly-decorated dress I had been working on, almost since the day that Levi and I were betrothed. It was late afternoon by the time that I slipped the graceful garment, which was gathered at the shoulders, over my head, allowing it to drop to my ankles before smoothing it down. The fine linen next to my skin felt smooth and luxurious compared to the coarser woollen garments I usually wore. I had bought the linen from the stall of one of the traders in Jerusalem, and like much of the linen in the city, it was made from flax grown near Jericho, and laboriously woven from fine thread.

'You were right about the colour,' said Abigail with a smile.

I looked down at the lilac and nodded in agreement. 'It's just as well – the dye cost enough. The man who sold it to me kept explaining how difficult it was to obtain the dye. It was all I could do to stop him giving me a full description of how he personally extracted it, *from only the finest of myrtle trees in all of Judea.*'

Abigail laughed as I did my best to mimic his voice, and added, 'They *will* talk and talk, if they think it will persuade us that their wares are worth more than we are willing to pay.'

'Well, I didn't give him what he initially said it was worth.'

'I should hope not!' exclaimed Abigail, adjusting how the garment sat on my shoulders before stepping back to view the effect.

'He only got a half of what he was asking for. And that was with the yellow dye for the veil thrown in as well.'

'You did well, my friend. I ought to take you with me when I have to barter in Jerusalem.'

I laughed. 'Many of the traders know my father, although that doesn't stop them telling me that they are *practically giving* me whatever they're selling, even when they're still charging me far too much!'

Mary was patiently holding the linked metal belt, ornamented with beads of many colours, that was to go around my waist. She had already dressed in the deep-red linen tunic that I had made for her, the ends of her simpler chain belt jangling slightly as she stepped towards me. 'I helped decorate the belt,' she proclaimed proudly. It had taken the two of us several hours of patient work one afternoon to thread beads onto twisted thread and attach them to the belt. But it was nothing compared to the hours that it had taken me to add the extensive embroidery and beading around the neck, sleeves and hem of my garment and around each edge of the veil.

Abigail and Mary carefully draped the belt around my waist, taking care to pull in the material of my dress evenly as they did so. The jewellery came next, with – most importantly – the gold bracelets that had been given to me by Levi on our betrothal, and the headband with its coins. They also adorned me further with various rings, earrings, a necklace made from strands of gold with purple and green beads, and an ankle chain. When all were in place, I slipped on the new sandals of embossed and painted leather, far more ornate than the more practical ones that we wore every day.

Mary stood back and studied the completed outfit, smiling. 'You look beautiful, sister.'

'Levi is a fortunate man,' added Abigail, deliberately catching my eyes. And the words of my friend, sincerely spoken, both warmed and calmed my heart and brought colour to my cheeks.

Then we waited, knowing that the groom and his party would not arrive until the working day was over, but not knowing whether that would be closer to sunset or midnight.

I was surrounded by a number of other girls from Bethany, including Levi's sister Tamar. But the courtyard was also full to overflowing with family members from Bethany, Jerusalem and Galilee. The cool but pleasant evening air was filled with excited chatter and with laughter, particularly that of my aunt Tabitha. And, of course, my father was there, dressed in a fine new linen garment, dyed bright blue. Although he was standing across the courtyard from me, our eyes frequently met. Whenever they did, his expression was always one of immense pride, with a smile brimming over with the same love I'd known throughout the whole of my life. And, although the absence of my mother tinged my joy with wistfulness, I silently thanked God for the man whom I had always known as *Abba*.

A sunset of gentle pinks that merged into orange coloured the evening sky. It was only when a number of stars had appeared that we heard the raucous blowing of horns, announcing that the procession, which would wind its way from Levi's family home to our house, had begun. That was the way it had been done for as long as anyone could remember. The groom coming to collect his bride, to take her back to what would be her new home and family.

I slipped inside one final time with Abigail and Mary. My sister handed me the small vial that my father had given me the year before. As I opened it, the heady scent of myrrh rose up to meet me, and I inhaled deeply as I had done before in my father's workshop. Abigail leaned over to breathe in the scent, and then exhaled slowly, her eyes closed, savouring the expensive perfume. 'Levi won't be able to resist you!' she said.

'Where do you want the myrrh?' asked Mary.

'Everywhere!' I replied with a laugh.

'And how much do you want to use?' asked Abigail.

'All of it!' By the time they had finished applying the

myrrh to my clothes and skin, the whole room was filled with the beautiful fragrance. All that remained to be done was to place over my head the embroidered veils, covering not only my head but my face.

The girls led me out into the courtyard again. Although I could see very little through the material of the veil, I felt everyone's eyes upon me. My heart beat faster with a nervous anticipation. I was thankful that I did not have too long to wait before I heard the traditional cry go up: 'The bridegroom is here!' The voice was that of Manaen, who had been like a brother to Levi for most of his life, and the honour of being the Friend of the Bridegroom had fallen to him.

Levi's torch-lit procession had come as far as the threshold of the courtyard, but had not, as tradition dictated, come any further. It was for me, a sixteen-year-old bride, to go out to meet the one to whom I was promised, my groom of almost nineteen years. Abigail and Mary led me out through the doorway, and an expectant hush fell on the gathering. Moments later the veil over my face was being lifted up and removed by Levi. And the first thing I saw was his radiant face. The courtyard erupted into shouts of joy. I flushed with pleasure and delight. I would have been more than happy for him to kiss me then and there. But that was for later.

Instead, Levi leaned over and whispered in my ear. I giggled slightly, and those who had accompanied Levi laughed and shouted again. I whispered back, 'My bridegroom is the most handsome man in Bethany!'

He grinned, 'Come, Martha, my bride, I have waited long enough for you.' And then he took my hand and began leading me, away from my family home and my childhood, and towards my new life as his wife.

Those who had been waiting at the house with us spilled out onto the street, their own torches and lamps having been lit. The noisy – and now much larger – procession then started back to Levi's house, where Matthias was waiting to receive us. It felt as if the whole of the village had come out to watch. The music of lyres and horns, drums and tambourines, blended with the joyful singing of both men and women, as we walked and danced through the streets of Bethany.

The rest of the evening – and indeed the whole of the seven days of feasting that followed – were an exhilarating whirl. The brief ceremony that joined us as husband and wife and the blessings said over us. Our crowning as king and queen of the festivities. The two of us entering the wedding chamber to consummate the marriage as the festivities continued. The food and the wine, the singing and the dancing, the laughter and the story-telling, all of which seemed to be in a never-ending supply.

But eventually the week of feasting came to an end and the celebrations were finally over. Our guests all departed after many extended goodbyes and much well-wishing – and my new life really began.

It felt strange at night, lying next to my husband and hearing his slow, steady breathing in the darkness. But, for me, the new and unfamiliar were woven together with a large remnant of my previous life. I was still a daughter needed by her widowed father, and (as had been agreed at our betrothal) I continued most days to help bring up my siblings and cook for the family. Although Levi and I slept in our new rooms, built onto the house of Matthias and Esther – and furnished and decorated by my father's generous dowry – many of our meals were still taken at my father's house.

It was a pattern that persisted through the changes that occurred in our lives and in our land. And of those changes, two were most notable. Levi reached the age of twenty, and began to fulfil all the roles of a priest at the temple. And, at the start of our fourth year of marriage, Pontius Pilate was appointed as Gratus' successor and the latest Roman prefect to govern Judea. I knew that my father was grateful for my continuing help, and he assured me, more than once, that when children came all would change. And I did not doubt his words.

But children never came. What came instead was the one thing I could never have foreseen.

Chapter 12

Widowed

'He does not willingly bring affliction or grief to anyone.'
(Lamentations 3:33)

Autumn AD 28/Spring AD 29

'Martha, come home.' The words were spoken gently and quietly by my father, as he laid his hand lightly upon my shoulder. I did not immediately turn to face him, but stood staring at the tomb, still numb from the shock of what had happened so quickly and with no warning. Only four days earlier, Levi had been full of life. He'd just returned from the autumn Feast of Tabernacles and had barely been able to control his laughter, as he recounted a mishap at the temple involving a priest, a clay pitcher full of olive oil and a rather unfortunate goat. The fever had started that evening and had quickly taken hold, and despite Jonathan's skills as a physician, Levi was dead within three days. And it was all so unreal – and so quiet as I stood there.

It had, of course, been a very different story a short while earlier. Then, there had been wailing and Esther's inconsolable sobbing, as she and Matthias laid their eldest son – my husband, and Bethany's youngest serving priest – to rest in their family tomb. Eventually, with all the necessary rituals of death completed, the mourners had gradually returned to the house of Matthias or to their own homes. But I had remained at the tomb. My father stood nearby, and my sister sat a little way off, beneath an olive tree. She was comforting Lazarus – now eleven – in the loss of the one he'd come to adore, and look up to as a brother, over the previous six years.

And as I stood there in silence, all I could think of was the day, several months earlier, when Levi had returned from temple duty. He had flung open the courtyard door, his face flushed with excitement, and had announced, 'I can now die a happy man!' I'd put down the pestle and mortar I'd been using to grind mustard seeds, and waited with curiosity for his explanation. He came over and wrapped his arms around me, and whispered in my ear, 'I was chosen – the lot fell to me to burn the incense in the temple!' He gave me a kiss and then stood back, with his hands still on my waist and his eyes shining. 'Just think of it, Martha – it's not even four years since I started serving there, and I've been honoured with the duty that some priests wait their whole lives to perform. The Lord's blessing is surely upon us!' And I'd known that meant he believed that children would not be long in coming. But he was wrong. And the purposes of the Almighty had never seemed more inscrutable than at that moment, as I stared at the sealed tomb.

'Martha…' my father began again, and I finally turned to face him. He'd suddenly aged, as worsening health had slowed him down in the preceding two years, and his years had become etched more deeply upon his features in recent months. But even on his now-weary face, I could still see the same love that had always been there. His smile, although weak, was full of compassion. I responded in the only way I could: with a silent nod, a deep sigh that made my whole body shudder, and a last look at the tomb. We then began the slow walk back to Bethany, and to the house of my childhood that was once again my home.

The laws of inheritance in our land were hard on widows. I had no part in the little house that Levi and I had shared. It would, of course, have been different had I borne him a son. But I was grateful that I still had a home to which I could return, and a family of which I was a part.

The six and a half years between me and my sister felt as if they had melted away in the time since my wedding. Then, she had been a child of barely ten whom I'd had to mother. But she'd slowly and beautifully transformed, leaving her childhood behind, and now, at the age of fifteen, she stood beside me as my sister once again. And we drew closer, as we spent more time together after my return. Although I was in charge of running the house, she was often at my side as we prepared and cooked food. We cooked for our small family, for the friends or relatives who shared our Sabbath or evening meals, or for those in Bethany whose homes had been touched by the joy of childbirth or the sadness of loss. We also wove, dyed our fabrics and made our clothes together, and slowly – with the help of Mary's laughter and infectious joy – my heart began to heal over the months that followed. Though I still had scars that smarted, when the wrong questions were asked or difficult issues raised.

My father looked around at the numerous small clusters of people, standing around outside the synagogue in the sunshine of a Sabbath, early in March. Although the service had finished some time earlier, most seemed happy to be out in the first real warmth of the year – exchanging news, telling stories, meeting friends. My father had finished the lengthy and animated discussion he had been having with the other elders – presumably over some point that had been raised in the address Jonathan had given. He'd come over to stand with me, after Abigail, and her ever-growing number of small children, left for a meal with Judas and Salome.

After surveying the crowd, he finally spoke. 'There are still others in Bethany who would make a good husband for you, Martha.' I could feel my chest tightening, and didn't respond immediately. I did not for a moment begrudge Abigail her husband and children, but their presence had once again been a difficult reminder for me of what was not mine. He went on: 'And there are plenty of others in the family in Jerusalem besides – '

'But how many would want a barren widow?' As soon as the words were out of my mouth, I regretted my angry and bitter tone.

My father replied patiently and kindly, however, sighing deeply before he spoke. 'My dear Martha, you are a widow, yes, but remember how long it was before the Lord blessed your mother and me with you. You only arrived after ten years of waiting – you and Levi were only married for five.'

'Yes, but Mama had already conceived more than once before I was born.' It was not the first time that we had spoken of such things. Despite all of my father's assurances, I still doubted that any family would willingly consider a young widow, who had never born children in five years of marriage, as a good match for their son.

My father decided to direct my thoughts in other, more helpful directions, although he still did so with great tenderness in his voice. 'Martha, you cannot know all the ways in which the Lord works his purposes out. We have to trust that those purposes are good.'

I quickly and abruptly turned my head away, betraying my deep feelings of turmoil, even anger, towards the God whose ways were strangely perverse and so difficult to comprehend. I was in no mood to try to fathom His ways, and so changed the subject quickly. I looked over to where Mary was standing with my aunt Elizabeth, to whose home we were invited that day. 'Mary has just turned sixteen. Have you chosen for her yet?' I knew my father had been considering the issue, but had not yet confided in me any firm decision.

'Until the whole period of mourning for Levi is completed, I will do nothing definite for her – ' He turned and gave me his familiar smile, ' – or for you, my daughter.'

I was grateful that my aunt Elizabeth came over to join us. Her face now showed the lines of age, but there was still a gracefulness and gentleness about her that reminded me of my mother.

'Shalom, Heli,' she said with a smile, before greeting my father with the customary kiss.

'Shalom, Elizabeth.'

'You have not forgotten your invitation to join us today?'

He shook his head with a laugh, 'I wouldn't dream of it! And will Matthan and his family be with us? Has he returned from Galilee yet?' The conversation quickly moved on to various different members of family, but my father, in his wisdom, did not want our previous discussion to remain – in his eyes – unfinished. Or leave me estranged from the God whom he loved and trusted more than I did.

My father deliberately slowed his pace, as I accompanied him on the short walk back to the home of John and Elizabeth. Soon, there was enough distance between us and the rest of the family to talk without being overheard or interrupted. He raised his head and gazed upwards, following the path of several birds against the sky, which was the colour of the flax flowers that were adorning many of the fields of Judea.

'Even at my age, the Lord's wonders still never cease to amaze me – and the mystery of a bird in flight is one of them.'

I presumed that his words were a gentle way of steering our conversation back to the greater mystery that troubled my heart. I watched the swallows swooping and soaring against the clear blue sky. Without looking at my father, I said quietly, 'Why does the Almighty seem to bless with one hand and curse with the other?'

My father didn't give an answer immediately, although in truth I wasn't really expecting one. It had been more a statement of fact than a question in my mind. As we walked slowly, we continued to follow the ever-changing arcs traced by the birds above us. They appeared to rise effortlessly on their wings, blissfully free from any of the cares and sorrows that burdened my heart.

At last, my father spoke. 'We do not even understand the flight of the smallest bird, Martha. The mysteries of the Lord are many and great. But through the prophets He has assured us of His love, and that *He does not willingly bring affliction or grief to anyone*.'

I did not recognise the Scripture of which he spoke, but had no doubt that my father had quoted it truly. I tore my eyes away from the carefree swallows, and turned towards my father. 'Then why does he afflict or grieve us at all? Why do his purposes, if they're good, bring us so much pain?' I searched my father's face, but only found there a quiet thoughtfulness, as he considered how best to answer my anguished questions. Deep down, I longed for a faith as strong as his. His own life bore no less sorrow than mine, and yet his trust in the Almighty seemed to be, for him, an unshakeable rock on which to build his life.

The peacefulness of the Sabbath day was suddenly broken by the laughter of my uncle John ahead of us, as he and the other members of the family finally reached the house. My father slowed his pace even further, so I did the same. 'Do you remember, Martha, when your brother broke his arm when he was four?' I nodded, remembering the cries that had brought me running from the courtyard to the olive tree from which he had fallen. 'When Jonathan arrived, Lazarus screamed and screamed, and kept on trying to prevent him touching it.' It wasn't difficult to recollect the shrieks that most of our neighbours must also have heard. My father went on, 'Lazarus was too young to understand that Jonathan was helping him. All your brother could think of was the further pain he was causing, binding it up.'

I understood perfectly well what my father was trying to say to me, but blurted out, 'But what of a death? First Mama, and then Levi. What possible good could God bring out of those?'

As ever, my father not only imparted his own wisdom, but also directed me to the great stories of our people, through which God had made Himself known. He began again, 'Do you remember how we spoke of Joseph after Mama died?' I nodded, remembering how my father had spoken of how God was still at work, even in the many hardships endured by the son of Jacob. 'But the Scriptures also tell us of the sufferings of Job.'

The sombre tale of the godly man who had lost his wealth, his health and his children when God allowed Satan to afflict him, had always been one that troubled me. 'But what good came of *his* sufferings?' I asked.

'Job may never have known the reasons for his pain and loss, but he found something more precious.' I remained silent and waited for him to elaborate. 'He saw the greatness and wonder of God, and was then willing to trust that the Lord's ways were higher than his.' My father paused before adding, 'The pathway to beholding the glory of God often leads us first through places of pain.'

When I looked up into the sky again in the silence that followed, the swallows were nowhere to be seen. The final words of my father echoed through my mind again – and would come back to me, some four years later. But as we finally reached the house together, the familiar phrase of my father – *When the Messiah comes* – slipped once again into my mind, and my heart longed for the time when all would be put right.

As Elizabeth placed on the table a basket of bread, baked before the Sabbath had begun, my father asked her with a twinkle in his eye, 'And does your latest grandson look like his father or his grandfather?' My aunt laughed. She had recently returned from visiting her youngest son, Seth, in

160

Galilee. He had married one of our mutual cousins and settled in the north, where work for a mason was easy to come by.

'Neither,' replied Elizabeth. 'If anything he looks more like his mother.'

'And Seth isn't regretting making his home in Galilee?'

My uncle settled himself down at the table opposite my father. 'On the contrary – it seems to suit him well. It is still a good time to be a mason there, even though the work on Tiberias has been completed.'

'And does Herod's brand new city on the lake honour Caesar, as he wished it to?'

Uncle John chuckled. 'Herod Antipas should have been more careful in his planning. Apparently he has built his new city on an old Gentile graveyard, so no self-respecting Jew will live there as it makes them unclean. I hear he has had to fill his city with slaves and those who have been freed from prison!'

My father roared with laughter until tears were running down his face. My aunt smiled as she placed another pottery bowl filled with salad on the table. I recognised the design of diamonds and circles, embossed around the edge of the bowl, as being the handiwork of our friend Judas. When my father had eventually caught his breath enough to continue, he asked, 'So is he still expanding Sepphoris?' I remembered the name of the city in Galilee that Herod Antipas had spent considerable time and money rebuilding. The answer to my father's question had to wait, however, until my uncle had spoken the blessing over our simple meal.

'His building plans are certainly continuing for the moment,' John finally answered. 'Not good news for all who pay taxes, but at least Seth has his tax returned to him in his wages.'

'And does he find life under Herod Antipas any better than under a Roman prefect?' asked my father again.

John shrugged as he reached for the bowl of olives. 'Herod may not be a Roman, but his desire to please the emperor is no less than that of Pilate. The best course of action with both of them is to pay your taxes and keep out of their way.'

'At least that's not difficult with Pilate, given that he spends most of his time in Caesarea,' added Elizabeth as she passed a plate of freshly made cheese around the table. My knowledge of the politics of our land was nowhere near that of my father. But I did know that whilst Pilate was away at Caesarea (his base further up the coast), the power in Jerusalem and much of Judea was largely delegated to the high priest appointed by him.

'Have you ever seen Pontius Pilate, Abba?' asked Lazarus.

'Once – two years ago at Passover. I was in the Upper City near Jacob's house, and he was on his way to Herod's palace. You couldn't miss him. The soldiers cleared the way for him and made sure we all kept our distance.' I had seen enough of Roman soldiers to know that I would not want to get too close to any of them.

'Why doesn't he stay at the Antonia Fortress when he's in Jerusalem?' asked Lazarus. And it was a good question. *Why would a Roman ruler not want to stay in their stronghold, surrounded by his soldiers?*

My uncle laughed. 'What – and miss the luxuries that Herod built into his palace before he died? Your grandfather Eleazar did some stonework there. He used to tell us how it was full of mosaics, statues and fountains. Old Herod certainly knew how to impress his Roman friends, and it's little surprise that Pilate has taken the finest building in Jerusalem, after the temple, to be his quarters whilst he's here – '

'Like every governor before him,' added my father.

'So why doesn't he live in Jerusalem all the time?' asked Lazarus.

My father shrugged his shoulders and joked, 'It's probably too Jewish for his liking. He only comes to Jerusalem when he has to – at the time of the festivals.'

My brother looked puzzled. 'But if he's not a Jew, why does he come for the festivals?'

'Because he knows that if there's going to be trouble, then it's more than likely to be at one of the times when Jerusalem and its temple are packed with pilgrims,' replied my father. 'It's no accident that the fortress overlooks the temple.'

'I suppose he also thinks it prudent to swell the number of Roman soldiers in Jerusalem with those who travel with him,' added my uncle.

'Aren't there enough of them already in Jerusalem?' I asked, in a voice that didn't entirely hide my dislike of *any* number of Rome's soldiers.

'They only keep five hundred or so at the fortress – '

'And isn't that enough?' I interrupted.

My father laughed. 'We should be thankful Martha. Pilate largely relies on the temple guard to keep order in Jerusalem. If it wasn't for the several thousand guards who are under Caiaphas, we'd be seeing far more soldiers in Roman uniforms in our city. But enough talk of Rome.' My father's face brightened as he turned the conversation away from our human overlords, and back to our true identity as God's people. 'What did you all make of Jonathan's address this morning?'

The conversation around the table was lively and animated as we debated what had been said. Lazarus, who had recently turned twelve, was increasingly able to make contributions, given his continuing schooling at the synagogue under Joseph the scribe. When he made a relevant comment about the words of Moses to Joshua, commanding him to lead the people of Israel across the Jordan River and into the Promised Land, my uncle turned to my father with raised eyebrows. 'Well, it seems that my young nephew is paying attention to what Joseph is teaching him.' And he said to Lazarus, 'You are becoming a fine student of the Law!' I wasn't sure who took greatest pleasure in John's comment – my brother or my father. My uncle continued, 'I hope you realise how fortunate you are, Lazarus. Many of the boys your age are already working in the fields each day, or helping to run the family business. There is no greater privilege than to be educated in the ways of the Lord, so that you may know Him better and serve Him in this world.'

Although he wouldn't say it to my uncle or father, Lazarus often found the lessons that he had to sit through tedious. He didn't mind memorising large amounts of Scripture, or learning its stories. But having to remember the minutiae of the traditions of the elders left him bored. The direction in which our conversation suddenly turned, however, was anything but boring.

'And speaking of the Jordan, have you heard, Heli, of the new preacher who is baptising in the river?'

My father nodded in reply, swallowing a spoonful of

yoghurt and honey from the bowl that Elizabeth had just set in the middle of the table. 'There seems to be little else spoken of in Jerusalem at the moment.'

I was suddenly curious, as were my brother and sister, judging by the looks on their faces. 'Who is he?' asked Mary.

'All I've found out so far,' began my father, 'is that he seems to have come from the desert, and has been preaching all around the Jordan area. And that suddenly droves of people from Jerusalem are going out to hear him – and to be baptised.'

'But I thought baptism was only for Gentiles, when they wanted to become part of our people,' said Lazarus.

I shared his perplexity. I was used to the ritual baths that I had to take each month, and to those we also took after childbirth or when defiled by contact with the dead. But the ritual of baptism was different. It was an immersion in water that allowed a Gentile to take on the faith of the Jews, despite not being born as one. It signified a break with all they had been before and a new birth into the people of God. I was eager to hear what my father had to say.

'Well,' he began, 'it certainly isn't Gentiles that he's preaching to – or baptising – at the moment. And whatever he's saying, it's having an effect.'

Elizabeth glanced between the two men at the table. 'Will either of you go to hear him?'

My father smiled. 'I'll hear anyone once.'

Chapter 13

The priest's son

*'A voice of one calling: "In the wilderness prepare the way for the L*ord*."' (Isaiah 40:3)*

Spring AD 29

I stared at the crowds, dumbfounded. Every available space around the river and on the nearby vantage points – trees, rocks, mounds – appeared to be taken. The constant slow milling of people seeming as ever-changing as the flow of the Jordan itself. Trees near the water's edge formed a line of green stretching along the banks of the river, whose waters had been swollen by the rains of the winter and the early spring. But the landscape was mainly of rocky slopes, curving down to the valley through which the river ran. It streamed from the Sea of Galilee in the north, to the dead Salt Sea that lay to the east and south of Bethany. I had never seen crowds like it outside of Jerusalem at festival time. I couldn't begin to number the people gathered there, and so whispered to my father, 'How many are here do you think, Abba?'

He scanned the crowd that was made up of all ages and all walks of life. It even included – much to my surprise – some in the uniforms of Roman soldiers. 'Three or four hundred, maybe? It's hard to tell…'

The people were all standing round in little groups, talking quietly, as were we. But the attention of every person was on the solitary figure standing by the river, staff in hand, eyes closed, as if in prayer or listening attentively to a voice that was beyond our hearing.

Two days earlier, my father had suddenly announced that we were all going to visit his youngest brother, Matthan, who lived in Jericho, twelve or so miles to the north-east. We had travelled down the winding road that descended from Jerusalem to Jericho, through the rugged and barren hills, almost white in the harsh sun. The city was like a green oasis in the surrounding countryside, and known for its springs and palm trees. But, as I soon discovered, the purpose of our trip was not only to visit Matthan and the family. To the east of the city was the river Jordan – and the baptist who was causing such a stir.

I wasn't sure what I'd been expecting. Certainly, when I saw the baptist – John, as we had discovered his name to be – he looked nothing like any preacher who had ever visited our synagogue to speak. If there was one word that described the person who stood on the opposite bank of the river, then it was *wild*. Even from where I was standing, I could see that his garments were fairly rough and ready ones, held together with a thick leather belt around his waist.

My father tore his gaze away from John. He turned to a small group standing nearby, clearly eager to glean what he could about the identity of the unlikely preacher. 'Do any of you know what family he comes from?'

I had already decided it must be a poor one, given his dress. But a white-haired, older man, who gave the impression of knowing more than any of the others around him, said to my father, 'I've heard that he comes from a family of priests, the only son of elderly parents.'

The answer stirred up fresh discussion as to whether he had ever served in the temple or not, but my father's attention was back on John. He had been transfixed by the baptist ever since setting eyes on him. But he was suddenly deep in thought. 'What is it, Abba?'

It was a few moments before he responded, and when he eventually spoke, it was more to himself. 'Yes, he would be about the right age.'

'Abba?' asked Mary, as confused as I was.

'The priest's son,' replied my father, with wonder on his face. He lowered his voice so that only we could hear. 'Martha, do you remember the story that Matthias told, about an angel appearing to an elderly priest in the temple?'

'Yes, I remember it!' I exclaimed. Although I had first heard the tale recounted by my father before either my sister or brother had been born, I had subsequently heard it again when Matthias had been my father-in-law. The strange events in the temple had to quickly be retold in their entirety, however, to my siblings – and then my father's comment about John being about the right age became clear.

Lazarus stared at my father, wide-eyed. 'Do you think John is the one the angel spoke of, the one who would be great in God's plans?'

'Maybe we should hear what he has to say first...' my father answered. And with that he fell silent and gazed again at the figure standing, head still bowed, on the other side of the river.

The crowd continued to move slowly around us, as

more people arrived. 'They say his clothes are made from camel's hair,' confided a woman to a friend, as they took their place near us.

Without looking away from John, my father quietly asked my brother, 'And in the Scriptures, Lazarus, who dresses in a garment of hair with a leather belt around his waist?'

Lazarus thought for a moment, evidently doing his best to remember all that Joseph had taught him. 'The prophet Elijah?'

'That's right. He dresses as Elijah.' His words were spoken softly, as if they carried great significance. Although why John wearing the same clothes as one of our greatest prophets should be important was lost on me. Still, I had to admit that he *was* exactly how I'd imagine one of the great prophets of old to be. Even before he spoke, there was air of authority about him, as if he were afraid of no man and answered only to God. And when he finally did speak, I immediately knew that I had heard nothing like it before.

The murmuring of the crowd suddenly came to an abrupt halt as John opened his eyes. He scrutinised the crowd, as if he were looking into the hearts and minds of all gathered there. He then lifted his head, and his voice carried clearly across the multitude: 'Repent, for the kingdom of heaven is near.'

Unlike so many of the addresses I'd heard over the years in the synagogue, John's message was straightforward and simple. He spoke of the need that we all had – Jews or not – to turn from the sins that stood as a barrier between us and a holy God. He warned us of God's coming judgment, telling us that being descendants of Abraham would not save us. And he implored us to change, saying it was not too late to set our lives right with God.

When voices in the crowd called out, asking John what they should do, he spoke plainly. 'Anyone who has two shirts should share with the one who has none, and anyone who has food should do the same.' Tax-collectors were told, 'Don't collect any more than you are required to.' And when soldiers asked what they should do, he replied, 'Don't extort money and don't accuse people falsely – be content with your pay.' None of it was difficult to understand.

John called each one of us to demonstrate a desire for both forgiveness and a change in our lives, by confessing our sins and being immersed in the waters of the Jordan. The more I listened to him, the more my heart stirred within me. I was only too well aware of my short-comings, and, as he spoke, I found myself longing to be rid of those things of which I was ashamed. And there were tears on my sister's cheeks.

I wasn't sure how long we listened to him, but my attention hadn't once strayed elsewhere. And when John stepped down into the waters of the Jordan, calling on each person there to be baptised, my father immediately began to move forward. I gasped, 'Abba! You have no need to repent.'

He looked over his shoulder, back towards me, and I was stunned by the depth of sorrow in his eyes. 'Child, we *all* stand sinful before a holy God. There is not a man alive who can claim to be without sin.' And with that he looked ahead once more, moving slowly forward with the crowd, as we also did, each silently waiting our turn to be immersed in the waters by the baptist. But even as

I stood and waited, I couldn't help noticing that not all were responding to his call.

It wasn't difficult to understand why those in power were watching John, with people there to report back all that was said. I suspected from their dress that among those standing back from the river were a group of Sadducees. I had spent enough time with Levi to recognise the elite group of rich, to which the high priest and the whole family of Annas belonged. But I was more surprised to see a group of Pharisees there, also standing at a distance. Given their commitment to the Law and to living holy lives, I couldn't understand why they would not also want to respond. It was a fleeting question in my mind, however. My thoughts were soon back on my own need to repent.

A sudden anxiety gripped me as my father made his way somewhat unsteadily into the water, his ever-increasing age displayed once again. But I needn't have worried, as all was well. I do not know what sins my father confessed to John before going beneath the waters, but when it was my turn, I stood nervously before John with my head bowed. The words tumbled out of my mouth, as I confessed with shame my anger towards God and my lack of trust in the Almighty. I also confessed my lack of love for God and for others, and was glad that it was only John and the Lord himself who heard my jumbled words. The cool waters of the Jordan only covered me for a moment, and as I came up my eyes finally met those of John – and I was utterly taken by surprise. I had expected a stern expression, and an air of holiness under which I would wither. Instead, I found a warm smile that accompanied three simple words: 'God forgives you.' And as I waded back, my heart felt lighter than before.

I stood beside my father on the shore, as we waited for Mary and then Lazarus to be baptised. The four of us then watched as the flow of people continued down into the river. As the warm spring sunshine began to dry our clothes and our hair, Lazarus was clearly turning something over in his mind. 'John can't be the Messiah, can he Abba? Not if it's true that he comes from a family of priests, because that would make him a descendant of Levi.'

'That's right,' replied my father, nodding.

'When the Messiah comes, he'll be a son of David, won't he? From the tribe of Judah, not the tribe of Levi.'

My father smiled, as did my sister and I, not only at the correct answer, but also because my brother had picked up his favourite phrase. Lazarus suddenly added excitedly, 'Maybe the Messiah has already been born!'

'Surely we'd have heard of it,' I responded, convinced that the coming of the greatest ever descendent of David would be obvious to all of God's people.

My father shrugged his shoulders. 'Remember, Martha, he will be a son of David, not of Herod. He cannot come from those who rule our lands now. Herod and his family cannot even claim true Jewish descent, let alone being of David's line.'

His comment brought our discussion of the Messiah to an end, and we continued to watch the baptisms taking place for most of the rest of the day. It was only shortly before we left, however, that we heard the words that were to stir up our questions once again. A small group had approached John as soon as he returned to the banks of the river. Whatever question they had asked was inaudible to us. John's reply, however, was not.

'I baptise you with water for repentance,' he cried out. A hush fell once more over the whole crowd. John's commanding voice rose above the gentle sound of the river continuing its journey down to the Salt Sea. 'But there is one who will come after me – one who is more powerful – whose sandals I am not even worthy to untie.' He paused, looking round the crowd, and I could feel my heart beating with excitement. 'I baptise you with water, but he will baptise you with the Holy Spirit and with fire.'

The words of the baptist were often spoken of in the weeks that followed. I became aware, however, that the unorthodox preacher not only drew crowds but also divided them. Most of the people in Bethany and in the other villages around, though, seemed happy to listen to John and be baptised. But as the spring slipped into summer, I became increasingly worried about my father's health. I noticed him being bothered more and more by sudden pains, which he did his best to hide, and he often found it difficult to catch his breath. He began taking more days of rest, when even the short walk into Jerusalem was too much for him. Three score years and ten, the span of our lives spoken of in Scripture, was attained by some but by no means all in our land. Many who reached fifty – as my father had done the previous year – did not see much beyond that. And as summer began to slip into autumn, I knew that my father was preparing me in different ways for a responsibility that might soon be thrust upon me.

In the cool of a summer evening, as I sat in the courtyard beside him, my father turned his tired face towards me. 'It is time for Lazarus to begin learning the trade of his father. Your uncle John will take him into Jerusalem – '

'But Abba, he can go into the city with you.'

'Martha, I will not be with you forever, and I must make provision for all my children.' I fell silent, unwilling to accept what I saw every time I looked at my father. He continued, 'Jacob will teach Lazarus alongside Thomas in the workshop. Jacob is also aware that it will soon be time for a husband to be found for Mary.'

'Abba, please don't say such things.'

My father patted my hand, 'My dear Martha. We are not like the ancient olive trees on the Mount. We only ever *flourish like a flower of the field*, as the Lord himself has told us. Here one day and gone the next. But the Almighty still remembers us. You must trust Him, Martha. Trust Him as I have always taught you to. His ways may be beyond our understanding at times, but He will not fail you.'

I smiled weakly, 'I will try to, Abba.'

My father's eyes suddenly brightened. 'And look for the Messiah, Martha! I fear that I will not live to see his day, but you… If the words of the baptist are true, then you may see his day, and see it soon. Be ready for him, Martha – be ready for him!'

He sounded so like Lazarus in his infectious excitement, and for a moment the sadness that had hung over our conversation was dispelled. I smiled back, 'I will, Abba – I promise. We all will.'

And then my father spoke again, but in a hushed tone: 'One of the prophets speaks of Elijah coming before the day of the Lord.'

He dresses as Elijah. The words my father had spoken near the banks of the Jordan back in the spring of that year suddenly returned to me. And I finally understood their significance.

And my father, much to my surprise, suddenly chuckled. 'To think of it. That I should have lived long enough to see the fulfilment of the prophet. And that my own children might actually see the dawning of the day of the Messiah!' We then sat in silence, and a faraway look came into my father's eyes. But then the moment had passed. 'Fetch your sister for me, will you, Martha? And the wooden box on the table by my bed. Whatever you do, don't drop it!' I smiled, and without a further word rose to fulfil my father's requests.

As soon as my father lifted the lid of the box and I saw what was inside, I knew what was coming. He carefully lifted out the alabaster jar and handed it to Mary. She looked enquiringly at him, as I had done some years before, when he had placed into my hands the precious jar of myrrh. 'It is your dowry, Mary. I have decided to give it to you now, rather than wait until your betrothal.' Whether my sister realised what lay behind his words was not clear, but she continued to look at both of us for further explanation, unsure of the contents of the jar. My father glanced over in my direction. 'And let's see if your sister can guess what is inside…'

I smiled. Myrrh had been my favourite. But Mary's preference, as I had supposed in my father's workshop all those years earlier, had been different. 'Is it nard?'

'Ah, your sister has a good memory, Mary. It is indeed – a pint of the purest nard, all the way from India.'

Mary gasped. She, like me, understood the immense value of what she now held in her hands. 'Oh Abba, thank you!'

'Now all we need to do is find a man who is worthy of that dowry – and worthy of you, my daughter.'

And after she had embraced our father, he once again produced a small vial for her wedding day. She lifted the stopper, and I caught the faintest hint of the rich perfume. And I wondered how long it would be until – as had happened at my wedding – the fragrance filled the whole room.

It was my uncle Jacob who took on the responsibility for my father's funeral. In the autumn, shortly after the rites of mourning for my husband were completed, Mary, Lazarus and I laid our father in the family tomb close to Bethany, where the bones of my mother and her parents lay. Many came from Jerusalem to mourn with us. And as I stood at the tomb, surrounded by the weeping and the wailing, I silently promised my father that, whatever else happened, I would keep my promise. When the Messiah finally came, I would be ready for him.

And once again, as we mourned, there was a distant figure – still afflicted with leprosy – who also mourned the loss of Heli, son of Saul: not as a father, but as his closest friend.

Chapter 14

The Son of David

*'"The days are coming," declares the L*ORD*, "when I will*
raise up for David a righteous Branch,
a King who will reign wisely and do what is just and
right in the land."' (Jeremiah 23:5–6)

Spring AD 30

It's a miracle.

Lazarus was right.

If Simon's unblemished skin was the first thing I noticed about him, as I stood dumbfounded in the square in the centre of Bethany, the second was his shaved head and face. And immediately I knew their significance. Simon stopped in his tracks as soon as he caught sight of me. 'Martha! My little Martha!' And with that, he simply threw his arms around me, and embraced me as he would a long-lost daughter. 'It's been fourteen years, Martha – fourteen long years.'

The questions in my mind were too many and too muddled to form into a coherent sentence. All I could do was return the embrace in stunned silence. As I did so, I saw Rachel over Simon's shoulder, tears of joy streaming down her face. And James, standing beside his mother, his face beaming with a smile that seemed almost as wide as he was tall.

As Simon and I finally stood apart, I found that I, too, had tears in my eyes, as I searched for any signs of leprosy on his face or hands but found none. 'How is that possible?' I whispered in a wavering voice.

Then I saw the face of Matthias. He was standing on the other side of Rachel, and he smiled. 'I, too, am waiting for the answer to that question, Martha. He's been examined and pronounced clean by the priests at the temple, but he hasn't yet told me how it happened.'

Although the years had added wrinkles and lines to his face, Simon had a grin that was almost childlike. 'All in good time, my friends, all in good time. After all, don't you have some introductions to do first, Martha?'

I suddenly became aware of my siblings at my side – the ones who had almost dragged me there in the first place. 'My sister, Mary, and my brother, Lazarus,' I said, indicating each with my hand. 'And this,' I said to them, 'is Simon, son of Jonas,' adding rather pointedly, 'the *Silversmith*.'

It wasn't until that evening that we were finally given our explanation. Simon's house was packed with family and friends from Bethany, all eager – as we were – to hear about his miraculous recovery, and how, after fourteen years, his leprosy seemed to have disappeared overnight. Mary and I helped Rachel and her daughters (who had returned with their husbands) to serve wine, olives and cakes of raisins and figs to all the guests. The room, crammed full as the temple at festival time, was alive with animated and excited chatter. Eventually, when all had been served, Simon held up his hand to indicate that he was ready to speak. The lively conversation rapidly became an expectant hush, and I was reminded of how it had felt on the banks of the Jordan the previous year. Light from the little pottery lamps, scattered liberally around the room, illuminated the eager faces of old and young alike – all turned in the same direction. Towards Simon, as he began to speak.

'Thank you, friends, for joining my family and me this evening.' Simon paused as he surveyed the room, smiling at the faces of those who were dear to him, and from whom he had been separated for so long. 'I know that you have all been asking the same question – how it is that my leprosy has left me so suddenly, after all these years.'

There was a gentle murmuring and nods of agreement. An unfamiliar voice piped up from the back of the room, echoing Lazarus' earlier words: 'It's a miracle!'

The murmuring increased, and Simon said, 'Yes, friends, I believe it is.'

'But how did it happen?' The slightly exasperated voice was that of Matthias.

'I see that fourteen years have not made my friend the priest any less impatient.' A ripple of laughter went around the crowded room. 'Well, you shall get your answer now, Matthias, but the story really starts with James.' All eyes shifted onto Simon's son, who immediately appeared self-conscious with all the sudden attention. 'Tell them how it started, James,' said Simon.

James kept his gaze mainly on the floor, but glanced up from time to time, as he told his part of the story. 'It was just before the end of the Passover, and I was in the workshop. One of the pilgrims had come to buy a silver bracelet. He told me, however, that he'd just come from the temple. There had been quite a stir, because one of the other pilgrims had been healing people in the temple courts. I asked who this person was, but the man didn't seem to know. He just said that he had seen a lame man made completely better, and that he had never seen anything like it – a man healing the sick with just a word! After I'd served the customer, I locked up the workshop and hurried up to the temple, but I didn't see anything unusual. I went back the following day, though – the last day of the Feast. I just wanted to know if there was any chance of healing for my father.' James paused, but when he looked up from the ground again his eyes were shining. 'And this time I saw him. He was – ' James trailed off, as if he were searching for just the right words to describe what he'd seen. ' – he was doing wonderful things!'

Apart from James speaking, a complete silence had fallen upon the room. He continued: 'He made the blind see – and I saw the lame walk for myself.' James glanced around the room. As if to answer any unspoken doubts, he added in a quieter voice, 'It was really happening, right in front of me.' After letting his words sink in for a moment, he went on. 'The crowds were getting larger all the time, but suddenly he was gone. He'd somehow just slipped away in the crowd. I ran as fast as I could back to the Leper House, and called for my father. If this man could heal leprosy, I couldn't let it pass.'

As James looked down at the floor again, Simon said, 'I have a good son,' and then continued the story himself. 'James explained to me on the way back to Jerusalem what he had seen. To be honest, I didn't know what to make of it, but there was nothing to lose – not after fourteen years. It wasn't easy with all the pilgrims beginning to leave Jerusalem, though.' Simon didn't need to give us a fuller explanation. It didn't take much imagination to see the difficulty of a leper trying to reach Jerusalem with pilgrims coming and going. Lepers were required to make sure they kept their distance from others – although others were more than happy to give them a wide berth.

'You must have been popular,' joked Judas. As laughter once again rippled around the room, I could only imagine the comments that must have been made, as the progress of the pilgrims was slowed by a leper trying to go in the opposite direction.

When the room was quiet once more, Simon continued. 'As you know, I'm not – or rather, was not – permitted to enter Jerusalem, let alone the temple.' Around the room, a number nodded. It was one of the many restrictions placed upon those with the terrible disease, and one of the most heart-rending. 'But thankfully, I have not only a good son, but a clever one.' Despite the dim lamplight, I was close enough to James to see him redden slightly. His father's raised eyebrows and nod invited him to explain.

'Although I didn't know anything about the healer, I'd heard him speak,' began James. 'He had a northern accent – a Galilean one. I reckoned that if he was leaving Jerusalem with other pilgrims, and going back up north to Galilee, he'd probably leave through the Susa Gate. So that seemed the best place to wait to see if he came along. My only fear was that we might already have missed him.'

'As I said, I have a clever son,' said Simon, a look of pride on his face. 'We must have waited about two hours near the gate, and I was beginning to wonder whether it would have been better to stay at the Leper House. But

181

then James spotted him, and pointed him out to me as he came up the road.' Simon paused once more, as if he were savouring again in his imagination the moment he first glimpsed his healer. 'As he came closer, I didn't know how I would get his attention. But, all of a sudden, he looked in my direction, and I found myself calling out to him, *Can you help me, Teacher?* He stopped, and said nothing for a moment. He just looked at me. Then he smiled and walked over to me. And he reached out and touched me.'

Simon fell silent again, letting the significance of his words sink in. *Touching a leper*. I wondered how long it had been since he had been touched like that – *had it been fourteen years?*

Simon then went on, 'And all he said was, *Be clean*. And then…' Simon's voice began to waver with emotion. Rachel, sitting beside him, brushed away tears, as they began to roll down her cheeks once more. Simon took a moment to collect himself and then began again. 'And then I felt something change, as if my body had come alive under his touch. And when I looked down at my hands' – he held them up for us all to see – 'they were as you see them now.' His sleeves slid back to reveal his arms. There was no hint of leprosy in sight – no disfigurement or ugly blemishes – and his skin resembled that of a much younger man. He finished, 'And I knew I was completely healed.'

A buzz of excitement suddenly filled the room. When I caught sight of my sister, her face was radiant, and she was looking with rapt attention and wonder at Simon.

'What then?' piped up another voice from across the room. Once again, silence descended as we all eagerly waited to hear more.

'I think I stuttered out a *thank-you*, but to be honest, I was so overwhelmed I'm not sure what I said. But then he told me to go and show myself to the priest, and offer the sacrifices required by the Law.'

'And then?' asked Matthias.

'He smiled. And he was gone. He walked away up the road. Part of me just wanted to run after him, but he didn't look back. So I went to the Chamber of the Lepers in the temple, as he'd told me to.'

I remembered it as one of the four chambers at the corners of the Court of the Women. Levi had once described to me the rituals of cleansing that recovered lepers had to go through, including presenting themselves to a priest at the Nicanor Gate, who alone had the authority to pronounce them clean. And so I understood, perhaps better than many others in the room, Simon's next words.

'The priests examined me, and told me to wash and shave as I was clear of leprosy. I was pronounced clean, and then spent the necessary week in seclusion with relatives in Jerusalem. Then I offered the last of the sacrifices for purification this morning. And so here I am – restored to health, restored to my family, and restored to all of you, my friends.'

There was a moment's pause, and then the room suddenly erupted with questions. And one question was being called out more than any other. Simon held up his hand to quell the clamour, and the room again fell silent. '*His name?* His name is Jesus – from Nazareth.'

I'm not sure what I had expected, but the name of the healer was nothing unusual. The Aramaic form of the name Joshua was popular, and I could immediately think of three others in Bethany who went by the same name.

'Nazareth?' called out Judas. 'Are you suggesting something good has come out of there?'

We all knew of the place in Galilee, and the laughter around the room was because none of us would ever associate it with greatness. But Judas then asked, 'And what of this Jesus? What else do you know of him?'

'That he is a teacher,' replied Simon. 'And now I have told you everything I know.'

From that point on, the packed room was filled with animated discussions, as each small huddle debated what they had heard and seen that day. The lack of information about Simon's healer did not, however, stop speculation. And more than once, I heard a word whispered, and always in the same questioning tone: *Messiah?*

Eventually people began to drift away, but only when the lamps were beginning to sputter and die, and the young children had fallen asleep in their mothers' arms. By the time we were the only guests remaining, Bethany had largely fallen silent. Mary and I helped Rachel clear away the empty cups and bowls, every olive having been consumed and every jug of wine emptied. When the rugs and mats had been straightened, and the house returned to more or less its normal appearance, we still lingered. We were reluctant to leave, and Simon and Rachel seemed reluctant to see us go. Simon beckoned us to sit back down with him, and we gladly sat on the cushions and rugs, as did James and his wife, who was holding their young baby in her arms. James's five-year-old daughter lay asleep on Simon's lap. He was stroking her hair, able at last to hold and touch the grandchild that he had previously only seen from a distance.

Simon finally tore his gaze away from the sleeping

girl. 'It broke my heart, not being able to stand with you when you buried Susannah and then Heli.' He paused and sighed deeply. 'They were such good friends – I missed them terribly when the disease tore me away from them.'

'And they missed you,' I replied. 'But I did see you there when we laid them in the tomb.'

'I hate to think of the years that the leprosy stole from me,' said Simon wistfully.

'But you're better now!' exclaimed Lazarus, the excitement of the day still lingering in his voice.

'Ah yes – and how I would have loved to share *this* with my friend Heli.'

A thoughtful silence hung over us, until Mary broke it with the question that was burning in my own heart. 'This Jesus – do you think he might be the Messiah?'

'How can he not be the Messiah if he's doing miracles?' asked Lazarus, his eyes once again full of the almost wild excitement that I had seen earlier in the day. 'Not even John the Baptist does miracles!'

Rachel nodded silently, agreeing with my brother's sentiments. But I desperately wanted to know what Simon thought – he was, after all, the one who had been healed.

'*The Messiah…?*' began Simon slowly, with the same faraway look as my father. 'I don't know. All I know is that there was such kindness in his eyes, and such compassion in the words he spoke – '

'And that he healed you,' added James quietly.

'Yes, and that he healed me. Or maybe I should say that the power of the Almighty flowed through him to heal me.' He paused for a moment's thought before adding,

'Whether he is the Messiah or not, I cannot say. But is he sent from God? I do not doubt it. I've seen priests and Pharisees and teachers of the Law, and many of them are good men. But have I ever met a true man of God? All I can say is that I have now.'

As Mary, Lazarus and I walked the short distance back to our house, it appeared that my brother and sister had already made up their minds about this man, who they had not even set eyes upon yet. I, however, was more cautious. 'Nazareth sounds like a strange place for the Messiah to come from,' I began. 'He's meant to be the son of David, after all.'

'Yes, but even our family has moved around,' reasoned Lazarus. 'Grandfather Eleazar moved from Galilee down to Bethany. Surely this Jesus could be a descendant of David without having to be born in Bethlehem?' I had to admit that my brother's reasoning did have a certain sense to it.

'John the Baptist said another was coming after him who was greater than him,' added Mary. 'Why shouldn't this healer be the one John was talking about? As Lazarus said, John can't do miracles after all.'

'John *doesn't* do miracles,' I corrected. 'We don't know that he *can't* do them.'

Both Mary and Lazarus groaned, clearly frustrated that I wasn't ready to accept what they both thought was obvious. But I was happy to accept Simon's more measured conclusion, and the truth was that I felt responsible for my sister and brother. Although no longer children, their well-being was a constant concern to me now that our parents were gone. But as I pushed the door into our courtyard open, another matter was unexpectedly raised.

'You cannot let me be betrothed!' Mary suddenly implored, as she pulled the covering from her head, giving her hair a little shake, visibly glad to feel more of the cool night air upon her.

'What are you talking about?' I asked, somewhat confused by the direction that our conversation had suddenly taken.

'How can we possibly continue to live as if nothing has happened, getting betrothed and married as if that were the most important thing in life? Surely everything will change now.'

Before I had time to respond, Lazarus cut in, 'Mary's right. We must at least see this Jesus for ourselves first. And I am the head of the household now, after all. Mary doesn't have to get married unless I say so.'

The lateness of the hour, and the enormity of the questions being asked of me, suddenly made me feel very drained, especially after all the excitement and emotion of the day. Somehow it had brought back to me afresh the loss of both my father and mother, and all I wanted at that moment was for my mind not to be assailed by any more questions.

'It can wait until morning,' I answered wearily, securing the courtyard door behind me.

As I lay in bed that night, sleep did not come as swiftly as I'd imagined it would. I listened to Mary's steady breathing, with the different conversations from the evening and my sister's request swirling around in my mind. I whispered into the darkness, 'Abba, I don't know what I should do for the best.' And almost immediately, I knew the one thing that my father would definitely have told me to do. I thought for a moment, and then began whispering again: 'God of my fathers and Lord of heaven, show us the right path. Please make your ways known to us.' My prayer was simple and short, but heart-felt – and my troubled mind felt more at peace. As I finally slipped into sleep, there was only one thing in my heart and on my mind: a desire to see this Jesus for myself.

Chapter 15

Galilee of the Gentiles

'In the future he will honour Galilee of the nations, by the Way of the Sea, beyond the Jordan.' (Isaiah 9:1)

Winter AD 30/Spring AD 31

'Is it true?' I asked Matthias anxiously.

He nodded grimly. 'It's true alright.'

Lazarus had returned from Jerusalem that day with rumours that none of us wanted to believe: that John the Baptist had been arrested by Herod Antipas. If there was one person in the village who might know the truth or otherwise of the rumours, then it was Matthias. He had connections with the temple and with those who held the real power in Jerusalem – Caiaphas and the chief priests. And so it was to him we had rushed.

'How can Herod do that?' I exclaimed. I was at a loss to imagine any law that John might possibly have broken, and mystified as to how a ruler (supposedly following God's laws) could throw a person that many regarded as a prophet into jail.

'Herod's tetrarch of Galilee,' said Matthias, 'and he can do what he likes there, providing he doesn't cause a riot or upset the Romans. And I don't think our overlords care too much about the fate of one Jewish preacher.'

'But why?' I asked, still not understanding what John had done wrong.

'Well that's the easy question,' replied Matthias, with the grim expression still on his face.

But it was his wife who supplied the one-word answer: 'Herodias.'

As Matthias and I had been talking, Esther had been kneading a batch of dough on a table out in their courtyard where we were standing. She was apparently as indignant as me, but was taking it out on the dough instead. Her mention of the name of Herod's new wife was enough to suddenly make everything much clearer in my mind. Herod's marriage to a former wife of his half-brother Philip (whilst Philip still lived) did not go down well with most Jews. Many – including ourselves – considered it an outrage that Herod had married his sister-in-law, in blatant violation of the Law of Moses.

Matthias continued, though lowering his voice slightly. 'John had the courage to say publicly what nobody else would – that Herod was sinning against God's Law when he married Herodias. Whilst he was in Judea or Samaria and in Pilate's jurisdiction, Herod couldn't really touch him. But unfortunately for John, he was also baptising across the Jordan in Perea – '

'Which Herod also controls,' I completed, putting the pieces together. 'Is that where he was arrested?'

'I imagine so. But Herod's still playing with fire, given the following that John had – '

'And given who he is,' added Esther, punching the dough again. 'Herod is defying God!'

Like us, Matthias and his family regarded John as a

prophet sent from God and, like us, had also been baptised in the Jordan.

'What will Herod do with him?' I asked.

Matthias shrugged. 'I can't imagine Herod wants anything more than to keep him silent and out of the way.' He lowered his voice slightly again. 'He would be a fool to kill him.'

I shuddered slightly at even the thought of it, but Matthias went on. 'They say he's holding John in the Machaerus.' When I looked puzzled, he explained: 'That's Herod's fortress at the southern end of Perea. I suppose he thinks that keeping him locked away in his remote stronghold on the far side of the Salt Sea will keep him out of people's minds and harm's way.'

Esther's dough hit the table again with a loud *thwack*, and I wondered what my father would have made of the arrest of the priest's son.

Our thoughts, however, soon turned northwards, as the winter months turned once again into spring. Because it was out of Galilee that news began to flow – first a trickle and then a flood – about a new preacher. To be honest, we'd been surprised not to hear any news of Jesus in the months that followed Simon's healing. We had possibly expected everything to immediately change, and were bemused when it didn't. But John's arrest appeared to signal something new. Soon, every pilgrim, every merchant, every distant relative who travelled the roads from Galilee to Jerusalem, seemed to have a similar story to tell about a new teacher who was performing miracles. It didn't surprise us when we heard his name: Jesus of Nazareth. There were stories of many being healed with just a touch or a word – the paralysed walking, lepers being cleansed, and fevers suddenly disappearing. And stories of demons being cast out with power.

'We *must* go,' begged Lazarus, who had just turned fourteen years of age. 'And soon! We're missing it all here.' Despite my brother's usual voracious appetite, he had barely started on the dish of spiced lentils, onions and squash that the three of us were sharing for our evening meal.

'It won't matter if Lazarus takes a week or two away from the workshop,' reasoned Mary. 'Uncle Jacob will let him I'm sure, and it isn't as if we're short of money to live on.'

I was still concerned that Mary, who would shortly turn eighteen, was not yet betrothed. But somehow, Lazarus had used his youthful persuasion and his status within our small family to convince our uncle not to go ahead with a betrothal quite yet. And this preacher was the reason. But I was not without sympathy. The months since Simon's healing had not decreased in any way my desire to see Jesus and, in the end, I did not need much convincing by my sister and brother. Mary was, after all, quite right. Our father's business had left us comfortably off, and we wanted for very little. I scooped a little of the stew from the dish with the bread that was still warm. Having decided the lentils could have done with less garlic and more cumin, I finally made my decision. I swallowed the mouthful, and smiled at my brother and sister. 'I think maybe it's time that we visited Aunt Tabitha in Galilee.' My statement was immediately rewarded by two broad grins accompanied by a sudden onset of appetites.

We did not journey alone, however, as we were not the only ones eager to travel north. Simon had been waiting for a suitable opportunity when he, like us, heard the news from Galilee. He and James quickly decided to accompany us when we told them our plans, and it was only the need to stay with her daughter-in-law and young grandchildren that prevented Rachel from joining the five of us.

The journey northwards was uneventful. We all stayed a night in Jericho with my uncle Matthan, before following the Jordan valley due north for around forty miles towards Scythopolis. And as we talked to other travellers heading in the same direction, we discovered that many of them were also heading towards Galilee for the same reason as ours.

'It makes a change for pilgrims to be travelling north,' quipped James at one point with a grin.

'Jerusalem is not used to having a rival,' added his father and, although we laughed, the enormity of what he'd said was not lost on me.

We eventually turned north-west towards the large Galilean village of Japhia, where my aunt Tabitha and her family lived. We then parted company with Simon and James, who still had a few miles further north to travel to the small village of Rumah where they had relatives. By the time our journey was finally completed, it was nearing the fourth evening since we'd left. If we'd had any fears about arriving suddenly and unannounced, those fears were dispelled within seconds of hailing my aunt from the door to their courtyard. Age had done nothing to dampen the enthusiasm or the generous spirit of Tabitha. We were greeted by a very loud and joyful shriek, before being enfolded in her characteristic embrace.

After her usual comments about how beautiful my sister and I were looking, and about how much Lazarus had grown, we were given seats in the courtyard. Tabitha and her two daughters-in-law brought out water for us to wash our feet and our hands, and drinks and raisin cakes to refresh us. We'd barely finished washing when my uncle Reuben, by now too old to be working as a stonemason, returned from visiting a neighbour, closely followed by my cousins Simeon and Joseph after they'd finished their day's work at Sepphoris. And after all the necessary greetings and pleasantries, Reuben fixed me with a quizzical look. 'So what brings you north to Galilee – or can I guess?'

That evening, as we shared a special meal of a roasted leg of goat, we told the story of the baptisms by John, and then of Simon's healing. Our relatives, in turn, told us of all they had heard, particularly of what had been happening at Capernaum, fifteen miles away on the shores of Lake Galilee. And the stories were the same as those we'd heard told in Jerusalem: of many being healed of various kinds of sickness, and of demons being cast out. But not all that they had to tell us excited us.

'By all accounts, however, he didn't receive much of a welcome at the synagogue in Nazareth,' said Joseph, eight years my senior. 'I often work alongside another mason who comes from there, and apparently they almost threw him out of the synagogue and out of town, after he started quoting Scriptures about Gentiles to them.'

'But I thought he was *from* Nazareth,' said Lazarus with a note of surprise in his voice. 'Why wouldn't *they* welcome him?'

'Well, it seems that that was the problem,' added Joseph's older brother.

'What do you mean?' asked Mary.

Simeon continued: 'He told them that no prophet was ever welcome in his home town.'

'So he *does* say that he's a prophet,' said Lazarus excitedly.

'A prophet and maybe more than that,' replied Joseph. 'My friend tells me he also read from the prophet Isaiah – and then told them all that it was fulfilled in their hearing that day.'

'And *that* is a bold claim indeed,' said my uncle Reuben, raising his eyebrows.

Nazareth was a similar distance from Japhia as Jerusalem was from Bethany, and I was therefore sure that they must be able to tell us something of this prophet's background. 'What of his home and his family?' I asked. 'Is he from a family of priests?' I added, remembering what we'd learned about the baptist.

'From what we can learn,' began my uncle, 'his family is quite an ordinary one. Neither priestly nor rich, and not unlike our own – though maybe more humble. His father was a builder, and apparently so was this Jesus before he went down to Judea. Who knows, we may even have worked alongside them in Sepphoris. After all, Antipas had a small army from around Galilee working on the wood- and stone-works there.'

'So have you seen him?' asked Mary eagerly.

Reuben shook his head, 'No. He travels around the towns and villages of Galilee, and there are enough of those. People find out where he is, news travels, and the crowds flock to hear him and to be healed of their diseases.'

'And you haven't been to see him yet?' asked Lazarus, making no attempt to hide the incredulity in his voice.

My uncle shrugged. 'You hear different things. Some say he does wonderful things, but others that he treats God's Law with contempt, breaking the Sabbath. Many of the Pharisees say that he defiles himself by keeping company with the immoral and those who work for the Gentiles.'

If Tabitha shared my uncle's suspicion, then she didn't show it, perhaps because she was mindful of the prophet having healed our father's closest friend. 'You will have to make up your own minds, if you manage to see him,' she said.

'Where do you suggest we go?' asked Lazarus, with an enthusiasm that hadn't been dampened, despite my uncle's words.

'Capernaum,' answered Joseph. 'That's where he seems to call home these days.'

The rolling green hills of Galilee that surrounded us as we set off for Capernaum, early the following day, made a welcome change to the more rocky landscape of the south. Many of the hills were covered with vines, although the grape harvest wouldn't happen for some months yet. We'd left our donkey and cart at my aunt's house, and had decided to travel by foot. We had bags containing fresh bread from my aunt, some small rounds of cheese, a few small fish and cakes of figs wrapped in vine leaves. But we also had money shared between our bags, for food that we might need to buy along the way, or for a night's lodging at an inn. I had also been equipped with a number of names of cousins or more distant family members around

Galilee, where we would find a welcome and a roof over our heads.

The first day's travelling proved to be fruitless. We did, however, encounter a number of others on the road who had seen Jesus healing or heard him teaching. Unless they were travelling in our direction, our progress was always slowed, as we invariably stopped to hear their stories. We reached Capernaum without any joy, but were at least able to find where Jesus was living. It was a large house, similar to our own, and belonging – as we discovered from asking around – to the family of two brothers whom he'd apparently called to be his disciples. And not for the first time we were surprised. I was not unfamiliar with the pattern of respected rabbis gathering around themselves groups of well-educated pupils – disciples – who would then be taught by the rabbi. The disciples would follow their leader around, trying to emulate him in all aspects of life. But Jesus was clearly different.

'They're not educated men,' said the old man seated on the edge of the well, in the open market area at the centre of the town. 'At least, not as far as I know.'

We were each perched on a low wall that ran around the small garden of a nearby house, eagerly devouring what remained of the food our aunt had given us that morning. As we were eating, we were more than happy to listen to the local knowledge that Zacharias, our new acquaintance, was more than willing to supply. He seemed pleased to have a small audience, keen to hear for themselves what probably the whole of Capernaum already knew. And he was busy telling us about the following that this new teacher from Nazareth already had.

'The Twelve – that's what people are calling them –

his disciples, that is. As I was saying, they may have been taught at the synagogue like anybody else as they were growing up, but I don't think any of them have been trained under a proper rabbi. Take Simon, for example' – Zacharias broke off, and nodded his head in the direction of the house that Jesus apparently called home – 'he's a fisherman. Works in the business that his father Jonah runs with another local man, Zebedee. Him and his brother Andrew have gone off with this Jesus. It's just as well that their business has got hired men, because two of Zebedee's sons have also gone off with him as well.'

'But what do you know of Jesus?' asked Mary, more interested in the reason for all the disruption, rather than the details of a local fishing business.

'Well I can tell you something that not everyone knows,' said Zacharias, leaning forwards slightly on his stick, as if to share a secret. The words had the desired effect, with each of us visibly eager to hear more. 'My cousin Abel grew up in Nazareth. Knew the family. When all this business with Jesus started, he told me what he knew of him. He's one of five brothers – got sisters too – *two, three?* I forget how many. Anyway, he's the eldest, born shortly after the parents were married, though the same couldn't be said about when he was conceived.' He let the words hang in the air for several moments, as if for effect. I certainly didn't want to ask what he meant. Not that I needed to – the words could only really have one meaning. Zacharias went on, still leaning forwards and lowering his voice slightly: 'It's said that the father, Joseph his name was, denied the child was his when he found out she was pregnant – when they were betrothed, that is. And yet there was no trial for adultery, not even a quiet divorce as anyone would have expected. He went ahead and married her anyway.' He paused for a moment as if trawling through his memory. 'Mary. Yes, that's what her name was. But there was always a question about who the real father was.'

His words were not particularly welcome ones, and I was keen to move away from what felt like little more than local gossip. 'But have you heard Jesus yourself?'

Zacharias straightened himself up again. 'Heard him – and seen what he can do. Never seen nothing like it – just ordered a demon out and out it went.'

Mary's expression told me that she shared my slight revulsion. Neither of us cared much for talk of the powers of evil that could invade a person and take control of them. The idea frightened me, and I would have been happy to have left it at that in our conversation, but my brother was eager to find out more. 'What sort of demon was it?'

'Well, I don't know about that, but I do know what I saw. It was on a Sabbath, maybe a month ago, maybe two – my memory's not what it used to be. Whilst we were in the synagogue, this man with the demon suddenly started hollering at the top of his voice, asking if Jesus had come to destroy them, calling him the Holy One of God. There was something about that voice. Evil it was…' He paused, shuddering at the memory. 'Now, I'm old enough to have seen others trying to drive out demons. Using long rituals or their special remedies, doing their chanting and calling on the name of Solomon. But this? This was nothing like that. He just tells the demon to shut up and come out – and although it throws the man to the ground, it does what he says. It comes out of him without another word.'

Zacharias shook his head, and quietly and in deep thought said once again, 'Never seen nothing like it.'

We stayed in Capernaum that night, with a cousin on my uncle's side we had not met before. But, as Tabitha had assured us, she welcomed us warmly into her home. There was, once again, more talk of the local prophet, as we gratefully ate the chicken broth and fresh bread that was set before us. Another early start sent us off in a direction to the north-east of Capernaum, where Jesus was rumoured to have been some days before. And this time the Hand of Providence was upon us. We suddenly found ourselves caught up in a flood of people, all excitedly heading in the same direction. Snatches of conversation as we hurried along (with what was becoming a very large crowd) told us that as well as locals from Galilee, others were there from Judea and Jerusalem. And even some from further south – from Idumea, where the land became more barren and desert-like. Others had come from the lands across the Jordan, whilst some had travelled south from the coastal towns of Tyre and Sidon in Phoenicia. And it was clear that many were coming to be healed.

We continued with the crowds down the hill to a large, flat area. And then we spotted him.

If anyone had asked me to describe him at that moment, there would have been nothing about his appearance to set him apart from a hundred Jewish men in a crowd. That all changed when I saw his face. It was not that his features were noticeably different from those standing around him. It was his demeanour that set him apart. If any face could be overflowing with love, joy and peace – all at the same time – then it was his.

Although the crowds made it difficult to get close, patience and Lazarus' determination eventually got us near enough to have a reasonable view of what was going on – and of what Zacharias had seen. The scream of a demon made the hairs on the back of my neck prickle. There was something unearthly and terrible about the sound. But above the noise I heard the calm, authoritative voice of the prophet issue a command, and then heard the sudden gasps of astonishment from those nearby. The quiet authority in the voice of Jesus left me in no doubt about what had happened.

Before I could get any closer, I heard a voice behind me. 'Let us through, I beg you!' We were jostled, as the crowds parted as best they could. A man with a strained expression came through, carrying a young boy that I took to be his son. One of the boy's legs was dangling awkwardly.

'He must be lame,' murmured Lazarus beside me.

The constant surging of the crowd meant we couldn't see what happened. But several minutes later the man returned with joy on his face – and with the boy almost dancing at his side, chattering excitedly and happily to his father. I gasped – the useless leg now no different to his other. As had been the case with Simon's healing, I found my cheeks were wet with tears. I, too, could echo the words I'd heard before: I had never seen anything like it.

Jesus healed every person who came to him. Although we couldn't always see what was being done, a constant stream of reports were excitedly passed along by the crowd, only adding to our sense of awe and wonder. But eventually a hush began to descend over the large crowd, and we too fell silent, wondering what was coming next.

Once again we heard the same calm but powerful voice, not this time commanding a demon, but addressing all of us gathered there.

'Blessed are you who are poor, for yours is the kingdom of God…'

We were oblivious to either the passing of time or the aching of our feet, as we stood listening to the teacher. And once again I was encountering something utterly new. John's message had been one that called us to repentance, but this went further. Jesus spoke of love for enemies, of the kindness and mercy of God, of the need to not only hear his words but to put them into practice, and of storms raging but our lives standing firm.

I had been listening to teaching in the synagogue for as long as I could remember. But so much of it had been dull or difficult to understand. The minutiae of God's Law were expounded in long sermons in which the teaching of various rabbis was quoted and compared. And I was left feeling that God was at best distant, or at worst angry. But when Jesus spoke, his words had an authority I had never encountered before, even with John. He had no need to quote the words of others. He spoke clearly, as if he knew and understood God better than any other living man. And having heard him speak, I felt as if I knew what God required of me as never before. It was both more beautiful and more challenging than I had ever imagined.

In the days that followed, we constantly sought out Jesus. Some days we found him, and delighted in watching him as he healed many, and in listening to him as he spoke of God. But other days it almost felt as if he did not want to be found. Certainly he travelled around the region in ways that were hard to predict. He didn't seem to follow any pattern that we could recognise. But even when we didn't see him, we heard the rumours that spread, though never knowing whether these came to us second-hand, third-hand or embellished beyond recognition.

'He was violent, screaming and shouting. I heard he lived among tombs and no-one would go near him. But Jesus cast the demons out into a herd of pigs. They ran straight down into the lake! And they say people hardly recognised him afterwards, he was so different!'

'It'd been going on for years and years. Doctors couldn't help her, but when she touched Jesus, the bleeding stopped – just like that.'

'I saw it with my own eyes. He got up off the bed and walked!'

And among those rumours, we heard tales of storms stilled and the dead raised. But whatever the truth of those particular tales, many testified to healings that they themselves or those in their families had received. And more than once I found myself wondering whether, if Jesus had arrived sooner, others might not have died. I thought of my mother and of my father, and I thought of Levi.

It was not only the healings that amazed and delighted us, however. We constantly longed to hear more of his teaching. We all felt as if our eyes were being opened to truths that we had previously only dimly perceived, if at all. And we listened eagerly to the stories he told as he described God's kingdom to us: stories of seeds and crops, of pearls and weeds. Not that we always understood the meaning behind them, especially as they were often told without explanation. But they always provoked discussions between my sister and brother and myself as we talked together about them, often late into an evening. Only much later did we come to understand that Jesus deliberately spoke in parables (as his stories were known) with the meaning buried, to test whether we were willing to dig. But in those stories we mined treasures of the kingdom of God: an understanding not only of the purposes of the Almighty, but also a better understanding of the God of Israel Himself.

But eventually the time came when we had to return south. Despite the protests of both my brother and sister, the simple fact was that we had exhausted our money and supplies. Lazarus also needed to return to the workshop. Besides, Passover was almost upon us, and it would be our turn to receive visitors.

But our lives in Bethany had changed. I wanted to begin to live as Jesus had told us to. Although I remembered his teaching about not being anxious, I still struggled with the ever-present worries for the welfare of both Mary and Lazarus and for the upkeep of the household. The responsibilities weighed heavily upon my shoulders, like some invisible sack of grain. I did, however, promise them both that we would return to Galilee to see Jesus again, and we eagerly listened out for any news of him that came our way.

We finally managed to travel north again as summer was drawing to a close, and the pattern of our visit was not unlike the first one. But once again, we eventually had to tear ourselves away, and were – reluctantly – back in Bethany before the Day of Atonement. Though each of us felt as if we'd left our hearts in Galilee and we longed to return.

In the meantime, however, we continued to talk of all that we had heard and seen. For the truth was, that although Jesus gave us the answers to many questions, there were plenty of others to take their place.

Chapter 16

When the Messiah comes

'He had no beauty or majesty to attract us to him.'
(Isaiah 53:2)

Autumn AD 31

My brow furrowed, as I asked Simon another question. 'But if Jesus *is* the Messiah, then why is he *so* different from anything we expected?'

Of course, I *wanted* to believe – as my brother and sister seemed so readily to do – that Jesus of Nazareth was the Messiah. It was just that I had lived for so long with a picture of what he would be like, and of how it would be when the Messiah finally came. And I was finding it hard to reconcile the miracle worker from Galilee with the expectations that I was not alone in holding.

It was far easier to ask these questions in Simon's house, for it was becoming abundantly clear that Jesus was not universally received with the same elation that we felt. Even in my own wider family, I was aware of unease. I'd seen furtive glances when the name of the preacher from Galilee was spoken. It was at times like these that I missed my father and his great wisdom terribly. But sitting with Simon in his courtyard, as Rachel did the final preparations for the evening meal, was, to me, the next best thing.

Simon sighed deeply, apparently sharing my perplexities. 'I don't deny – ' He broke off and corrected himself. 'I *cannot* deny the power that Jesus wields – my own body reminds me of that every day. And I, like you, witnessed countless demonstrations of his power in Galilee. But you're right, Martha. His coming has changed so much, but…' He broke off, trying to find the right words to express his own questions.

'But so much remains the same?' I offered.

Simon nodded. 'The Romans still rule over us and Jesus barely even mentions them. I've certainly heard nothing from his lips that even hints that he intends to drive them out.' Simon paused and lowered his voice. 'And I believe that he could do so if he wanted.' After another pause and a slight shake of the head he added, 'But he almost seems content to let them be, as if they're no concern of his…' His voice trailed off and whatever other thoughts were going through his mind remained unspoken.

In the silence that followed, broken only by the scraping of pestle against mortar as Rachel ground some herbs together, I pictured again what I had imagined since childhood. The Son of David entering Jerusalem in triumph to the sound of a fanfare, mounted on a powerful steed, and ready to establish God's rule throughout the earth with His people, the Jews. My vision was embellished with gold and glory, soldiers and swords – all things noticeable by their absence in what Jesus did.

The sound of grinding suddenly stopped, and Rachel looked questioningly at Simon. 'From what you've told me, it sounds as if Jesus has more criticism of our own leaders than those of Rome.'

Simon nodded again. 'I could understand him

speaking out against the Sadducees and their desire for wealth and power. But some of his fiercest criticism is for the Pharisees, which seems strange as they're the ones who care most about keeping God's Law.'

It was one of the questions that had also perplexed me. And yet the more I thought about it, the greater the gulf seemed to be between Jesus and our religious leaders – or at least, most of them. Their myriad rules and stern demeanours (which had frightened me as a child) stood in stark contrast to the simplicity and joy of Jesus' approach. It was little wonder to me that children were always perfectly happy to be around Jesus – and that he was equally happy to have them there.

Similar questions and debates were taking place around Bethany, on its dusty streets and in its homes. Barely a week went by without some new story about this radical teacher and healer reaching our ears. As had been the case in Galilee, we were not always sure whether the stories we heard were recent ones, or older stories that had travelled far and wide before finally arriving in Bethany, often via our workshop in Jerusalem.

'…and Jesus then told him not to tell anyone, but to go and show himself to the priest, just like Simon had to do!' Lazarus said the last phrase with particular excitement, as he finished relaying another story of a leper's healing, shared that day by a customer who'd come to buy a small alabaster pot of fragranced ointment.

'If Jesus told him not to tell anyone, then how do we know what happened?' asked Mary, as she helped finish the preparations for the evening meal, peeling the skin from an onion that would eventually end up in a salad.

'Maybe bystanders saw and heard what happened,' offered Lazarus.

'Or maybe he simply didn't do what Jesus told him – ' I suggested, giving the dough one final knead, before beginning to shape it into the rounds that would soon be baked in the courtyard oven. ' – not everybody does.'

'But why would Jesus instruct someone he'd healed *not* to tell others about it? Surely he'd want others to know what he's doing.'

Mary's question silenced Lazarus temporarily. This sort of question had already arisen more than once, and I wasn't sure we had any answer to it. We had seen in Galilee how Jesus had not always gone about publicly. We'd heard stories of how he'd (seemingly deliberately) healed people away from the gaze of the watching crowds. It added to my perplexity as to why Jesus was so different to the Messiah that I'd expected – if he was indeed the Messiah. *Surely the Scriptures spoke of the glory of God's chosen king. Or had we, in some way, misunderstood the Scriptures?*

The troubling thought was soon dispelled, however, by Lazarus' quick mind and creative thinking. 'What if Jesus is simply waiting for the right time to set up God's kingdom here? He said, didn't he, that the kingdom of God is *near*? Maybe he's building up his following around the country, showing everyone what he can do, and then, when most of the Jews are gathered together in Jerusalem at one of the festivals, everything will change. Surely there would be no better time and place for him to be made king?'

'But that's also when the Romans are there in force,' I countered.

Lazarus rolled his eyes in exasperation. 'Martha!

You've seen his power. Do you seriously think that the Romans would be able to stand against him?'

'Somehow I can't imagine Jesus wielding a sword,' said Mary, rubbing her forearm across her watering eyes, as the pungent smell of the onion that she was now slicing started to fill the room.

'He won't *need* to wield a sword!' exclaimed Lazarus confidently. 'God might send fire from heaven to destroy them as he did with Elijah. Or send his angel out to destroy their soldiers, as he did with the Assyrian army in the time of King Hezekiah. Our God is with Jesus!'

My brother had always loved the stories of battles and God's triumph in the Scriptures. And even I had to admit that it was difficult to see what the Romans could do, if God chose to wield the armies and power of heaven through or for Jesus.

'But Jesus told us to love our enemies,' responded Mary as she paused, momentarily defeated by the onion and needing to wipe her eyes once more.

'But that doesn't mean that *God* might not remove the Romans!' declared Lazarus in reply, raising his eyebrows as he did so, as if in anticipation of God's triumph. Any further discussion, however, had to wait for another opportunity, for whatever colossal changes might or might not happen in our land, our daily bread still needed to be baked.

If Jesus were waiting for one of the Jewish festivals to make a triumphal entry into Jerusalem, then it was neither the Feast of Tabernacles that autumn nor the Feast of Dedication in December. That was not to say, however, that Jesus did not come. But we didn't find out about his visit until afterwards, and although Jesus had come for a festival, revolution – at least against the Romans – seemed far from his mind.

Late one afternoon, the door into the courtyard was suddenly flung open by Lazarus. And judging by his breathlessness, he had run most of the mile and a half back from Jerusalem, after the first day's work of the new week. He bent over double for a moment, with his hands resting on his thighs, gulping in air as he tried to recover enough to speak. He finally raised his head, a pained expression still on his face, but he couldn't wait any longer. Between deep breaths he gasped, 'He…was here…in Jerusalem.'

I immediately put down the walnuts I was shelling, whilst Mary's embroidery fell to the ground as she leaped to her feet in excitement – and neither of us needed to ask who Lazarus meant.

'When?' asked Mary.

'Yesterday!' exclaimed Lazarus. He collapsed on the nearest stool, the pain of exertion still showing on his face. He looked pleadingly at me, evidently needing sooner rather than later the water that I normally served him on his return home. I hurried down to the cistern, pitcher in hand, and returned with cool water as fast as I could. By the time Lazarus had downed two large cups of water, one straight after the other, Mary and I had drawn up two other stools, and were eagerly waiting for the tale he had to tell. And Lazarus needed no encouragement, although his story still had to be delivered in short bursts as he continued to catch his breath.

'Everyone's talking about it. He was in Jerusalem for the Feast. No one mentioned the Twelve, so he may have been on his own. Anyway, Jesus went to the Pool of Bethesda.' He paused to take another gulp of water. Both Mary and I knew the place to which he referred. It was an old and rather ornate pool to the north of the temple, in the area we knew as Bezetha, the New City, built to house Jerusalem's growing population. The pool was supposed to have healing properties, which is why the lame, blind, or those suffering some other affliction, often gathered there.

'Did Jesus perform healings?' asked Mary excitedly.

'Well, he certainly healed one of them – a man who'd been an invalid for thirty-eight years apparently.'

'That's more than twice as long as I've lived,' murmured Mary, who'd turned eighteen that spring. I shared her amazement, finding it hard to comprehend what it must be like to have been ill for so long.

'Jesus just told him to get up and walk – and he did!' Mary's eyes were shining, and my own heart soared, although I also longed to have been there and seen the healing – and Jesus – for myself. But Lazarus hadn't finished. 'Apparently some of the Jewish leaders were furious though – '

'What, because Jesus performed a wonderful miracle?' interrupted Mary indignantly.

'No. You see, that wasn't all,' said Lazarus. 'Jesus told him to pick up the mat that he was lying on as well.'

Although I understood perfectly the significance of what my brother was saying, Mary stared at him in incomprehension for a moment. 'So?'

'It was the Sabbath!' exclaimed Lazarus with a certain amount of exasperation. 'Carrying your mat on the Sabbath is against the Law!'

We continued to feel the ripples that Jesus had sent through the Jewish establishment for some time after the healing. Lazarus returned a few days later, fuming, from one of his regular lessons at the synagogue school.

'Joseph calls Jesus a law-breaker and a blasphemer,' said Lazarus, his voice unsteady. Tears of anger and frustration welled up as he struggled to contain his feelings. 'I had to sit through the entire lesson listening to him denouncing Jesus. He says that people shouldn't listen to a word Jesus says, because he tells people to disregard God's Law. He says he's of the devil because he speaks blasphemy. He says that when Jesus calls God his Father he's making himself equal with God, and so deserves to be stoned to death!' A tear finally slipped down my brother's cheek. Despite him being fourteen, I put down the washing in my hands, and went over to him and put my arms around him. I could feel him shaking with anger, and I did my best to comfort and soothe him.

'How can he *say* that?' asked Lazarus more calmly, but with his voice still trembling.

'I don't know,' I said quietly. 'He may not have seen or heard Jesus for himself as we have.'

'But he's seen Simon.'

'I know. And I don't understand either how people can be so blind to the wonderful things that Jesus does.'

Lazarus loosened his grip on me, so I stepped back. I could then see a look of determination on his face. 'God would not give him the power to do all the things he does if he was evil,' he said with conviction. My brother had made up his mind about Jesus, and no one was going to persuade him otherwise.

'I know,' I replied, and then smiled. He might now

be counted an adult, but certain childhood weaknesses would never change. 'Some yoghurt and honey?' I asked. 'I might be able to find some fresh figs too.'

My brother looked at me for several moments, and then nodded with the hint of a smile on his face.

Not all disquiet in our community, however, could be quelled with the fruits of the land flowing with milk and honey. We invited to our house the following Sabbath eve not only Simon and Rachel, but also Matthias and Esther and their younger children. Matthias had been at the temple during the festival, and had been well aware of the controversy that Jesus had caused. He also knew more of what Jesus had reportedly said. We sat together around the low table covered with dishes, from which arose the aroma of grilled sardines, garlic, and the ever-present fresh bread.

'It's not the healings themselves that are the issue,' explained Matthias, after he had finished his mouthful of fish. 'It's the way that Jesus does them. It's almost as if he went to Bethesda deliberately looking for someone to heal on the Sabbath – as a direct challenge to the authority of the leaders.'

'Do you really think that was his purpose?' asked Simon.

Matthias shrugged his shoulders. 'I don't know. But surely he must have known what effect it would have.'

'It was still something wonderful that he did, though,' added Rachel, voicing my own feelings.

'I don't doubt it,' said Matthias. 'But then there are the claims he is making…'

'Calling God his Father?' asked Lazarus, and I

thought of the recent lecture he'd had from Joseph at the synagogue.

Matthias nodded. 'Yes. That is one of them.'

'And yet no one can doubt that he speaks of God in a way that none of us have ever encountered before,' said Simon. 'He knows and understands the Scriptures far better than any educated scribe, and honours and lives out God's standards better than any Pharisee that I have ever known.'

'Except keeping the Sabbath?' added Matthias, almost as a challenge to Simon.

Simon savoured a mouthful of stew rather than responding immediately. 'Excellent, Martha. I swear every meal we eat here is even better than the one before.' In the gentle lamplight I could see the faces of all those around the table relax into smiles. Simon took a second mouthful, swallowed, and then spoke. 'One thousand, five hundred and twenty-one types of activity prohibited on the Sabbath. Is that what the Almighty's day of rest has become for us?'

'You agree with the teaching of the Galilean?' asked Matthias.

'It makes sense to me,' answered Simon, looking steadily and calmly over the table at the priest.

Matthias was the first to look away. He then shook his head and sighed. 'Our Galilean preacher has disturbed the established order. He has come into the temple and has made what some see as outrageous and blasphemous claims, deserving of death. Saying not only that God is his father, but that God has entrusted him with the task of judgment, and that those in their graves will hear his voice and will live.' Matthias must have seen the looks of surprise on our faces. 'He didn't say these things in a corner, if you doubt me. He addressed them to a number of the leaders at the temple. His claims are bold – and dangerous.'

I wondered who would dare to speak next and break the heavy silence that suddenly hung over the room. But it was Matthias himself. He drew a deep breath and let it out slowly, before shaking his head once more. 'But then I hear of all the lives that he is changing for the good, and I look at you, Simon, whom I have known all my life. And I find myself almost ready to think the unthinkable.' Matthias did not elaborate on the exact meaning of his words. Instead, he took a mouthful of the dish of vegetables, and smiled. 'Simon is right, Martha. You excel yourself.'

I returned his smile, and rose to re-fill the now-empty basket of bread.

Matthias took the opportunity to move the conversation onto unrelated matters – the recent harvests, the price of silver, the progress of my brother in his trade – clearly not wanting to be the cause of too much controversy over our Sabbath meal. But towards the end of the evening, it was Simon who changed the subject once more with a simple question to Matthias. 'Have you heard about Sejanus?'

'Yes – it doesn't take long for news like that to cover the miles between Rome and Jerusalem.'

Esther's young daughter was, by now, dozing, with her head in her mother's lap, but her older brother was still very much awake. He suddenly seemed very eager to find out what lay behind the conversation of the adults, which had just gone from the art of grinding myrrh to something far more interesting. 'Who's Sejanus?' I was familiar with the name, as I was with Tiberius, the Roman emperor. But the connection between them was, at the very least, somewhat hazy in my mind.

Matthias smiled at his son. 'He was, until very recently, more or less in charge of Rome.'

'But Tiberius is emperor,' said Lazarus, somewhat bemused.

'Yes, but he spends much of his time outside Rome these days. He seems to prefer the country in his old age. He must be, what – over seventy now?'

'Something like that,' replied Simon.

'So,' continued Matthias, 'he appointed one of his trusted soldiers, Sejanus, to be in charge in his absence. But it appears that Sejanus got a little too powerful for Tiberius' liking.'

'Meaning?' I asked.

'Meaning that Tiberius had him – and all his family – executed,' answered Matthias.

A silence fell once again on the room, only broken by Simon muttering quietly to himself: 'And they call themselves civilised!' The sordid details of the executions were undoubtedly felt unsuitable both for a Sabbath meal and for the women at the table. Simon himself obviously did not want to dwell on the details in his mind either. 'What will it mean for Pilate?'

Matthias shrugged. 'It's probably too early to say.'

'What's it got to do with Pontius Pilate?' queried Lazarus, who appeared as fascinated by the conversation as his young counterpart.

'It was Sejanus who appointed him governor here, not the emperor,' explained Simon.

'So will the emperor want to get rid of Pilate too, then?' asked Lazarus.

'As Matthias said, it's probably too early to tell what will happen to him. But at the very least, he will not want to do anything to upset Tiberius. Sejanus was never a friend of the Jews, but with his support now gone, I imagine Pilate may want to avoid any trouble here and keep on good terms with the Jewish leadership.'

'So that's a good thing,' stated Lazarus, and the men nodded in agreement.

But it wouldn't be long before they came to think exactly the opposite, when the working of God's purposes drew together the strands of history – and of the Roman prefect and our Galilean preacher.

Chapter 17

Bread of heaven

'In their hunger you gave them bread from heaven.'
(Nehemiah 9:15)

Spring AD 32

The shock waves reverberated around small villages like Bethany as much as the great city of Jerusalem and beyond. We were at the house of my aunt and uncle when we heard the news. Their home was filled not only with sons and their wives, but also with grandchildren whose number and antics were reminiscent of a small flock of sheep. The evening meal we were sharing was just coming to an end when we heard the voice of Judas the Potter in the courtyard.

'John! Elizabeth!' His voice was urgent, and he entered immediately, without even waiting for a response. The look on his face brought the laughter of the adults to an abrupt end. It was clear that something was wrong – and very wrong.

My uncle rose swiftly and was soon having a whispered conversation with him, and then his expression suddenly changed. 'Rachel, Sarah, Miriam – take the children into the courtyard for a while, please.' His daughters-in-law obliged, scooping up those too young to walk into their arms, and shepherding the rest of the young children out through the door. As soon as the room was clear, John turned to Judas. 'Tell them what you've just told me.'

'A cousin of mine has just arrived from across the Jordan in Perea. He knows some of those who work at the Machaerus.' The mention of the fortress where Herod had incarcerated John the Baptist filled my heart with a sense of dread, and I suddenly realised that all of us in the room had been baptised by him. My uncle and aunt had been slower than my father to journey to hear the preacher. But as more and more heard and responded to John and his message, they and their family had eventually also gone under the waters of the Jordan, to prepare themselves for the Lord and for His Messiah. In fact, by the time John had been thrown into prison, it felt as if most of Judea and Jerusalem had been baptised by him.

All our eyes were now fixed on Judas, who took a deep breath and then began. 'Herod's had –' He paused, a look of deep anger on his face, and then began again, throwing any caution to the wind: 'Herod's murdered John.'

We gasped. *How could Herod Antipas put a prophet to death?*

'Fool!' exclaimed my uncle. 'What on earth possessed him to do that?'

'Herodias – and a foolish promise made in front of dinner guests,' said Judas darkly. 'There is only one merciful thing in all this – his death was quick. Herod had him beheaded, so at least it was not the abomination of crucifixion.'

I remembered the smile that I had received from John, and my stomach lurched. But even the little that Judas had shared was too much detail for Mary, and she ran from the room sobbing. As I ran to follow her, I caught a look of guilt on Judas's face, and heard him mutter a quick apology as I went past.

As I stood holding my sobbing sister, I thought back to how I'd held my brother several weeks earlier. *How could those unquestionably sent by God be rejected by those who were supposedly His own people?* And with that thought, never had my childhood dreams of the glorious Son of David seemed so far from reality.

I shuddered later, when I discovered the greater horror in John's death. The manner of execution had been dictated by Herodias, who'd prompted her daughter to ask for the baptist's head to be brought to her on a plate. But if one good thing came out of his death, it was that it propelled us north once again. All three of us felt it had been far too long since we'd heard and seen Jesus for ourselves, and the news of John's death stirred up in us the desire to see him again as soon as possible. Several months had passed since we were last in Galilee. Since then, we had always been listening out for news of Jesus, and had sat and eagerly listened to the reports of any who had seen him, particularly those who considered themselves – as we did by now – his followers.

Our journey along the roads to Jericho, Scythopolis and Capernaum could not pass quickly enough for us.

'Lazarus! Be careful! The donkey and the cart have got to get us all the way to Galilee.' It wasn't the first time I'd had to stop my brother from driving our animal too hard.

'Don't worry. It'll be fine!'

'It won't be fine if the wheel comes off,' I warned. Lazarus appeared oblivious at times to the fact that our cart was laden with more supplies than ever, to enable us to stay as long as humanly possible.

When we were finally – and safely – back in Galilee, with our cart and its contents safely entrusted to my aunt Tabitha once more, finding Jesus was just as difficult as it had previously been. Rumours and counter-rumours concerning his whereabouts abounded. But when a growing number of people began to stream in one direction, we joined ourselves to the flow, hoping and praying for the best, and were eventually rewarded, although not until we had walked several miles.

The hill on which we found Jesus teaching was in a remote area, but close to the shore of the Sea of Galilee. Lush grass covered its slopes, the results of the rains that had fallen in the winter months. But the grass was rapidly becoming obscured by a crowd that seemed larger than anything I had seen during our previous trips to the north. The sheer numbers of those eager to hear Jesus drove far from my mind the opposition to him we'd encountered in Jerusalem and Bethany. And when we heard him speak of God again and saw him healing the sick, any fears that remained dissipated in the face of his matchless authority. At one point, my eyes fell on John the disciple, one of the fishermen from Capernaum. And I suddenly thought of his namesake. *What had the death of the Baptist meant for Jesus?* I quickly forgot the question, however, in the wonder of Jesus' teaching.

It seemed we had been there only an hour or two when Lazarus nudged me and whispered, 'Is there any food left?'

I was amazed at how far the afternoon had advanced. I shook my head, 'Not anymore.' Although we had left that morning with ample supplies – I had packed far more than I thought we needed – they had steadily dwindled throughout the day as we'd shared with those around us who had come with little or nothing.

Mary had barely touched a thing, her growling stomach going largely unnoticed, as if food were something of an unwelcome distraction. Although Lazarus also listened with rapt attention, I had never yet known him to miss a meal, except on the rare occasions when he was sick as a child. 'What are we going to do, then?' whispered Lazarus back.

The look of deep concern on his face almost made me laugh. I answered as quietly as I could. 'We'll go hungry like everybody else, and eat when we get back.' When Lazarus' face fell even further, I did laugh. 'It won't kill you!'

A gentle *Ssshh* was all that Mary had to say on the matter.

But only a short while later, our curiosity was suddenly aroused. Jesus had apparently finished teaching and healing, but was not dismissing the crowd as we might have expected. We stood on tiptoes, trying to work out what was going on.

'It looks as if he's talking with the Twelve,' said Lazarus. He had turned fifteen just over two months earlier, and although I was ten years his senior, he was already towering over both my sister and me. He therefore had the advantage any time a good view was required. 'Now he seems to be giving them some sort of instructions,' he continued. And a few minutes later, we discovered what those were.

'Everyone sit down. Get into groups of fifty if you

can,' said a voice from somewhere nearby. As those around us began to sit down, I realised it was Andrew, one of the Twelve and the brother of Simon Peter, who was particularly close to Jesus. Their home in Capernaum was where Jesus stayed.

'What's Jesus going to do?' asked a man taking his place on the grass.

Andrew grinned and shrugged his shoulders. 'Feed everyone?' An excited murmur went around the crowd, and Lazarus brightened up considerably at Andrew's suggestion.

When the immense crowd was eventually seated, clumped around the green hillside in groups that seemed more or less evenly sized, all attention turned again to Jesus, with the Twelve gathered around him once more. He lifted high what was little more than enough food to fill his two hands. 'Blessed are You, O Lord our God, King of the Universe, who brings forth bread from the earth.' Having given the blessing in a voice loud enough for us all to hear, he then lowered the handful of food. As he broke what was in his hands, he handed it to the men gathered around him. Each of the Twelve then took a basket and began spreading out amongst the groups on the grass. Andrew went among those seated near us, handing out what appeared to be fish and small loaves of bread. He went to one group and then another.

'His basket should be empty by now,' whispered Lazarus, his eyes wide with wonder. And he was not the only one in our group whispering excitedly. By the time Andrew had finished the third group and was making his way towards us, we began to hear voices all around us murmuring the words that had by now become familiar: *It's a miracle!*

'More?' asked Andrew for a second time.

'Lazarus!' I hissed in embarrassment, as my brother nodded enthusiastically.

But Andrew just laughed as he handed my brother two more of the small loaves and another fish. 'There's plenty, believe me.' And he was right. Even Mary regained her appetite now that Jesus had finished teaching. It may have been my imagination, but the barley loaves tasted as good as if they'd been baked within the hour, and the fish as fresh as if newly drawn from the waters of Galilee nearby.

The mood of the crowd could not have been more joyful. All around us, we heard the same sorts of comments being made: 'He feeds us like Moses fed the people in the desert!'

'Surely this is the Prophet that Moses foretold,' said another voice.

'He must be the Messiah,' said another with conviction. And more than once we heard whispered the word that more than any other spoke of revolution: *king*.

For me, however, it was enough simply to be there. I could scarcely believe that we found ourselves not only witnesses to, but also partakers in, an extraordinary miracle. *Maybe now I understood a little more of how Simon must have felt.* I wished my father could have been a part of the momentous days we found ourselves in – days that he had longed for all the time I had known him, from my birth to his death. And I felt a sudden pang of sadness.

'Any leftovers?' Andrew had once again approached our group with his basket. But this time it was empty, and he was filling it with any pieces of bread and fish that had not been eaten.

One of the men sitting nearby in the group called out, 'How much food was there to start with?'

Andrew took two fish halves and tossed them into his basket, and said in a matter-of-fact voice, 'Five small loaves and two fish.' A murmur of amazement rippled around those seated near us.

Another voice called out, 'And any idea how many are here today?'

Andrew reached down, smiling, and took a piece of bread from the hand of a small girl holding it up for him. 'Matthew's had a go at counting – he's the one who's good at numbers – and he reckons there must be around five thousand men, besides women and children!' Matthew was another of the Twelve, though why counting was a skill of his wasn't explained. It seemed of little consequence, however, in the light of what we'd just been told.

When Andrew reached where we were sitting, Lazarus placed a whole loaf and an untouched fish in the basket. I gave him a withering look, but he ignored it. Andrew must have seen what had silently passed between us, and laughed again. 'Don't worry! It won't go to waste.' And then he continued with a grin, 'After all, with Jesus, we often don't know where our next meal is coming from. This should, at least, keep us going for a while – well, us and half of Capernaum!'

At the mention of his home town, an idea suddenly came to me. A wild idea. *I was meant to be the sensible and level-headed one!* But it felt strangely right. So I leaped up. I needed to act before I reasoned myself out of it. I caught up with Andrew and he stopped, a look of curiosity on his face. And I began stuttering out shyly what felt like an almost ridiculous suggestion.

'I know that Jesus has stayed at your home in Capernaum, and I was just thinking... if Jesus visits Jerusalem again and needs somewhere to stay... Not just Jesus, I mean, but all of you who travel with him as well... Though obviously I don't mean *everyone* who follows Jesus...' I could feel the colour rising in my cheeks as I fumbled to find the right words to offer my invitation. But Andrew was smiling, so I started again. 'I have a good-sized house in Bethany, with my sister and brother. It's less than two miles from Jerusalem.' I glanced over to where Jesus was standing. 'And it is at his disposal, should he need a place to stay near Jerusalem.'

'I'll tell the Master.' The kindness and sincerity in his voice assured me that my invitation was not considered foolish.

I felt myself flushing slightly again, but this time because of a sudden warmth in my heart rather than embarrassment. 'Just ask for the house of Martha. I'm the only woman in the village of that name.' Andrew nodded, thanked me, and then he was gone.

'What was that all about?' asked Lazarus when I returned, visibly amazed that I had gone over to speak to one of the Twelve.

'Just an idea,' I said, unwilling to raise any expectations or – more likely in my mind – invite any teasing from my brother.

'Martha!' cried Lazarus, clearly not satisfied with my vague response.

But it was Mary who came to my aid, as she said happily, 'If I know Martha, it was probably a suggestion as to how to use up leftover fish and bread.'

I gave a little smile that I hoped would leave them

thinking that she might be right, and changed the subject.

The following day saw us crammed into the synagogue in Capernaum, with what felt like hundreds of others. After a night spent under the stars, we had been fortunate to find places in a small boat crossing the lake. It had become apparent, shortly after sunrise, that Jesus was no longer there, despite him not having been with the Twelve when they left by boat the previous evening. I hated the time in the boat. The fact that I could not swim constantly played on my mind, although Mary appeared unconcerned, despite having the same inability. My brother, on the other hand, positively enjoyed the movement of the boat on the waters. He seemed to find the larger waves exhilarating. I just clung on more tightly. I spent a good part of the crossing with my eyes closed, silently praying that the Almighty would bring us safely to the other side.

Our efforts and the unpleasant boat-ride were rewarded, however, when we learned that Jesus had gone to the synagogue to teach. Despite it not being the Sabbath, every bench was filled, and others stood wherever there was room. And it was soon clear that the miraculous feeding of the crowd was still very much on everyone's mind. It was not unusual for questions to be asked during teaching at synagogue, but the answers that were given by Jesus could in no way be called typical. When some seemed to be asking for a return to the miraculous forty-year provision of manna in the desert, the assembly became quiet. All were presumably mindful, as was I, of the miracle that had filled our stomachs.

Jesus' strong and steady voice broke the silence: 'I am

the bread of life.' He paused, though not waiting for our attention, for he already had it – as if there were no other voice in the world but his. 'Whoever comes to me will never go hungry, and whoever believes in me will never be thirsty.' Jesus looked around the packed building and then continued his teaching. And as he spoke, one phrase in particular burned in my heart: *everyone who looks to the Son and believes in him shall have eternal life, and I will raise them up at the last day.*

It sounded no less revolutionary and uncompromising than the words he had spoken in Jerusalem, reported to us by Matthias. *Could it really be true,* I asked myself, *that the man standing at the front of the synagogue was the answer to the deaths of those who had been closest to me? To all death? Was he, in some way, the key to life beyond?* The idea was almost too incredible to take in. But even as these questions were occupying my mind, I suddenly became aware of murmuring around the synagogue. I wondered what had been said as my mind had momentarily wandered. The indignant whisperings soon provided the answer.

'Who does he think he is, saying that he's come down as bread from heaven?'

'Heaven? He's from Nazareth!'

'It's not as if we don't know who his mother and father are…'

But Jesus acted as if he were unconcerned by their grumbling and, if anything, only antagonised his listeners further. 'No one has seen the Father except the one who is from God; only he has seen the Father.' Some of those nearby shifted uncomfortably, and there was a harsh edge to the murmurs.

But worse was still to come. 'Unless you eat the flesh

of the Son of Man and drink his blood, you have no life in you.' His words were certainly shocking – and I was shocked. But I was also frightened. The murmurings were intensifying, and, as well as the hostility of many around us, arguments were breaking out throughout the synagogue.

'How can he give us his flesh to eat?' asked one raised voice, angrily.

The crowds who had been willing to make Jesus their king only the previous day now seemed to be turning against him.

Outside the synagogue and back in the sunshine of a spring day, it was clear that many of those who had entered the building so eagerly were now walking away, shaking their heads and muttering. We lingered, however, and Lazarus – still fiercely loyal to Jesus – said quietly but firmly, as if needing to persuade himself afresh of what his heart undoubtedly wanted to be true: 'He *is* the Messiah – he *must* be!' Mary was quiet, visibly shaken and confused by the hostility we had seen. But we were not the only ones who stayed, and we found ourselves on the edge of a group, at the heart of which was Jesus and the Twelve.

Jesus' gaze slowly swept around the small knot of men who were closer to him than any others: 'You do not want to leave too, do you?'

There was a moment's silence, and then Andrew's brother, Simon, spoke. 'Lord, where would we go? You have the words of eternal life. We believe and know that you are the Holy One of God.'

And at my side, I heard a defiant Lazarus whisper, 'That's right!'

I wasn't sure I was ready to respond with the same heart-felt conviction, but I could echo Simon's question: *Lord, where would we go?* Somehow I could no longer comprehend a life without Jesus. So much of our lives now revolved around him and our desire to know more of him. He was never far from our thoughts, and our world would now seem as empty as the Judean wilderness without him. And even as these thoughts were going through my mind, Jesus looked in our direction – and smiled. And I had the uncanny feeling that he knew exactly what I had been thinking.

We stayed as long as we could in Galilee, missing Passover in Jerusalem. Jesus – for whatever reason – appeared to have no intention of travelling south for the festival. And we were rewarded, ever more frequently, by finding ourselves part of a smaller group of Jesus' followers, sitting closer to him – and being recognised by him. It wasn't, however, that he just remembered our faces. Mary, Lazarus and I all felt as if he knew us well, and in some strange way, had always done so. He treated us and those we sat alongside with an easy familiarity, as though he counted us as disciples, and knew without asking that we had been following him and hanging on his every word. I wondered whether he'd seen us in Galilee when we'd been there before. *But maybe all who spent time with Jesus simply felt noticed by him*.

And so we learned the names, not just of the Twelve, but of others who, like us, were often close to all that was happening. Particularly other women who supported Jesus and his followers, providing them with meals and with shelter when possible. Women like Mary from

Magdala, Joanna (whose husband was the manager of Herod's household), and Salome, whose sons James and John were part of the Twelve. And in return, our names became known to them.

Even when we did finally return home, our hearts remained in the north, with Jesus. As spring turned into summer that year, we travelled once again to Galilee. We took any opportunities we could to see and hear him, growing ever closer to him, and – miracle of miracles – speaking with him ourselves. And as summer then mellowed into autumn, I began to wonder whether Jesus had any intention of returning to Jerusalem – and whether Andrew had remembered my offer. But both of those questions were about to be answered.

Chapter 18

The better thing

'There is a time for everything, and a season for every activity under the heavens.' (Ecclesiastes 3:1)

Autumn AD 32

The first I was aware of something out of the ordinary was when I heard my name and that of my sister being called. I then saw Lazarus, through the window of the kitchen, careering down the steps from the roof to the courtyard. He dispensed with the last few steps completely, leaping down to the ground instead. I hurried out from the kitchen, ready to admonish him for his recklessness. *What was he doing anyway? He'd precious little time left to complete the roof-top shelter for Tabernacles!*

But I was stopped in my tracks. 'Jesus is here in Bethany!' he blurted out. 'I just spotted him from the roof!' Mary, who had been working with me in the kitchen, was already at my side. My mind immediately began to fill with myriad questions. But Lazarus went on: 'He's coming down the road.' And then he added, eyes wide with childlike excitement, 'Do you think he might like to stop at our house for some food?'

My heart was pounding. I said in a rather small, strained voice, 'I already invited him.'

'What?' exclaimed my brother and sister in unison.

'When was that?' demanded Lazarus, barely able to contain his excitement.

'In Galilee,' I replied, 'when Jesus performed the miracle with the loaves and fish.' But already my mind was elsewhere. I looked around at the courtyard in quiet desperation, wishing it were tidier and that I was better prepared for providing the hospitality I had offered months earlier. I was already mentally taking stock of the contents of my food-store. *Vegetables? Yes. Plenty of flour. But not enough meat! How much more could I still buy from the stall in Bethany?* Even as the three of us went out through the courtyard door, I was counting up in my head the number of cups we possessed, deciding I would need to send Mary or Lazarus to Simon's house for more.

As we stood watching the group coming towards us, I told myself that Jesus' presence in Bethany did not necessarily mean he was intending to stay with us. *Though if he had come from Galilee and was heading straight to Jerusalem for the festival, he was unlikely to come through our village.* Andrew then hurried towards us, as Jesus paused to speak to a small group in the road.

I bowed my head as Andrew reached us, my heart pounding. 'Shalom, friends!' he said with a smile.

'Shalom, Andrew,' I replied. I was glad to have Lazarus at my side as I greeted in the street a man to whom I was not related. The wonderful truth was, however, that Jesus and the Twelve had begun to feel like family. 'Our house is at the Lord's disposal,' I began nervously, now daunted by the prospect of Jesus coming under our roof. *Would I be able to honour him as he deserved?*

Andrew smiled warmly and glanced back at Jesus

before answering: 'The Master would be grateful of your hospitality, Martha. Thank you.'

'You're *all* welcome,' I replied, bowing my head again, with my heart still beating furiously. I gestured towards the door of our courtyard. 'Please come when you are ready.'

'We may be a little while,' he said with a grin, turning back to return to the others,

Before either my brother or sister had time to do or say anything, I was giving them instructions. 'Mary, ask Rachel if we could borrow five or six cups, please. Lazarus, run down to Elias – see what meat he has left, and get as much as you are able. Tell him I will settle the account with him tomorrow.' Both of them were clearly torn, wanting rather to join the small crowd that was beginning to form around Jesus. But they went anyway. I silently thanked the Almighty for Lazarus' speed and for Elias' provision when my brother returned – even before Mary did – with a reasonable quantity of goat meat.

'Mary, could you fill the water jugs and the bowls for washing, please? And fetch some towels.' As Mary disappeared down the steps to the cistern, I hurriedly began to assemble the spices and vegetables that I would put with the meat, and the extra ingredients that would be used for the accompanying dishes. 'And Lazarus, could you wait by the door, please? Let me know when Jesus arrives.'

I would have wished for days rather than a small portion of one hour to prepare for our honoured guest and those with him. My years of cooking for the family – and for the numerous friends and neighbours who came into our home on a regular basis – meant, however, that the food-store was always well stocked and ready for any unexpected visitors. I also sent another silent prayer of thanks that the impending Feast of Tabernacles, and the feasting that went with it, meant that I had even more food in my kitchen than usual. The house and courtyard had also been thoroughly swept and washed earlier in the day, even if the task of tidying away the brooms, bucket, and freshly-beaten rugs airing in the courtyard, had not yet been completed.

Just as I was finishing returning the rugs to the floor (whilst in my head dividing the tasks to be done in the kitchen between myself and my sister), Lazarus called out, 'Martha, they're here!'

I smoothed down the skirt of my dress, pushed back the hair from my eyes, adjusted my head-covering, and hurried to the courtyard door. Mary was already at Lazarus' side, and within moments we were greeting our guests. We offered them cups of cool water for their thirst, and bowls of water to wash their tired and dusty feet, after what we assumed had probably been a long, hot walk from Jericho. I then showed them into the cool room in which I had laid the rugs, around which were also scattered a large number of cushions on which they could recline. Lazarus, as a young man, was free to sit with Jesus and the Twelve, listening to what was being said. Mary and I could join them later, after preparing the meal.

I gestured to Mary to follow me. Together we filled bowls with olives, almonds, pistachio nuts, roasted grains, and goat's cheese that I had marinated in oil and herbs. I sent her in to the gathering with a tray on which was balanced practically every small bowl that we possessed. We had never had such an honoured guest in our home, and I wanted to give Jesus and those with him the best that I could offer. The moment that Mary had left the kitchen, walking very carefully with the heavily laden tray, I began the task of cutting the meat into small pieces. I wanted to start it cooking over the fire in the courtyard as soon as possible. That way, the meat would have as much time as possible to simmer with the herbs and spices, becoming tender and juicy by the time it needed to be served.

As soon as the meat was on, I began grinding together the garlic, coriander seeds and cumin that I would add to the cooking pot. I was grateful that chick peas had already been soaking for the evening meal that I'd planned before we had guests. I could make them into a hotter, spicier dish to accompany the stewed goat. I knew how many measures of flour I would ask Mary to use, having decided that it would be best for her to start on the bread dough as soon as she returned. But by the time I had added the fine paste from the mortar to the simmering pot, Mary still hadn't reappeared. *Where was she?* I could feel myself becoming slightly irritated by her lack of haste, given the number of tasks that needed doing if we were to provide the feast that was growing ever more elaborate in my mind. *This had to be far better than any Sabbath meal!* I didn't understand. *Mary was usually so willing and helpful. And yet here I was, preparing the most important meal I'd ever cooked, and she'd chosen this day of all days to linger elsewhere!*

As I began kneading the dough myself, Mary had still not returned. Irritated, I punched and pulled the dough with particular vigour, all the while thinking of the jobs that she should have been doing. *Surely, if she had been listening to the Master's teaching on love and service, she would be helping me, rather than letting me do everything myself?* By the time the smooth dough had been returned somewhat ungraciously to the mixing bowl with a loud *thwack*, I could bear it no longer.

I threw a small cloth over the dough – *I would put it somewhere warmer when I returned with Mary* – and walked purposefully across the courtyard. I paused for a moment outside to compose myself before going in to the gathering. Although we were familiar with Jesus and his disciples by now, I didn't want to appear ill-mannered before the one whose teaching on love had spoken so powerfully to our hearts. I took a deep breath and pushed aside the curtain over the doorway and went inside.

Jesus stopped mid-sentence. My eyes flitted across to Mary, who was sitting near Jesus' feet. I had no doubt that it was her responsibility, as a woman and as my younger sister, to assist me with the preparation of the meal. She had clearly decided, however, that she could join the men instead and sit listening to Jesus – leaving everything to me. But it wasn't just that. *Hadn't Jesus wanted us to treat others as we'd want to be treated?* Yet he'd allowed Mary to just sit there. *It was so unfair!* Silence had fallen and every eye was upon me. And I suddenly felt less sure of myself. Despite my best intentions, I wasn't wholly successful in keeping the irritation out of my voice. I found myself blurting out, 'Lord, don't you care that my sister has left me to do the work by myself?' And I didn't seem to be able to stop myself adding, 'Tell her to help me.'

Instead of answering immediately, Jesus looked steadily at me for several moments. He then spoke with a tenderness in his voice that the tone of my own words did not merit: 'Martha, Martha…you are worried and upset about so many things.'

His words took me by surprise. It felt as though he were looking into my heart, seeing beyond my irritation to the heavy load I had been bearing ever since my mother died. My worries of looking after the family, of providing for and taking care of both Mary and Lazarus, of now being responsible for their well-being. And in that moment, it was as if he knew me and cared for me as no other human being had ever done, not even Levi or my parents. But he hadn't finished.

He went on gently, 'But only one thing is needed.' And I knew to what he was referring. 'Mary has chosen what is better, and it will not be taken away from her.'

And he was, of course, right. If he was the Messiah, how could I tear my sister away from him – or make food preparation more important than hearing his words? *And yet, was it so wrong to want to honour this man with a special meal and the best that I could give?* I hesitated, and could feel the colour rising in my cheeks as I continued to be the centre of attention. But it was Mary who saved me. The one with whom I had been annoyed, only moments earlier, smiled at me with unaffected sweetness from where she sat on the floor. I still hesitated, but Mary stretched out her hand to me, inviting me to join her – and I gave in. Though not without a sigh of slight exasperation as I thought of the dough now abandoned on the kitchen table, muttering to no one in particular, 'The bread probably won't rise now…'

'Then we'll pretend it's Passover!' Andrew's reference to the flat, unleavened bread that we ate at that festival had everyone laughing. Even I had a smile on my face by the time I was sitting beside my sister at Jesus' feet. She squeezed my hand, and an expectant hush then fell on the room, with Jesus once again the focus of our attention as we waited for him to begin speaking again. I thought I caught the hint of a twinkle in his eye, reminding me of my father. And then he began.

'What is the kingdom of God like? What shall I compare it to?' He looked around the room at all those gathered there, and then his gaze fell upon me and he smiled. 'It is like yeast that a woman took and mixed into a large amount of flour until it worked all through the dough.'

And as I listened to Jesus teaching, I felt the warmth of his love melt away the final vestiges of my turmoil. And once again, the time slipped by without us noticing, as he spoke and as we asked questions, marvelling at the wisdom and understanding of each and every one of his answers.

When Jesus finally paused, the shadows out in the courtyard told me it must be late afternoon. I suddenly realised with a jolt that I had left the stew unattended, and silently and desperately prayed that I had put sufficient water in the pot. My thoughts were interrupted, however, by the sound of Jesus' voice: 'There is a time for everything, and a season for every activity under the heavens...'

If we were puzzled by Jesus' words, quoted from one of the books of wisdom but spoken with humour, then it wasn't for long. It soon became apparent that it was *now* the time for work. The shelter on the roof for the Feast of Tabernacles, started by Lazarus some hours earlier, still needed to be completed – and there were now thirteen additional pairs of willing hands, including those of a carpenter. Lazarus led the men up onto the flat roof, where he'd already assembled a huge pile of branches (complete with their leaves) and had begun constructing what had initially been planned to be a rather modest structure.

Soon, peals of laughter were coming from above. It was little wonder that Jesus drew people – including children – to himself. Never before had I encountered such joy in one human being.

So it was time to build, but it was also now time to cook – and this time, Mary gladly joined me. 'What can I do to help, Martha?' she asked.

'Could you check the fire out in the courtyard – and the pot, please?' As Mary disappeared, I drained the chick peas that had been soaking. She reappeared moments later.

'The fire's only just alight, so the meat's fine – it hasn't dried out. Shall I stoke up the fire now?'

'Yes please, and add some wine and these chick peas to the pot whilst you're at it.' She took the dish from my hand. 'I'll chop some carrots and onions to go in too.'

Somehow the bread was also redeemed, and everything came right with the Hand of Providence upon us – and with a good measure of the female ingenuity with which that same Hand had also blessed us. And as Mary stood at my side and worked with me, she told me what Jesus had said before I joined them. As I sliced some small salad onions thinly and Mary mixed fresh lettuce leaves in a bowl, I listened as Mary spoke of a Father in heaven who knows what we need before we ask Him. And I believed it was true.

Whilst what we served that evening was a simpler meal that I had originally envisaged, there was still enough to feed sixteen mouths – and more. Simon and Rachel had belatedly been invited to join us – and were overjoyed to be there – for the first of our Tabernacle meals, eaten up on the roof with Jesus and the Twelve. Rachel and Mary helped me serve the food, although we made sure that we were never out of the sound of Jesus' words for more than a few moments. It felt as though heaven were touching earth as we sat eating together under the stars, in one of the largest – and sturdiest – shelters we had ever had at Tabernacles. And as we shared festive cups of spiced wine, we listened to Jesus as he spoke to us of the Lord of creation, and our hearts soared. But we also shared stories and laughter, and whatever joys paradise might offer, I would have been content to forego them if that evening could have gone on forever.

But it did, of course, eventually have to end – but not before the lamps had burned low. When the dishes, including those of the many sweet platters I'd managed to produce, were cleared away, our guests were provided with blankets, some of which came from Rachel's stores. Mary and I then made our way to a separate booth on a different part of the roof, as was only appropriate. We lay beside each other, whispering together about all we'd heard and seen, or just listening quietly as the noises of the night – the dogs, the foxes and the owls – broke the silence around us. Slumber overtook Mary before it did me, and as I lay there, I quietly thanked the Almighty for the honour that had been bestowed on us. The words that my father had spoken so often ran through my head once more: *When the Messiah comes…* And as I drifted off to sleep that night, a smile came to my face. *Abba, you'll never guess who came to our house today…*

The cock crowing early in the morning, as the first light of day began creeping into the sky, made me groan inwardly as sleep departed. Still, I could hear no sounds of our guests stirring, so I allowed myself to lie there, revelling in the memory of the previous evening, until I heard the cock crowing for a second time. I glanced across at Mary, whose breathing was still regular. The growing light of the new day illuminated her sleeping face, which had a look of deep peace. I decided not to wake her just yet, and quickly pushed the blanket aside, shivering slightly in the coolness of the early autumn morning. I hurried down the steps into the courtyard, and a fire was quickly kindled in the bread oven. Although my body yearned for more sleep, especially after the lateness of the previous night, there was something about the quietness and peacefulness of the early morning that always lifted my heart.

The goats stood impassively – chewing the cud as ever – as I milked them. But my mind was not on the frothy white milk that was filling the bowl. I was, instead, pondering the words of Jesus, turning them over in my mind as I then set aside the bowl. I added a spoonful of the yoghurt I'd made the previous day, so that the everyday miracle of souring milk to become creamy yoghurt could once again take place.

By the time the first of the guests was making his way down the steps, Mary had joined me, as had Lazarus (keen not to miss out on anything that might be happening). The smell of baking bread was once again filling the courtyard. It felt strange to have a company of men who were not relatives staying with us, with neither Mary nor me married. Although Lazarus, being the only male, was supposedly the head of our household, he was still only fifteen. I had, however, recently turned twenty six, and was certainly the one who ran the home. But so much was changing with the coming of Jesus. Although the Twelve were all men, he bestowed on women such as Mary and me a dignity and value that made us feel equal to men in his sight, even though I was a widow and Mary unmarried.

'Smells good!'

'Martha makes the best bread in Bethany,' Lazarus said with a grin to the disciple we knew as Matthew.

I felt myself redden, and quickly changed the subject. 'I hope you all slept well.'

'Yes, thank you,' said Matthew, and then directed his gaze at the roof. 'And *are* still sleeping well,' adding with a smile, 'helped by the excellent meal last night.'

Although I was used to receiving compliments for my food, I never found them easy to accept, and once again re-directed the conversation. 'Are you the only one awake so far?'

'Yes. Apart from Jesus, that is. He's gone already.'

'Gone?' said Mary, disappointment etched on her face.

Matthew smiled as he pulled up a stool to sit upon. 'Don't worry – he'll be back. He often leaves before sunrise to pray.' He let out a satisfied yawn and stretched before continuing: 'He's probably just gone up to a quiet spot at the top of the Mount of Olives to pray. He'll be back when he's finished.'

Lazarus dragged another stool across the courtyard and sat down near Matthew. 'Tell us more of Jesus – and how you became his disciple.'

'Let our guest eat some breakfast first,' I interrupted, offering Matthew some of the fresh bread, which was by now in a basket. Mary followed my lead, holding a bowl of yoghurt and honey into which Matthew could dip the warm bread. A look of contentment came to his face as he savoured the combination, and he didn't refuse when I offered him more.

'Were you a fisherman, too, when Jesus called you?' asked Lazarus, unable to contain his curiosity any longer.

Matthew spluttered on the food in his mouth, and apologised before giving my brother the correct answer. 'Heavens, no! I was a tax-collector.'

And before I could shoot Lazarus a warning look, he'd exclaimed with incredulity, 'You worked for the Romans?'

Mary, however, swiftly countered our brother's unintended slight. 'But if Jesus wanted Matthew to be one of his disciples, what difference does it make what he did before?' My eyes met those of Mary, and I smiled in an attempt to convey my gratitude to her. That didn't, however, mean that I wasn't also surprised that Jesus had chosen one of those usually despised by our countrymen, because of their collaboration with our enemies.

Matthew shrugged and smiled again. 'Jesus seems to make a habit of choosing and including those whom others wouldn't.' He was right. It was one of the things that needled many of our leaders. I was beginning to get used to the fact that Jesus seemed to spend a surprisingly large amount of time with those considered outcasts – the prostitutes, the immoral, and, *yes,* the tax-collectors. And then I thought of our friend Simon. He'd also been an outcast – a leper – and yet, because of Jesus, he was among us once again. And as I thought of him, I was glad that Jesus *did* reach out and touch the lives of those whom others considered untouchable.

Matthew then shared with us the story of how Jesus had called him from his tax-collector's booth, and then he laughed. 'Who'd have thought it – a tax-collector bringing good-news!'

'What do you mean?' asked Lazarus. 'Isn't that what Jesus does?'

'He does, yes, but he's also been sending us out to do the same throughout Galilee.'

'How do you know what to say?' asked Mary with curiosity.

'Jesus tells people the good news about the Kingdom of God – that the rule of God in people's hearts is near – and therefore so do we.' Amazement must have shown on our faces, because he laughed and then continued: 'It's not as difficult as it sounds. We're really just repeating what we've already heard him say. After all, we've heard the same things so many times by now.' And when he saw our surprise, he added, 'He doesn't always say different things in different places.'

I thought for a moment, and then suggested, 'I suppose each place where Jesus travels needs to hear the same truths about God.'

'You're right,' replied Matthew. 'Although he does sometimes use a parable to make one point in one place, and then to make another elsewhere.' He paused and then added, 'It's as if he has an ear open to a silent voice that we don't hear, but which directs him. But either way, we know many of his words off by heart by now, and are able to pass them on to others. After all, Galilee has – what? – maybe two hundred towns and villages. He sends us out in pairs, so we can spread his message more widely than he could alone.'

As I listened to Matthew, I was reminded afresh of how we relied so much on memories of the spoken word. It was part of our heritage, and formed the basis of Lazarus' learning at synagogue. But the news about Jesus was different – far more important. And suddenly I felt as though it shouldn't only be left in the memories of fallible men. 'You should write it down!' I exclaimed. 'You were a tax-collector – you must be used to making records.'

Matthew laughed. 'And when am I going to find time for that, travelling around with Jesus? Maybe I will one day,' he said jokingly.

But then Lazarus cut in, making his words more of a statement than a question: 'You believe that he is the Messiah…'

Matthew drew in a breath and nodded. He then lowered his voice. 'He raises the dead – twice I've seen it. How can he not be?'

'We'd heard rumours about that,' I said. 'We wanted to believe it, but weren't sure that we could trust the stories we were hearing.'

'You can trust those stories,' said Matthew, adding with a smile, 'providing you can trust me.'

Then Lazarus suddenly asked a question that he must have been carrying around in his mind ever since a discussion that followed Simon's healing, more than two years earlier. 'Is Jesus a descendant of David – he must be, surely, if he's the Messiah?'

'That's right, Lazarus,' replied Matthew. 'He is.'

My brother couldn't quite hide his smugness at finally having proved his point. 'I told you he could still be a descendant of David, even if he came from Nazareth!'

'*Came from Nazareth*, yes, but that's not where he

was born.' Matthew leaned forward, as if he had a secret to share – and he did. 'Don't be fooled by his Galilean accent – I found out he was born in the south. In Judea. In Bethlehem.' He let his last word hang in the air – and we knew what it meant: the city of David.

And my brother whispered a triumphant *Yes!*

Chapter 19

Living water

'Come, all you who are thirsty, come to the waters.'
(Isaiah 55:1)

Autumn AD 32

It was something of a mystery to us that Jesus didn't immediately go to the temple. Not that we minded. All three of us were elated to have him in our home and to have so much time with him. None of us wanted to be separated from him, and we were amazed at the affection he showed us. More than once I saw Jesus' hand on my brother's shoulder, as Lazarus sat beside him, utterly engrossed, as the one we knew as *Lord* imparted wonderful truths about God. But, even so, we were still puzzled.

The Feast of Tabernacles had started, and yet, despite having come all the way from Galilee for the festival, Jesus gave the impression of being in no hurry to join the crowds in Jerusalem. He seemed more interested in staying out of sight, and it had surprised me that he'd only arrived with the Twelve, given the numbers of others that often followed him around.

'We travelled south in secret,' said Matthew, when I took him aside to ask him about it. 'Did you hear about what happened when Jesus was last in Jerusalem?'

I nodded, 'Healing a man on the Sabbath, and telling him to pick up his bed and walk. And I heard about the opposition that it stirred up. We felt it even here in Bethany.'

Matthew glanced over towards Jesus, who was sitting and talking quietly to my brother and sister, both of whom were listening in rapt attention. 'I think he's aware of the opposition – he seems to have been deliberately staying away from Judea.'

'Then why come now – and why come and *not* go to Jerusalem?'

'The Master always has his reasons,' replied Matthew with a wry smile, 'even if we rarely seem to know what they are.'

Only when the festival was halfway through, did Jesus finally decide to make the short journey into Jerusalem. We went with him and the Twelve, and joined the throngs of men, women and children – all waving festive lulabs of myrtle and willow – as they streamed towards the city and the temple for the daily celebrations. As we walked the familiar route, down the Mount of Olives, and then up from the bottom of the valley into the city, jostling with the crowds through the Susa Gate, I had little idea of what Jesus would do. But I had at the back of my mind the earlier conversation with Matthew. I wondered what the reaction would be of those like Joseph, our local scribe, who had been so vehemently opposed to Jesus the last time he had visited the city.

When Jesus found a place to sit in Solomon's Colonnade – the usual place for rabbis to teach their followers – a crowd quickly gathered around him as he began to teach, and as news spread that the teacher from Galilee had arrived. Mary was standing close to Jesus, but I found myself on the edge of the gathering and decided to stay there, rather than push through the crowd as Lazarus had done. But standing on the edge, I could see the looks of amazement on the faces of those listening. And I heard snatches of their whispers: *not educated…carpenter from Galilee…*

My mind suddenly snapped back to what Jesus was saying. Despite the general festival clamour behind us in the Court of the Gentiles, Jesus' voice rose clear and calm. 'My teaching is not my own' – it was as if he was perfectly aware of the whispered conversations of the crowd – 'it comes from the one who sent me.'

As I continued listening to Jesus, I tried to gauge the reactions of those standing nearby. They were largely listening intently, until, that is, Jesus asked a question that shocked me. Judging by the reactions of those around me, it surprised others too. 'Why are you trying to kill me?'

From where I was standing, I could see the confused look on Mary's face. She appeared unable to conceive that anyone could possibly want to harm Jesus. But amongst the crowd I could sense that not all had Mary's attitude towards Jesus. I heard a voice nearby mutter, 'Who does he think he is?'

Another voice jeered loudly, 'You've got a demon!'

Yet another called out, his tone implying that he didn't believe what Jesus was saying, 'Who's trying to kill you?'

The crowd quickly quietened as Jesus began to speak again, but I still felt uneasy. Part of me wished that I had Mary's carefree trust, which never doubted that, with Jesus, all would be well. I was the one, as Jesus had so clearly seen, destined to worry, regardless of whether it was over meals or the Messiah. And as Jesus began to challenge those around him about their animosity towards him, caused by the miracle he'd performed on the Sabbath, it did nothing to lessen my unease.

Jesus continued staying with us during the festival, with our days spent at the temple listening to him teach, and our evenings back at Bethany with hastily prepared meals. When the last day – the greatest day – of the Feast arrived, we joined once again the vast crowds streaming towards Jerusalem, many of whom had been staying in local villages or camping out on the nearby hillsides.

I remembered back to the time in my childhood when I had watched all the celebrations with my aunt. I suddenly felt a little stab in my heart, seeing the other young women and their families in the crowd. I was neither a wife nor a mother, the roles that defined a woman in our society, and it was at these special times that I felt that most acutely. But then I looked at Jesus – around ten years my senior – and suddenly realised that he was neither a husband nor a father. *Hadn't he spoken of a new way? Of those who did God's will being his family?* And I felt the pain in my heart begin to dissipate. *Maybe I, too, was an outsider in my own way. But Jesus had included me amongst his friends. What more could I want?*

We arrived at the temple just as the procession, returning from the Pool of Siloam, was making its way across the Court of the Gentiles and towards the heart of the temple. Caiaphas, holding the golden pitcher full of water, was at its head. The contrast between our religious leaders and Jesus had never felt starker. The power wielded by Caiaphas was inextricably linked with everything that went with his position: his high priest's robes and roles, his wealth and his connections, and the authority he had over the temple guards. For Jesus, his power lay only in himself.

If Caiaphas was aware of Jesus' presence, he didn't show it. His procession soon disappeared into the Court of the Women. The singing and shouting of the crowds, and the blasts of the ram's horn, indicated that Caiaphas had made his way up the ramp and onto the altar in the Court of the Priests. We knew he was about to pour the water from the pitcher into the silver bowl, symbolising the prayer for rain. But then Jesus suddenly cried out above the noise: 'Let anyone who is thirsty come to me and drink.'

His words left the crowd around us stunned and silent. Jesus was, it seemed, deliberately interrupting one of the most dramatic moments of the festival. But he hadn't finished. 'Whoever believes in me, as Scripture has said, rivers of living water will flow from within him.'

Once again, I could hear murmuring in the crowd around me, but this time whispering questions with the words *messiah* and *prophet*. But I also heard doubts about a Galilean messiah. *Though I now knew the truth about his birth.* But beyond the edge of the crowd, a group of temple guards were watching Jesus carefully, and listening to all that was going on. Although they would be reporting back to Caiaphas, my disquiet was lessened by the expressions on the guards' faces, which appeared to be closer to curiosity than hostility.

The water libation was not the only image from the Feast to be used by Jesus. In the Court of the Women, where the huge lampstands that blazed during the final night loomed above us, he spoke of being the light of the world. But his words did not go unchallenged. Even as many put their faith in him, the Pharisees questioned his words to his face – and Jesus did more to provoke than placate them.

Jesus stayed beyond the end of the festival, but was not always with us. It was only after one particular Sabbath spent in Bethany – Jerusalem being beyond the distance we were permitted to walk on the day of rest – that we heard he had once again healed on that day. This time, he had sent a blind man to wash in the Pool of Siloam, from which the water had so recently been drawn at the Feast. And the man who had been blind from birth was able to see for the first time ever. I knew it was likely to cause more offence, and I witnessed the repercussions closer to home a short while after Jesus had left.

I was spending the afternoon with Salome, helping out at her house. Her daughter-in-law (Benjamin's wife) had fallen ill, as had one of her grandchildren, and I was in the kitchen, helping start off their evening meal as she tended to the sick. I heard the sound of voices outside in their small courtyard. It didn't take long for me to realise that Jonathan had arrived to bring some medicine, which he was giving to Judas. I could see the two men reasonably clearly out in the bright courtyard. But I remained out of sight to them in the darker kitchen, behind the thin piece of muslin that hung across the kitchen window, keeping out any flies that were still venturing out on the warm autumn day. From the conversation, I gathered that Judas was paying for the medicine. But I suddenly paused when he added, 'It's a shame Jesus isn't still here in Bethany – if he were, I suspect I wouldn't be needing your services.' I couldn't tell whether he spoke the words with a smile. Or whether they were deliberately said to provoke a reaction, because that was certainly the result.

Jonathan responded sharply, 'I know you claim that he could be the Messiah, and yet I hear from other Pharisees that he breaks God's holy law by working on the Sabbath!'

I quietly laid the knife down and listened. I wondered if I should make my presence known, feeling slightly uneasy about being party to their conversation without their knowledge. But before I had made any decision, Judas was speaking again, and I could hear the impatience in his reply: 'He *heals* on the Sabbath, if that's what you mean.'

'There are six other days on which to heal.'

'Jonathan! You're a physician yourself. If a member of your own family was dying and your skills could heal them, I *know* that you wouldn't let them die simply because it was the Sabbath. If it was Naomi or one of your children you would act, regardless of what day it was. And *you* would think you were doing the will of the Almighty.'

'But that is saving a life, not carrying out a healing that could wait until the following day – '

Through the muslin, I could make out Judas shaking his head in exasperation. 'You speak as if miracles are no different to administering a poultice! The healings that Jesus is doing can only be done by the power of God!'

'So you say…'

'And surely God would not give such powers to a man if he were displeasing to the Almighty.'

Jonathan had no answer, as he then tried another approach. 'Answer me this then: if Jesus is the Messiah, why does he bring such division? Why is it that the leaders of our people are not proclaiming him as the Lord's anointed? Why do those who study and know God's Law not embrace him with open arms? Surely the true Messiah would unite our people and be welcomed by all.'

Judas fell silent and, from Jonathan's stance, it looked as if he were standing with his arms folded. But then Judas returned to one certainty that he knew to be true. 'Simon's healing – how do you explain that then?'

'Those with leprosy can get better. That's why God's law has provision for such events, telling those who are healed to go to the priests – '

'But people are not healed in an instant!' exclaimed Judas, cutting in. This time it was Jonathan's turn to fall silent. So Judas continued, and it sounded as if he were almost pleading with the other man. 'Jesus knows God in a way that no-one else does. You've heard him teach. No man speaks with such authority – '

'And yet he claims far more than any man should!' responded Jonathan. 'Did you hear what he said about our father Abraham?' And without waiting for Judas to reply he continued, 'He claimed to have seen Abraham for himself. And do you know what he said then? He said, *Before Abraham was born, I am*. I AM! He calls himself by the title that only the Almighty uses. Is it any wonder that those who heard him wanted to stone him for blasphemy? He is claiming to be God when he says such things!'

I suddenly realised that I was holding my breath. Some of what was being said was new to me and startled me, but all I could do now was keep quiet. I also knew, however, what I would say had it been me facing Jonathan and not Judas. But Judas said the words for me: 'Surely

256

he wouldn't be able to open the eyes of a man born blind if he weren't from God.' Before Jonathan had a chance to respond, Judas went on: 'And don't tell me his power is from Satan! Everywhere he goes Jesus heals and casts out demons. They say he has even raised people from the dead. Will the Messiah do more signs than him?'

Jonathan fell silent once again, and I suspected that he was torn. I had heard him speak about Jesus before. It had seemed to me then as though he were saying words that he felt he ought to be saying, yet without the conviction that was so evident in Judas. Many of the other Pharisees had made their disapproval of Jesus abundantly clear, as had Joseph the scribe at the synagogue. I imagined that Jonathan was perfectly well aware of what the personal cost would be, were he to give his approval to the preacher from Galilee. And I suddenly wondered whose approval was most important to these men of God whom we regarded so highly.

Through the muslin I saw Jonathan shake his head, but I suspected it wasn't in answer to Judas's question. He said quietly and simply, 'Would the Messiah treat our laws so lightly?' He then turned and left. Judas stood still and watched him go. Then, with the medicine in his hand, he turned to enter the rooms where his daughter-in-law and grandchild lay sick. And I breathed freely once more.

It was certainly true that there was much in Jesus' teaching that we did not understand. Whilst he was in Jerusalem he had spoken many wonderful words: about his teaching setting us free, about bringing life in all its fullness, about being the good shepherd for his sheep. And yet there were also words whose meaning was hidden to us. He spoke of being lifted up, and yet also of laying down his life and taking it up again. But despite the impenetrability of some of what he said, I found that increasingly I could no longer deny who he was.

We saw Jesus once more that year, when he visited the temple in winter for the Feast of Dedication. It was a time when we remembered what had happened almost two hundred years earlier, when a foreign tyrant had forbidden our people to worship our God. The family of the Maccabees had liberated Jerusalem and cleansed the temple and rededicated it. And by kindling lights, we celebrated the miracle that had occurred then, when the seven-branched, golden candlestick in the temple had been relit, and had burned for eight days, despite only having oil enough for one.

As I lit our own festival lights one evening, Mary suddenly asked, 'Do you think Jesus will cleanse the temple again – as the Maccabees did?'

'Well, if *they* could drive out the enemy and put everything right, imagine what Jesus will do!' replied Lazarus confidently.

Jesus *would* be victorious – though not in a way that any of us could ever have imagined. But first we would walk a path that would take us to the depths of despair and the heights of glory.

Chapter 20

The resurrection and the life

'You, my people, will know that I am the LORD, when I
open your graves and bring you up from them.'
(Ezekiel 37:13)

Early AD 33

'Aren't you hungry?' I asked Lazarus, when his breakfast of bread and yoghurt remained untouched. He just shook his head.

It was around four months since Jesus had stayed with us, and my brother hadn't been his normal self for a day or two. I raised my hand to his flushed forehead. 'I think you might be running a fever. You should go back to bed. I'm sure the workshop can manage without you today.' Although Lazarus had just turned sixteen and the coolness of winter had not yet passed, the walk into Jerusalem and a day's work alongside my uncle Jacob and cousin Thomas would not help any fever. When Lazarus meekly complied, any remaining doubts about the state of his health were dispelled. Any confinement indoors was usually met with a loud protest.

The passing of the day and some tonic procured from Jonathan did nothing, however, to improve his condition. When he wasn't sweating, he was shivering with a chill. His only words were to complain of aches. By night-fall I was sufficiently concerned to want to stay near his bedside through the hours of darkness. I kept a lamp burning during the night, and although I occasionally dozed, I was fully awake the moment I heard Mary creeping into the room, at what I judged to be some time after midnight.

'Any change?' whispered my sister, concern on her face.

I shook my head, and whispered back, 'No, he still seems feverish.'

Mary studied me in the flickering light of the lamp for several moments. 'It *will* be different this time, Martha.' It was as if she'd read my thoughts, and she didn't need to mention Levi's name for me to understand her meaning. I'd sat with my husband through two sleepless nights as he'd battled his fever and then lost the fight. I sighed and nodded. Mary continued, 'Jesus loves Lazarus – he won't let anything happen to him.'

I didn't reply immediately, but turned my gaze back on my brother, my mind flitting back to the time that Jesus had stayed with us. It had warmed my heart more than I could say to see the affection that Jesus had for Lazarus. My brother's youthful enthusiasm only ever met with smiles and encouragement. Jesus always seemed to have time for him, which only strengthened my brother's fierce commitment to him. I remembered how Lazarus had adored Levi. But his astonishment at being both known and loved by the one he believed to be the Messiah had ignited a passion in him that far exceeded anything I had ever seen before.

Mary sat on the edge of the bed and gently stroked our

brother's head. 'If he's no better by morning, we could send word to Jesus.'

'We'll do that,' I said, having already come to that decision myself. When I stifled a yawn, Mary turned to me and smiled. 'You go to bed, Martha. I'll sit with him for the rest of the night.' I looked at my sister, who had grown into a young woman whose inner beauty more than matched that of her outward appearance. And I knew that the love and joy that flowed from her had their source in the one who had changed each of our lives. I smiled wearily in agreement, whispering a quiet *thank you* as I rose to my feet. I kissed her lightly on the forehead, then pulled aside the curtain over the doorway and left.

Despite my sister's kindness, the rest of my night passed only in fitful sleep, and the coming of the first morning light brought with it no improvement in my brother's condition. His words, when he did speak, were confused, and both his sweats and his chills seemed more severe. I left Mary with Lazarus, hurrying the short distance up the road to the only place to go under the circumstances. The door to the courtyard was already open when I arrived at Simon's house. I found Rachel, despite her ever increasing years, kneeling on the ground next to her bread oven, coaxing the flames into life to bake the first batch of the day's bread. Surprise quickly turned to concern on her face, and she rose stiffly to her feet.

'Martha, my dear, whatever is the matter?' she said, as she began walking towards me with a slight hobble.

'It's Lazarus. We need James's help.'

Neither Simon nor Rachel had any hesitation in sending James north with a message for Jesus. Ever since his father's healing, James had believed that Jesus was the Messiah, and we knew he would believe that Jesus could heal Lazarus too. But he was also now in his early thirties, and able to travel both swiftly and light. Not that the journey would be a short one. Jesus had gone to Batanea, to the east of Galilee and across the Jordan, where John had been baptising in the early days of his ministry. It was away from the reach of Herod, in the region ruled by his half-brother Philip. But it was also the best part of four day's travel. Within the hour, however, James had departed with our simple message: *Lord, the one you love is sick.* And all that remained for my sister and me to do was tend to Lazarus' fever – and wait for Jesus' response.

As Mary and I took turns to sit with Lazarus, the simple reckoning on our fingers and in our minds was repeated over and over: James had left early on the third day of the week and, providing he encountered no delays, it was perfectly possible for him to arrive late on the sixth day before the Sabbath began. And we needed to keep Lazarus alive until Jesus could heal him. As the severity of Lazarus' fever increased, so did the fervency of our prayers, though an unspoken question lurked in our minds which I was the first to voice.

'Even if James arrives before sundown on the Day of Preparation, will Jesus travel south on the Sabbath?'

'He certainly heals on the Sabbath,' offered Mary in response, adding after a pause, 'and believes it is lawful to give help.'

I reached over and applied a fresh damp cloth to my brother's brow, my own brow furrowing as I faced once again a harsh reality. Even if Jesus *did* travel beyond the short distance that was allowed on that day, it would still take four days for Jesus to reach Bethany. I remembered all too well how quickly Levi had deteriorated. But, as if she had read my thoughts again, Mary laid her hand gently over mine and repeated the only certainty we had. 'Jesus loves Lazarus. He won't let us down.'

I turned over once again in my mind the seemingly impossible nature of our reckonings, but suddenly found a solution that seemed so perfect that I actually gave a little laugh. 'No – he won't let us down, because maybe he doesn't have to travel at all.'

Mary stared at me, perplexed, but then the light of comprehension dawned in her eyes. 'The story Matthew told us…'

I tried to remember the details of the account we'd heard of Jesus healing someone from afar. 'Jesus simply uttered a word and the centurion's servant was healed – he didn't even need to go to him! When Jesus hears that Lazarus is sick, surely he can do the same. Maybe it makes no difference whether he's in Bethany or Batanea'

Both of us looked back at Lazarus, almost expecting him to suddenly make a full recovery, even though we knew that James could not have reached Jesus yet.

Mary leaned over, and whispered, 'Hold on, Lazarus – Jesus will heal you.'

Among the visitors to our house as the days dragged by was Jonathan. He arrived unexpectedly on the day after James had left, and stood quietly in the doorway to Lazarus' room. He held out a small clay jar with a stopper, and said simply, 'This may help.'

I rose from the bedside, taking the bottle. 'Thank-you.'

'We've sent word to Jesus,' said Mary.

'I know – Simon told me.' But if Jonathan had any particular thoughts about that, he chose to keep them to himself. He crossed silently to where Lazarus lay, crouched down and placed his hand on my brother's fevered forehead and then on the side of his neck. 'He's been like this for how long?'

'A day and a half,' I replied.

Jonathan sighed. 'Do your best to try to get him to drink what I've given you,' and with that he rose, and went to leave, but he paused once again in the doorway. I had known the physician from my earliest days. He'd been there in our lives when first my mother and then Levi had died. More recently he had witnessed my father's decline – and then stood with us as we'd laid him in the tomb. But for a moment he looked uncertain of what to say. 'Let me know if there's any change,' he said eventually, and then he was gone.

As the Day of Preparation – the day before the Sabbath – drew to its close, we watched Lazarus even more closely for any signs of recovery. 'Maybe James hasn't reached Jesus yet,' murmured Mary. But when the lights faded and the trumpets sounded to announce that the Sabbath had at last begun, the only change was for the worse. Although his delirium lessened, he didn't come round and his breathing seemed shallow. His sickness had become a battle for life.

The seventh day slowly moved from long hours of darkness into a new morning, and then again later into the twilight that heralded its passing. Again and again in our increasing tiredness, we voiced every reason that we could think of to assure ourselves that Jesus would heal our brother. *The Messiah walked among us in our land and all would be well…surely.*

The end, when it came, was swift. Sometime after noon on the first day of the week I heard Mary urgently calling my name. I left the cloths that I had been washing and ran inside, and could immediately hear the change in my brother's breathing. By the time Lazarus drew his last laboured breath, both Jonathan and my uncle John were by our sides. A hand laid by Jonathan against my brother's neck followed by a quick shake of his head confirmed what our eyes told us but what our minds simply couldn't believe – Lazarus was dead. Mary looked as I felt: crushed and distraught. Our tears only held back by our shock. *Why had Jesus allowed this to happen? Why hadn't he been here when we needed him most? Why had he not spoken the word that would have healed our brother?* My brother was now lying utterly still and devoid of life, his sunken cheeks bearing the unmistakable pallor of death. The only sound was Mary softly saying *No*, as if the denial would somehow change what was before us.

'I'm sorry,' said Jonathan quietly, but in my mind, I heard his words differently: *where is your healer, your Messiah now?* But there was no malice in him. It was clear it gave him no joy to have his doubts about Jesus confirmed, and I was sure that he felt only pity for us. But despite my grief and utter bewilderment, I had seen too much to turn my back on the preacher from Galilee.

My uncle's words broke into my jumbled thoughts: 'I'll send word to Jacob and the others in Jerusalem. It's late in the day, but they'll be able to join us in the morning…'

And although he didn't say it, I knew what was implied: *when we bury your brother*. And the tears began.

Mary and I wept as we held each other, but soon the sounds of shared grief were no longer ours alone, as our friends and relatives from Bethany joined us. I was momentarily bewildered by the arrival of my cousin Thomas just as night fell. I stood staring at his tear-stained face, wondering why he should come at such a late hour – until I noticed the jars he was carrying. Although he was twelve years older than Lazarus, he'd always delighted in showing his young cousin the skills of their shared trade, and Lazarus had loved his cousin as ardently as I had done in my youth. And now Thomas was standing there with perfumes from our own family workshop for the rituals of burial – perfumes that he and Lazarus might have worked on together. And I wept once again.

The night passed in a blur, but even in my grief, I still found myself looking up each time someone entered the room, desperately wanting it to be Jesus, despite Batanea being too far away for that to be possible. All I wanted that night was for him to be there, for him to somehow make it right again. But he never came. Instead, as the hours of darkness rolled into a new dawn, we once again performed the preparations for burial that were becoming horribly familiar. Both Mary and I were numb and weary, with a grief that was laden with too many unanswered questions, but we both still wanted to do this one final act of love for our brother. So together with John and Elizabeth, we wrapped my brother's body in its burial cloths, sprinkling it with the mixture of myrrh and aloes that Thomas had brought.

'Why does death stalk our family?' I didn't expect an answer to the question that suddenly slipped from my lips in the quietness of the room – and none was given. Instead, I felt Elizabeth's hand upon my shoulder and heard her sigh. But neither she nor my uncle attempted to explain the workings of the God whose ways once more seemed too deep and too dark to fathom. The only words they offered during our grim task were when their voices blended together in singing a haunting but strangely beautiful psalm of lament.

> Relent, LORD! How long will it be?
>   Have compassion on your servants.
> Satisfy us in the morning with your unfailing love,
>   that we may sing for joy and be glad all our days.
> Make us glad for as many days as you have afflicted us,
>   for as many years as we have seen trouble.

And into the numbness of my heart and mind drifted a memory rekindled by the song from our Scriptures. *Martha,* my father had once said when I had struggled with why God had allowed my mother to die, *there will always be ways in which the Lord works that we will not be able to understand. But we know that the Lord is good, and we must trust Him when we cannot see His purposes in the things that happen.* The remembered words were like a small candle that had suddenly been lit in a deep darkness. Trust – *could I do that even now?*

I'm not sure how many I had expected to be there in the morning, but whatever number I might have guessed was far exceeded. As we made our way to the tomb, following behind the bier, our friends and neighbours from Bethany walked with us, together with all of John and Elizabeth's ever-growing family. But the numbers were swelled further by many from Jerusalem. Relatives from my father's side joined us, together with craftsmen from the city, who had known first my father and then Lazarus. There were priests and Levites from the temple, to whom the wares from our workshop had been sold, and other customers who had known our family for many years. It was a small comfort to see so many there, as Lazarus' body was borne to the cold, dark tomb that already contained the bones of both grandparents and parents. But still my eyes searched the crowd for the one face I longed to see, but did not find it.

Mary and I stood outside the tomb whilst Lazarus was laid to rest. 'Why wasn't he here when we needed him?' whispered my sister, staring at the gaping black hole through which our brother's body had disappeared. We had voiced that question a number of times already, but no answer made any sense.

All I could whisper back were the all-too-familiar words: 'I don't know, Mary. I just don't know.'

After the men re-emerged from the tomb into the dull winter morning came the moment that I had been dreading, when the huge, round stone was rolled across the entrance to the tomb. It had a horrible finality. The grinding of the stone, as it was pushed along the deep groove in which it sat, seemed to crush any last vestige of hope. *Jesus hadn't come, Lazarus had died, and now he was in the tomb.* It was as if our hope had been buried with him, and the third member of our tiny household was now a grief that felt almost too deep to bear.

On the day we buried Lazarus and the two days that followed, Mary and I had precious little time – or strength – to speak of Jesus and the questions that gnawed at our hearts. Many of those who had come from Jerusalem were there each day to sit with us in our desolation and comfort us in our loss. But two further realisations compounded our distress.

The first one concerned a consequence of Lazarus' death of which I had somehow remained oblivious, but which suddenly hit home with a sickening clarity. I immediately turned to my aunt Elizabeth, sitting next to me. 'What will happen to us?' I began. 'The house…'

Elizabeth's expression told me that the question was not unexpected. 'Martha, you must not worry – '

'But the house will no longer be ours,' I said. I understood enough of the rules of inheritance to know that neither Mary nor I were entitled to the house or wealth of our small family. On my father's death, it had all passed to Lazarus, although I had been running the household given my brother's relatively young age. But now that my brother was dead, it would pass to the male relatives on my father's side – to my uncle Jacob and to my father's other brother, Matthan, in Jericho.

Elizabeth patted my arm reassuringly. 'You and Mary will never be without a roof over your head. You needn't fear, Martha.'

I didn't doubt for a moment the truth of what she'd said – we were fortunate to be blessed with a wider family who loved us and could support us. But nevertheless, the future was now filled with uncertainty, knowing that Mary and I would be dependent on the goodness of others until husbands could be found for us, and I looked around with fresh sadness at the house I would most probably have to leave, and the kitchen which would no longer be mine.

Although this first realisation was difficult for my sister and me, it was, however, the second, on James's return, that brought us greater pain.

It was a moment or two before I realised that James had entered the room where we were sitting, surrounded by other mourners. I glanced up to see him staring at me, standing motionless as a Roman statue, with Simon at his side, a look of deep shock on his face. Both my sister and I rose quickly, and together we hurried with them out into the courtyard, seeking some sort of privacy for our conversation. We were barely outside when Mary asked James, 'Did you get our message to Jesus?'

'Yes. On Preparation Day – late in the afternoon. I told him Lazarus was sick…' The confused tone in James's voice told me that he, like us, could not then comprehend why my brother now lay dead in a tomb. 'I left Jesus and stayed overnight with some family who lived nearby. I rested on the Sabbath, but I thought…' James broke off, but he didn't need to finish the sentence for us to know what he was trying to say. After a moment, he said simply, 'I thought Jesus would be here by the time I got back.' The words *and I thought Lazarus would be healed* remained unspoken.

The certainty of knowing that Jesus had received our message, and his continued absence, only deepened our confusion and pain. But whereas I sought to grapple with my questions, Mary appeared to give up the struggle. The news that James had brought seemed to extinguish any light still burning within her, and the name of Jesus was no longer on her lips.

I wished those around us could just leave us alone in our anguish. Our customs required their presence, but my turmoil craved their absence. I wanted to be alone with Mary, to implore her to speak to me. And I wanted to shout at the heavens, for their silence was even worse than hers.

'Jesus, why did you ignore our message?' I whispered into the dark that night, my bed being my only place of solitude. 'Don't you care?' I then felt a pang of guilt. I had said those words to him once before, but he had always shown us love. *But why hadn't he come?*

But if James had been the one to deepen our grief, then he was also the first one to rekindle our hope, although not before Lazarus had been in the tomb for four days. I was out in the courtyard, needing to see the sky and breathe some fresh air, when James came through the door. The contrast could not have been greater, however, with his arrival the previous day. He was out of breath and all he could manage to say was, 'Jesus is coming.' I didn't bother to wait to find out how he knew, but rushed inside to Mary, who was surrounded by those still sitting with us in our grief. I lowered my voice and whispered the words that James had said to me. But Mary gave a little shake of her head, choosing to look at the ground instead of me. For a moment I was torn, wondering whether to try to persuade her to come with me, but I couldn't wait any longer. I turned and left.

Soon I was hurrying down the road, my bare feet breaking into a run as I finally caught sight of Jesus. He and the Twelve were coming down the Mount of Olives in the direction of Bethany. I didn't care what the disciples thought of me or my appearance. My eyes were fixed on a single figure, and it was only when I reached him that I finally stopped running. 'Lord – ' I began, needing to pause to catch my breath. The rest of my words tumbled out, as I said the only thing of which I was sure: ' – if you had been here, my brother would not have died.' I then looked up into Jesus' face, but found there only peace and same quiet authority that I'd always seen. No expression of sorrow or regret, no words of explanation. Only Jesus radiating love and life as he'd always done – and hope stirred within me. *Jesus would make it right again*, even though I did not know how. And I was suddenly sure of one other thing. 'But I know that even now God will give you whatever you ask.'

Jesus gazed steadily at me. 'Your brother will rise again.'

Was Jesus testing me? To what was he referring? Again, I spoke of what I knew for certain: 'I know he will rise again in the resurrection at the last day.'

But when Jesus lifted up his voice again, his words of power and triumph seemed to banish every grief and sorrow, as if he were challenging death itself. 'I am the resurrection and the life. He who believes in me will live, even though he dies, and whoever lives and believes in me will never die.' Then Jesus looked steadily at me once again, as if he were looking into my very soul, and asked, 'Do you believe this?'

And I found that I did. Seeing him standing there, I doubted neither his words nor authority, because my heart was finally and utterly sure of the true identity of the man standing before me. 'Yes, Lord, I believe that you are the Messiah, the Son of God, who is to come into the world.' And it was as if a heavy burden that I had been carrying for many years suddenly lifted from my heart. And my anguish, my grief, my questions, my confusion, all melted into peace in his presence.

Moments later I was running once again, but this time it was back to the house with a message. As soon as I was inside, I beckoned Mary away from the others and we sat together on a small bench. I took her hands in mine and whispered: 'The Teacher is here!' And when Mary finally lifted her gaze to meet mine, I added, 'He's asking for you.'

If we had wished again for privacy, it was not to be. As soon as Mary rose to follow me out, so did those who had been sitting with her, wanting to grieve with us, wherever that may be. When we finally met Jesus again at the edge of the village, we were therefore accompanied by a crowd of our family and friends. And Mary, like me, was unconcerned by what they thought. She fell at Jesus' feet as soon as she reached him, repeating the exact words that, unbeknown to her, I had voiced only a short while earlier: 'Lord, if you had been here, my brother would not have died.' And with that she began sobbing uncontrollably, her tears darkening the dust as they slipped to the ground.

Others around me also started to weep again, but my eyes were once more fixed on Jesus. His changed and troubled expression startled me. I saw deep anger or grief or pain – or all three. He looked around at those gathered there and asked, 'Where have you laid him?'

And Simon, our dearest friend and neighbour, said simply and quietly, 'Come and see, Lord.'

But I was not prepared for what happened next.

Jesus replied not with triumphant words but with tears, and wept with us as he walked beside us to the tomb. I could hear the murmuring of our neighbours and friends around us, and some of the whispered words that echoed those we'd already spoken: *he must have loved Lazarus… he's healed the blind – couldn't he have stopped him dying?*

We retraced the steps we had taken four days earlier, when Lazarus' body had been carried to the cave in which it now lay. Already, others in the village had heard of Jesus' arrival, and by the time we reached the tomb, the numbers had swelled considerably. And in the crowd, amongst many other familiar faces, I caught sight of Jonathan. His eyes, like those of all around him, didn't stray from the one person who might now change everything. Jesus stopped several paces from the entrance to the tomb, the expression of deep emotion still on his face. He turned to James and the other young men standing near him. 'Take away the stone.'

My heart was pounding. Despite the words that Jesus had spoken to me barely quarter of an hour before, I could only at that moment think of what lay within the tomb, and of the harsh realities of death and decay. 'But Lord, there will be a bad smell by now! He's been there four days.'

Jesus turned to me, the troubled expression suddenly replaced by the look of triumph I'd seen earlier. 'Didn't I tell you that if you believed you would see God's glory?' And his words, and the authority with which they were spoken, transformed my fear into a sense of awed anticipation, and silenced every other voice. The grinding of the stone as it rolled along its groove, which had so recently crushed my hope, now brought that hope back to life and my heartbeat quickened. I stole a quick glance at Mary standing beside me, and even when I slipped my hand into hers, her eyes did not move from the entrance of the tomb.

'Father! I thank you that you have heard me.' Jesus' confident words rang out as he lifted his eyes to heaven, and it felt as if the whole of creation had suddenly fallen silent and was listening. 'I knew that you always hear me, but I said this for the benefit of the people standing here, that they may believe that you sent me.' And then he called out in a loud voice, as if he were calling beyond the bounds of the created world: 'Lazarus, come out!'

I stared at the entrance to the cave and the darkness beyond it. For several moments it appeared as if nothing was happening, and I held my breath. But then I gasped as did every other person around me. For there was suddenly movement in the darkness. A figure then came shuffling out into the light, still bound from head to toe in burial cloths.

'Take off the grave clothes and let him go,' said Jesus simply.

As soon as he'd spoken those words, the stunned silence erupted into a cacophony of noise. My sister and I ran to Lazarus, as did James and my cousin Thomas. Our fingers fumbled as we tried to unwind the strips of linen as fast as we could, smelling neither disease nor decay – only the sweet smell of the myrrh and aloes we had used in the burial rites. And I gasped again when I finally saw my brother's face. Although he was squinting and blinking in the brightness of the late afternoon sun, the contrast with how he had looked when I had last seen him could not have been greater. Then he had been pale and still, his cheeks hollow from several days without food and his eyes sunken by the fever. Now he radiated life and health, his eyes bright and his cheeks full of colour. When he finally stood free of the burial linen, clothed now only in a simple tunic, and had stopped squinting in the light, he looked around at the large crowd, bemusement on his face. 'What…?'

But Lazarus got no further, as both Mary and I threw our arms around him and held him tight, crying and laughing as we did so, barely able to contain the joy that was flooding our whole beings. And through my tears and over Lazarus' shoulder, I witnessed a sight that only added to my joy, if that were possible. For Jonathan, Bethany's physician and the man I had known as the leader of the synagogue for as long as I could remember, was kneeling at the feet of Jesus.

Bethany had never known a celebration like the one that night. Laughter and singing filled the air, and dancing and feasting filled our streets. By the time the day had ended, there was not one person in our village who hadn't heard of the astounding miracle that had been done in our midst. We rejoiced together in the simple but stunning truth that one of Bethany's sons had been raised from the dead, a miracle that most had thought existed only in the scrolls of Scripture. Our house that had so recently been full of mourners, laments and sorrow was now overflowing with joy. Our friends and relatives, including those from Jerusalem, were there, but also what felt like half the village – the other half being out on the streets around our home. And many believed in Jesus that night. My kitchen, which had been rendered unclean as the result of the death in our house, was quickly restored to its proper use, though its stores were (happily and willingly) emptied as the night and the festivities wore on. And at the centre of all our joy and gladness were the two men dearest to my heart – my brother and my Lord.

Lazarus' first proper words after he'd been unbound that afternoon had been *I'm starving!* And he was undoubtedly trying to make up for lost time by eating whatever came near him with great enthusiasm. As I both listened to Jesus, and served food to our guests, I overheard Lazarus (when his mouth was sufficiently empty) speaking to Thomas and James. They were plying him with questions, most of which he was unable to answer. '*What did it feel like?*' I heard him say thoughtfully, repeating Thomas's question, and I paused to listen. His eyes suddenly seemed fixed on some faraway point, and he finally found something he could say. 'It felt a bit like when I was younger, and would be woken up in the morning by Martha calling my name. Only then I'd try to ignore her and go back to sleep. But when I heard Jesus calling me, it felt as if he'd woken me out of a deep sleep. Except this time I couldn't ignore his call, even if I'd wanted to. I just had to get up and go to him. I just had to.' And I treasured those words for the rest of my life.

'Martha! Come here and listen to what Jonathan has just told us!' I'd just gone outside into the cool night air, and I gladly accepted Judas's summons. I sat down beside him and Salome on a bench in the courtyard, and offered the bowl of olives I was carrying to the physician, seated on a stool next to them.

Jonathan declined the brined olives with a slight shake

of his head and hand, as if food were some inconsequential distraction, and began with words that I had never expected to hear him say. 'Forgive me, Martha, for being so slow to believe what you all accepted long before me.' He paused and then said quietly, 'There is now no doubt in my mind that the Messiah walks amongst us.'

Judas turned to Jonathan again, barely able to contain his excitement. 'But tell her what you just said.'

'Some of the scribes say,' began Jonathan, 'that the spirit of a person stays near the body for three days after death, and only after that does it finally depart for the place of the dead.'

'But Lazarus had been in the tomb for four days,' interjected Salome, with a note of triumph in her voice, adding with a knowing look, 'and we all know what a body would be like after that time…'

'Regardless of whether the scribes are right or not,' continued Jonathan, 'it is undeniably true that Jesus came only when death – and decay with it – had fully taken a hold on your brother. When all hope was gone and his spirit beyond this world.' He paused before adding in a solemn voice, 'This was an astounding miracle, unlike any other. He has what only God has – power to give life to the utterly lifeless!'

He left his words hanging in the air. After a few moments I murmured to myself more than anybody, '*The resurrection and the life.*' I then added quietly, 'So he waited for a reason.'

As people finally began to drift away and the sound of singing faded into the quietness of night, Simon and Rachel joined me in the courtyard before they made the short walk back to their house. We lingered for a little while in the cool night air, reliving together the momentous events of the day and sharing our joy.

'Matthias reminded me earlier,' said Simon, 'of the words that Jesus spoke in Jerusalem over a year ago: that those in their graves would hear his voice and live. He has shown that to be true. Can any now doubt that he truly is the Messiah?' Simon smiled broadly, but then added after a little pause, 'And yet I am becoming an old man and still need my sleep!' We all laughed and then they both embraced me. But before departing Simon said, 'One final thing, Martha. We would like to hold a dinner in Jesus' honour in *our* house. I, too, owe him my life.'

'*Only* if I can help,' I replied with a tired but mischievous smile and Simon laughed again.

'I'm sure Rachel and my beautiful daughter-in-law would welcome the help of the finest cook in Bethany.'

'Well, that's settled then,' added Rachel with a note of satisfaction in her voice. 'Now we can finally get to bed!'

As it happened, Jesus left Bethany before the meal could be arranged, although not before I had offered him our house once more, should he need it again. We did not, however, have long to wait for his return.

Chapter 21

Behold your king

'See, your king comes to you, righteous and victorious,
lowly and riding on a donkey, on a colt, the foal of a
donkey.' (Zechariah 9:9)

AD 33 – Late March

'Do you think he'll come to Jerusalem for the Passover?'

Matthias' question hung in the air for several seconds as we looked around at each other. I had invited Levi's parents to join us for the Sabbath evening, but had also invited Jonathan and his wife, Naomi. They had been frequent visitors since Jonathan had become a believer. Although we knew many other Pharisees were hostile to Jesus, it was a joy to open our home to another family friend in Bethany who now accepted Jesus as the Messiah. I had roasted some quail for our meal, serving it with fresh bread, a dish of squash, cumin and garlic, with a cucumber, onion and yoghurt dip, and we'd been eating with enjoyment and laughter. But suddenly I found the eyes of the other six on me, as if I alone possessed the answer to that particular question.

'He hasn't always come for Passover,' I offered hesitantly, remembering the time we had spent the festival in Galilee, after seeing Jesus feed the huge crowd with the loaves and fish.

'It feels as if everyone in Jerusalem is asking the question,' said Matthias. 'The city's already filling up with pilgrims from Judea and Galilee – '

'As is Bethany,' interjected Esther.

Matthias smiled at his wife before continuing, 'And I hear the name of Jesus being spoken by those pilgrims again and again.'

Lazarus grinned. 'And Jesus has certainly been good for business.'

'If you ever manage to find a spare moment to do any work these days!' I joked.

We all laughed, for some who had heard of what had happened to Lazarus only a few weeks earlier had also learned that he worked in Jerusalem. A steady stream had come to the workshop and purchased our family wares, even if the real reason for the visit was simply to satisfy their curiosity. And my brother often found himself recounting his story to a wide-eyed audience.

Jonathan suddenly became very serious, however, taking his cup in his hand and silently swilling its contents around, but staring at the wine rather than drinking it. After a moment, he looked up again. 'Does the name Nicodemus mean anything to you?'

We all shook our heads apart from Matthias. 'He's on the Sanhedrin, isn't he?'

'Yes. And a Pharisee – that's how I know him.'

'What of him?' asked Lazarus with curiosity.

Jonathan paused, and ran his hand through his dark but greying hair. He looked as if he was deliberating whether or not to share some knowledge with us. 'Despite the hostility of many of the leaders of our people,' he began, 'there are other Pharisees – and priests too – who accept that Jesus is the Messiah. I believe that Nicodemus is one of them. He certainly reacted gladly when I told him what had happened to Lazarus.' He paused again and took a deep breath before continuing. 'He told me that the Council – with the encouragement of Caiaphas – has given orders that if anyone knows where Jesus is, they must report it to them. They mean to arrest him. And I believe they want to kill him.'

'Should Jesus be warned?' asked Esther anxiously.

'What can the Sanhedrin do to him?' countered Lazarus, presumably believing there was nothing mere human leaders could do to thwart the Messiah. 'Besides, what are they going to do – ' he continued, ' – arrest him in front of the huge crowds that love listening to him? That'll make them popular!'

I remembered, however, a recent conversation I'd had with the disciple named Thomas, before Jesus had left Bethany. 'I think Jesus is well-aware of the hostility of others, Esther. He knows there are those who would like to see him dead – at least, that's what one of the Twelve said.'

'Well, if Jesus *does* come for the Passover, there'll be some watching his every move,' said Jonathan grimly.

'We certainly will,' responded Mary in a cheerful tone, as if nothing could dampen the spirits of my sister and brother. 'I do hope he comes,' she added with feeling.

And although I smiled, I remembered well the unsettling encounter I'd had with the high priest as a little girl. Although Caiaphas now filled that role, rather than his father-in-law, Annas, I knew the power that the high priest still wielded – and wondered what would happen if he ever came face to face with Jesus.

Fears and unease could not have been further from my mind, however, a little over a week later. Our question as to whether Jesus would come for the Passover had been answered the previous evening (six days before the Feast), when he had arrived in Bethany. But unlike his visit at Tabernacles, he had not come in secret. Or alone. Far from it. And he did not delay travelling the further short distance into Jerusalem.

As the city came into view over the brow of the Mount of Olives, the memory of the first time I had seen the temple flitted through my mind again. Then I had been seated on the shoulders of my father, but this time I was carried along by a large crowd, as we walked alongside Jesus, seated on a donkey. The crowd was not only made up of those who came with us from Bethany, including those who had travelled south with Jesus: many had also come out from the city to meet us. The number of those in Jerusalem wishing to see Jesus had been swelled considerably by the reports of the great miracle in Bethany, for a good number from the city (who had been mourning with us) had witnessed it themselves. And for a moment, I thought of the father who had given me life. *Oh Abba – if only you could have been with us today!*

But the moment quickly passed, as voices began to sing and shout out around me. 'Blessed is the king who comes in the name of the Lord!'

Other voices joyfully answered, 'Peace in heaven and glory in the highest.'

And my sister, brother and I added our own cries, 'Hosanna to the Son of David!'

As the name of my childhood hero passed my lips, I remembered how I'd imagined God's promised king arriving in Jerusalem: on a war-horse, clothed in shining armour and surrounded by his victorious army. But here was Jesus, humbly riding a common beast of burden over cloaks and branches being laid in his path, clothed no differently from the masses. He was followed and cheered on, not by troops, but by the strange and varied band of men and women who followed him with such passion. Among the Twelve, Simon the Zealot, who had previously despised and opposed the Romans, was now rubbing shoulders with Matthew, a tax-collector who had collaborated with them. The rich were in the crowd, but also the poor. Those whose families held influence – like Joanna, whose husband worked for Herod Antipas – and those who had none. I saw those esteemed by others and those considered outcasts. It was Jesus, and only Jesus, who had drawn us all together. He was not the king I had expected, but he was the king we needed – one who was there for all, whatever their background, and who wielded absolute power with love and grace.

'Hosanna to the Son of David,' I cried out once more, believing – as we all did – that the reign of the true king and the establishment of the Kingdom of God on earth was about to come to pass.

'Teacher, rebuke your disciples!' snapped a voice nearby.

I looked around, shocked, for the source of the angry words. Even as I spotted the stern figure in the crowd, I heard Lazarus muttering, 'Pharisees! How can they be so blind?'

I didn't even bother trying to answer my brother's question. But I believed Jesus' response: 'I tell you, if they keep quiet the stones will cry out.'

It *did* feel as if nothing could stand against the huge wave of fervour and joy that swept us along, although – strangely – Jesus didn't fully share our joy. I was close enough to him to see the tears he shed as Jerusalem and its temple loomed large over us. And close enough to hear the words he spoke that suddenly caused a little knot in my stomach: *you did not recognise the time of God's coming to you.*

When we finally reached the temple in the afternoon, the sun was already closer to the horizon than its zenith. I'm not sure what I had expected, but Jesus seemed content to simply look around, almost as if he were just one of the pilgrims, taking in the grandeur of our greatest building. Except it was neither the stones nor the decoration that Jesus was studying. It was the people – and people abounded. The temple courts were heaving with those who had come for the festival. The bleating of the animals that were being sold in front of the Royal Stoa only added to the noise resounding off the temple's massive stones. And as time slipped by, we began to realise that if God's king was going to establish his throne, then it wasn't going to be that day.

After our high expectations, we felt somewhat puzzled to be heading back to Bethany that evening, accompanied by the Twelve, with nothing more of note having happened. And even more puzzled when Jesus asked me for some cord when we arrived back at our house. He then sat in silence, methodically weaving together the cord made from flax that grew in the fields nearby. As a whip took form in his hands, it raised more questions than it answered.

A visitor to our courtyard drew me away from the gathering, and I smiled at our friend Simon standing there. 'A joyous day!' he began.

'I only wish my father had been there.'

Simon sighed, 'Ah yes. I suspect the voice of Heli son of Saul would have drowned out the rest of the crowd! How my old friend would have rejoiced to have seen this day.' I nodded wistfully, and Simon continued, 'And I'm also sure my old friend would not have begrudged me stealing the Messiah from his home for one evening.'

I laughed, remembering the request made by Simon the previous time Jesus was in Bethany. Before the evening was out, it had been decided that Jesus and the Twelve would be guests at Simon's house on the evening before Passover. And already my mind was filling with suggestions I would offer to Rachel about the meal we would prepare together, to honour the One to whom both our families owed so much.

Our questions about the whip were soon answered. Early the following morning we found ourselves back in the temple courts, which were already noisy and crowded, with worshippers jostling each other as they moved towards the inner courts. Jesus, however, walked purposefully across the Court of the Gentiles in the opposite direction, towards the Royal Stoa, and soon had a sizeable crowd following in his wake, curious to see what the preacher from Galilee was up to.

The table of one of the money changers was the first to be overturned. Jesus immediately grabbed the edge of another, and threw it over. He was clearly furious. As children ran gleefully to retrieve coins that rolled across the large stones on which we stood, and before the startled stall-holders were able to open their mouths in protest or rage, Jesus was quoting Scripture at them. 'It is written,' he began, with anger in his voice, '*My house will be called a house of prayer*, but you are making it a den of robbers.'

There was another crash as Jesus tipped over a third table, scattering coins and bags once again. He then overturned one of the benches upon which those selling doves had been perched. The merchants – who moments earlier had been buying and selling – now found themselves hurrying out of Jesus' way, as he used the whip to drive them out of the Court of the Gentiles, shouting, 'Get out of here! How dare you turn my Father's house into a market!' Childhood memories of my cousin Thomas speaking of corruption at the temple came back to me. Although I was seeing a side of Jesus that I had not encountered before, it somehow felt right.

'*Zeal for your house consumes me*,' said a voice at my side, and I turned to see Simon standing there, his eyes fixed on Jesus. 'David spoke those words in the Psalms,' he explained, still watching Jesus, 'and now the Son of David fulfils them. There is the true zealot who will usher in God's kingdom!'

But if Jesus wielding a whip was unfamiliar to me, his hands were soon being used for something far more familiar. The blind and lame were once again brought to him, and found healing – rather than a whip – in his hands. *Wasn't this*, I thought, *what God's temple should be about? God in our midst performing wonders, to the praise of His people?* The words that had been shouted out as we'd descended the Mount of Olives the previous day had been taken up again in the temple courts by children. They were running about, weaving a path through the pilgrims and shouting out to each other, 'Hosanna to the Son of David!'

But as we stood close to Jesus, revelling in the wonderful things we were both seeing and hearing, the crowds that were gathered around him suddenly parted, making way for a group of men who were anything but happy.

'Chief priests,' whispered Simon hurriedly to me, 'and teachers of the law.'

'Do you hear what these children are saying?' demanded one of the small knot of stern men, with as much indignation in his voice as on his face.

Jesus, still seated, looked up. 'Yes. And have you never read, *From the lips of children and infants you, Lord, have called forth your praise*?'

The robed priest, who appeared to be the group's spokesman, didn't reply, but stood glaring at Jesus. He eventually muttered something to those with him, causing the small group to retreat through the crowd, which again parted for them as they swept away and out of sight.

'*Have you never read…?*' chuckled Simon quietly. '*That* will offend the teachers of the law.'

In the two days that followed, as we again returned with Jesus to the temple courts each day, there seemed to be none of our leaders that Jesus *didn't* offend or challenge in some way. When the chief priests and Pharisees returned to question the basis of his authority, Jesus not only silenced them with a question of his own, but also offended them further with his stories. In the past, the meaning of his parables had often been hidden – these were different. None who stood in the temple courts, hearing Jesus speak of sons who did not do their father's bidding and of tenants who showed contempt for the owner of a vineyard, could miss the sense of his words. Jesus was comparing our religious leaders to the villains in his stories. And they did not miss it either. Or the offence in Jesus' comments that the tax-collectors and prostitutes, whom they despised, were entering God's kingdom before them.

But they were not the only ones whom Jesus challenged. When Sadducees came with a story of their own, trying to catch Jesus out, he told them they were in error, knowing neither the Scriptures nor the power of God. Every single time our leaders tried to trap Jesus in his words, they were silenced or wrong-footed – and the crowd loved it. And even as they gave up their devious questioning, Jesus became even more vocal in his denunciation of the established religious order, calling the teachers of the law and Pharisees fools, hypocrites – and worse.

As I stood in the Court of the Gentiles, aware of the truth of what Jonathan had said so recently about Jesus being closely watched, another distant memory suddenly stirred, bringing to mind a childhood horror. I recalled a sunny afternoon spent with Abigail, sitting by her father Judas at his potter's wheel, and hearing for the first time of God's people rejecting a prophet and mistreating him – and the memory scared me. We had rejected God in our past, and now those who were supposed to be our leaders seemed to be repeating the sins of our fathers. I tried to reason my anxieties away: *surely it would be different this time? God would not let anything bad happen to His chosen Messiah. Wasn't the Messiah, after all, the one who would put all things right?* That these thoughts were worryingly similar to my reasoning before Lazarus' death was something of which I was oblivious. And I pushed out of my mind the troubling detail that one of Jesus' stories spoke of the tenants killing the owner's son.

But it was not the safety of Jesus that was my only concern. A few days before the Passover, the man who had been my father-in-law walked into our courtyard. 'Matthias!' I said with surprise. 'What brings you here? I thought you'd be too busy with the Feast to be in Bethany.'

'You must keep Lazarus away from Jerusalem,' whispered Matthias urgently, once he had drawn me away from my brother and sister and from the others in the courtyard. 'There is a plot to kill him!'

'*What?*' I exclaimed in a lowered voice, both shocked and perplexed.

'One of the senior priests who's a good friend told me.'

'But why?'

'The chief priests know only too well how many people are putting their trust in Jesus when they hear Lazarus' story. It isn't just Jesus that they see as a threat now.'

'Are you sure?' I asked, desperately hoping it simply wasn't true. I knew enough, however, to fear that it was.

'Sadly, yes.'

I let out a deep breath. 'How on earth can I make Lazarus stay in Bethany whilst Jesus goes into Jerusalem? He won't be separated from him.'

'You must find a way,' said Matthias grimly.

I thought for a moment, looking over to where Lazarus and Mary were sitting. 'But surely no harm can come to him if he's with Jesus in public and surrounded by the crowds? Many of them recognise Lazarus now as well. Might he not be safer there, than hidden away back here in Bethany? After all, it's not as if they don't know where he lives.'

Matthias appeared to be weighing up my words. 'You may be right, Martha, but whatever you do, make sure he's never alone. And you will need to decide whether to tell him about this or not.'

'I'll certainly tell Simon and Uncle John. They can make sure that he's always with others, which shouldn't be too difficult with the crowds at the festival.'

Matthias nodded. 'That's probably wise.'

'And thank you for warning us.' I paused before continuing, casting my mind back to the conversation we'd had when Jonathan and Naomi had been there, less than two weeks before. '*Is* Jesus in any danger?' I asked, and our eyes met.

'If he were simply a radical teacher and no more,' Matthias began, 'then I would say, *yes*.' But then his features softened and he smiled. 'But what would your father have said?'

'*When the Messiah comes…*' I replied.

'Well, maybe there, dear Martha, lies the answer to your question.'

Despite Matthias' words, I continued to feel uneasy when I lay down to sleep that night, troubled by the fresh and unwelcome news.

'Mary, are you still awake?' I whispered, rolling onto my side to face her, and waiting to see if she responded before I blew out the small lamp.

Her eyes opened, and she said with a smile, 'Of course! It's hard to sleep with so many wonderful things going around in my mind.'

'Hmmm,' I responded, unsure of whether to tell her what was going around in mine. 'Some of what Jesus has said,' I began tentatively, 'cannot fail to have angered the chief priests and the Pharisees.' I then paused. 'Do you ever worry about what they might do?' I decided not to mention Lazarus.

Mary pushed herself up on one elbow, looking radiant in the soft lamplight, and studied me for a moment. 'Of course not, Martha.' Her eyes shone as she continued: 'You've seen Jesus' power. We all have. And each time the leaders have tried to catch him out this week, they've failed. They cannot touch him – he's the Messiah!' She chuckled to herself briefly before continuing: 'Remember what the Lord said to you, Martha – you worry about too many things!'

I smiled back at my sister, and leaned over and stroked her hair affectionately. 'You're right, Mary. I always have…'

And with that, I turned back and blew out the lamp. But I was still awake long after Mary had fallen asleep. I thought back to what I'd said to Jesus when Lazarus lay in the tomb: *I believe that you are the Messiah*. But I'd said more than that too. I'd called him *the Son of God*. I might not

292

have had the formal education of my brother, but I did know that the teachers of the law thought it blasphemous to say that of any man, a serious affront to the honour of God. And yet, having heard Jesus speak of the Almighty with such authority, and seen him perform deeds that we held to be the preserve of God alone, we could come to no other conclusion.

The Son of God. I said the words to myself again. Mary was right: *how could our leaders touch him?* And although I couldn't see where the opposition from them would end, of one thing I was sure: it was coming to a head.

Chapter 22

Prepared for burial

'While the king was at his table, my perfume spread its fragrance.' (Song of Solomon 1:12)

AD 33 – Wednesday 1ˢᵗ April

It was just as well that Simon's house was as large as ours, given the number of guests packed into their main room that evening. The meal we prepared to honour Jesus was almost as grand as any wedding feast I had seen.

Although it was almost exactly three years since his healing, Simon was still profoundly conscious of what Jesus had done for him. And the gratitude of my family was, of course, no less. Although both Simon and Lazarus, in different ways, owed Jesus their lives, Mary and I felt that Jesus had also bestowed new life upon us. For now we knew the Almighty in ways we simply could not have conceived of before. The Lord of history had stepped into our world and into our lives in ways we'd never imagined possible, and we rejoiced daily in the changes He'd wrought. The Lord's anointed walked amongst us – and had touched the lives of every person gathered in Simon and Rachel's house that night.

Jesus and the Twelve sat on cushions around the large, low table, joined by Simon, his sons-in-law and James.

Lazarus was there too, the youngest guest at the table, hanging – as he always did – on Jesus' every word. There were too many guests for us women to recline at the table with the men. But it was our joy to serve that evening.

'Could you carry in the stew and the platter of roast lamb, please?' Rachel asked her daughters, as she carried a second steaming pot of lamb and vegetables to the table.

'These spiced vegetables smell wonderful, Martha,' said Mary.

'Well, you helped prepare them,' I replied with a laugh, handing James's wife a big bowl of lentil stew. I followed her in with baskets of fresh bread.

Rachel soon passed me, on her way back to the kitchen. 'I'll start taking in the platters of salads.'

'Mary and I will bring the olives and cheese,' I replied.

Although we were serving, we still lingered around the table at every opportunity, listening to Jesus' words and joining in the joy and the laughter.

I reflected during the evening, as I flitted between the courtyard and the room inside, on how my own life had been changed by Jesus. The questions that had haunted me, after the deaths of first my mother and then Levi, had faded away. It was not that I had all the answers, but rather now knew the person who did – and I trusted him. The raising of Lazarus had taught me that, if the purposes of the Almighty were hidden from us, those purposes could be for an end more glorious than we could ever conceive. I remembered my father telling me after Levi's death about Job, who was able to trust God, despite his sufferings, when he saw the greatness of God for himself. I, too, in Jesus, had now seen God's glory, and could also put my trust in Him as my father had done so faithfully before me. And I understood for myself that our God was a God of unimaginable love.

As I looked around the room, my recent fears about the opposition to Jesus were far from my thoughts. Lazarus' eyes were firmly fixed on Jesus, his loyalty unwavering and solid as the foundations of the Temple Mount. Beyond a shadow of a doubt, he would willingly lay down his life down for the Messiah. I, for my part, gave Jesus the best I could – my service and my love. And I knew, of course, the depth of Mary's love. Or I thought I did.

'Where's Mary?' I asked Rachel as I emerged once more into the courtyard, grateful for the refreshing cool night air after the almost-stifling warmth of the crowded room. I had expected to find my sister outside, but she was nowhere to be seen.

'She said she had to run back to your house to fetch something,' replied Rachel, taking a fresh batch of bread from the oven as she did so.

I thought no more of it as I returned inside, assuming that she had hurried home to find an extra jug or platter for the meal. Until, that is, I looked up from offering the bread around the table – and gasped.

'What is it, Martha?' whispered Rachel, standing by my side.

I recognised the smooth alabaster jar that Mary was carrying, and remembered my father presenting it to her. I stood transfixed, my eyes beginning to fill with tears, because I knew my sister well enough to guess what she was about to do – and I loved her for it. I whispered back to Rachel, 'It's Mary – she's brought her dowry.'

As my sister approached Jesus, he looked up at her.

The eyes of all those sitting around the table followed Jesus' gaze, the chatter and laughter quickly dying down until there was an expectant hush. Neither Jesus nor Mary spoke. Instead, she pulled the heavy alabaster stopper from the jar, and began to pour its precious contents over Jesus' head. Within moments, the heady fragrance of the expensive nard began to fill the silent room. But Mary didn't stop there. Even as the perfume was still dripping down Jesus' head, Mary knelt down, and emptied the rest of the contents of the jar over his feet, lavishing her love on Jesus in an act of devotion that was reckless in its extravagance. She then uncovered her long, dark hair and began to wipe the perfume gently over each foot, filling not just the room but the whole house with the fragrance of the perfume. It was as if the moment were so holy, so beautiful, that none dared speak. At least, that's how it felt to me. But it soon became apparent, when the silence *was* broken, that not all felt the same way.

'Why this waste?'

The harsh words were an ugly and unwelcome intrusion, and I looked to see who had spoken them. It was the disciple called Judas. 'The perfume could have been sold and the money given to the poor,' he continued forcefully. But there seemed little love or care in his words that cut me to the heart. And, as if his objection were a signal, other disciples began to mutter amongst themselves, questioning what my sister had done.

Mary just stared at Judas, bewilderment on her face. And I could guess why. The word *waste* was such an insult to Jesus – as if he wasn't worth it. And such a hideous interpretation of her actions.

But it was Jesus who immediately came to her rescue.

'Leave her alone!' His quick rebuke silenced both Judas and the whispered comments around the table. He then went on: 'She has done a beautiful thing to me.' As peace descended on the room once more, the rich fragrance of the nard hung in the air. 'The poor you will always have with you,' continued Jesus, 'but you will not always have me.'

What did he mean? I did not want to think about what he might be saying.

'When she poured this perfume on my body,' Jesus continued, 'she did it to prepare me for burial.' Instead of explaining the perplexing words, his gaze fell again upon Mary, and he smiled at her. 'I tell you the truth, wherever this gospel is preached throughout the world, what she has done will also be told, in memory of her.' And I knew that Jesus treasured Mary's costly act.

I lay in bed that night, tired but happy. The peacefulness of the room was only broken by the sound of Mary's steady breathing. The rich and beautiful fragrance of the nard hung like a blessing in the air, as it floated across from my sister's hair. *If Jesus had come before I'd wed and I'd still had my jar of myrrh, would I have done the same for him?* I hoped so.

I wondered what our father would have thought of his daughter pouring out in a few moments the perfume that was worth many months of his labour. What would he have made of her anointing Jesus with the nard that was meant to be the provision for her marriage? I smiled. *Abba, you would have been proud of Mary, and overjoyed that your perfumes anointed the Messiah – the Anointed One.* For our father would have given his all for God's chosen king. *And Abba,* I continued in my thoughts, *did you not say that we needed to find a man worthy of that dowry and worthy of Mary? Well, we have found him, Abba!*

Peace flooded my heart as I finally drifted off to sleep. Everything would now be well.

Chapter 23

Passover

*'He was led like a lamb to the slaughter, and as a sheep
before its shearers is silent, so he did not open his mouth.'*
(Isaiah 53:7)

AD 33 – Thursday 2nd April

'Lazarus!' I called across the courtyard. 'Are you ready
yet?' It was still early the next morning, and Jesus had
gone off somewhere to pray. Matthew, Andrew, Judas and
Philip were sat, eating, in the corner of the courtyard that
was bathed in sunshine, where the morning light brought
some welcome warmth after a chilly night. And Lazarus
was with them. He grabbed another piece of bread, said
his goodbyes, and stuffed the bread in his mouth as he
rose reluctantly to his feet. He came over to where I was
standing, just outside the kitchen.

'Don't nag!' he said with a grin, when his mouth was
finally empty.

'Are you going to the temple with Uncle Jacob?' I
asked.

'What? To make sure he doesn't get lost?' he joked.

'No. To carry the lamb after it's been sacrificed,' I
replied drily. 'Your uncle isn't as young as he used to
be.'

'We'll go together after we lock up the workshop this afternoon.'

'Don't leave it too late,' I said, very aware of the huge Passover crowds that would soon be converging on the temple courts for exactly the same reason.

'Stop worrying, Martha! You and Aunt Ruth will have plenty of time to roast the lamb.'

The three of us would be joining my uncle and aunt and their family that night in Jerusalem for the Passover. But the lamb wasn't my only preoccupation. I was still very conscious of the plot we'd been warned about by Matthias. My brother hadn't, however, shared our concerns when he'd been told. 'And whatever you do, Lazarus,' I said with sudden seriousness, 'make sure you're always with a number of others and never alone.'

'Never alone? It's Passover, Martha!' replied my brother with a look of incredulity on his face. 'I'll be fine. They'll be people everywhere. Don't worry.'

'Be careful all the same.'

'If you say so,' said Lazarus, clearly humouring me. He then finally and somewhat half-heartedly headed off across the courtyard to make the short journey into Jerusalem, calling out, 'I'll see you later,' as he disappeared through the doorway.

We'd understood from Jesus that very little was going to happen that day until he and the Twelve celebrated the Passover. So my brother had been persuaded to make the most of the opportunity that a crowded Jerusalem afforded our family business. 'Does your brother always show such enthusiasm for his work?' asked Matthew with a grin, before taking a mouthful of the fresh batch of bread I'd taken over to them. It was the last that would

301

have leaven in before the house was rid of all traces of yeast later that day.

I smiled. 'It's just that he doesn't want to miss out on anything Jesus says or does.'

'He's such a likeable young man,' commented Andrew. 'Your father would have been proud of him.' And, despite my frequent chiding of him, I readily agreed.

Earlier in the week, I had offered (at my uncle Jacob's suggestion) their home in Jerusalem to Jesus for the Passover meal, but he'd indicated that other arrangements had already been made. To my surprise, there had been something in Jesus' eyes that I couldn't read. *Was it sadness or pain?* I couldn't be sure.

'Where are you celebrating the Passover?' I asked the small group.

'In the city – ' replied Philip, ' – somewhere!'

I found myself curious at his answer. 'You don't know?'

'Jesus hasn't told us,' explained Matthew. 'He's been strangely secretive about it. None of us know.'

I smiled again, 'Maybe he just wants you to have an uninterrupted Passover meal together. You know what it's like when people find out where he is.'

'You may be right, Martha,' said Matthew.

'Though I don't know why he won't even tell any of *us*,' added Andrew. 'It isn't as if we're going to go around telling everyone.'

I shrugged my shoulders. 'The Master must have his reasons.'

Judas was strangely quiet, but I put it down to the previous evening's rebuke from Jesus, and thought no more about it.

The Passover meal that Mary, Lazarus and I shared that evening with Jacob, Ruth and their family was a particularly joyful one. Jesus' name may not have been on our lips as we went through our ancient rituals, but knowing that the Messiah was in our midst made us treasure even more the re-telling of our story as the people of God. One of their young grandsons asked the traditional questions, as Lazarus had done not so many years earlier, but during the evening I caught my sister's eye more than once. I knew that she was thinking about Jesus, as I was, imagining him sharing the same meal, with the same words and the same hymns – presumably somewhere close by.

Although we wouldn't normally walk back to Bethany at night, a constant stream of our friends and neighbours (who had, like us, shared the Passover in Jerusalem) were also making their way back to the village. Not to mention many other pilgrims returning to their tents on the Mount of Olives.

My brother, sister and I walked briskly up the hill, under the light of the full moon which always marked the night of the Passover. Our exertion kept away the chill of the late hour, and we discussed together whether Jesus would be back teaching in the temple courts the following morning. The Passover marked the start of the seven-day Feast of Unleavened Bread, and Jerusalem would still be full of pilgrims. None of us could believe that the festival would end without something momentous happening. But our questions were no nearer finding an answer by the time we were back in Bethany and lying down for the night.

It felt as if I had only just dropped off to sleep when I heard the noise – and I was instantly awake. I had always been a light sleeper, which I put down to having spent many years looking after my brother and sister, always aware that they could call out for me at any time during the night. This, however, was neither Mary nor Lazarus. It was the sound of insistent hammering on the door of the courtyard and urgent voices calling my name. Mary stirred in her sleep, but I left her where she was. I hastily wrapped a cloak around me before hurrying out into the courtyard. I shivered slightly as I made my way to the door.

'Martha!' called the voice, which I suddenly recognised to be that of Matthew, and the loud hammering started again.

'I'm just here,' I said, fumbling with the latch of the door in the deep shadows. When I finally pulled open the door, the bright moonlight illuminated the faces of both Matthew and Philip – and their expressions of fear. They quickly looked up and down the street, as if to check they weren't being followed, then silently hurried inside, shutting the door behind them.

'Are any of the others here?' asked Matthew, as Philip made sure the latch was back in place. Both were slightly breathless, as if they'd been running.

I shook my head. 'No. Why? What is it?'

'It's Jesus,' replied Matthew. 'He's been arrested.'

A short while later, Mary, Lazarus and I were standing inside with Matthew and Philip. After being told of the arrest, I'd quickly lit some lamps, and roused my siblings. All drowsiness was instantly dispelled by the shock of the news. And now we were listening in horror as the events of the evening were briefly and quickly recounted.

'After we'd finished the Passover meal, Jesus led us all out to a garden on the Mount of Olives,' began Matthew.

'Gethsemane,' added Philip, naming the place. 'Jesus had prayed there before, so we knew it well.'

'Jesus spent some time praying on his own a little distance away from us,' continued Matthew. 'To be honest, we were all drowsy, and most of us dropped off to sleep. But then we suddenly heard a commotion. A large group of the temple guards and others were approaching, with torches, swords and clubs – and they arrested him.'

'And Jesus did nothing?' asked Lazarus, obviously finding it hard to believe that Jesus, with all his power and authority, would simply allow his enemies to apprehend him.

The two men both shook their heads. Matthew added, 'He spoke to them, but that was all.'

Lazarus looked from Matthew to Philip and then back again. 'So what did you do?' An uncomfortable silence followed, and Lazarus exclaimed indignantly, 'You just let him be taken and did nothing?'

'Lazarus!' I said sharply, aware that my brother's anger wasn't helping.

'There was such a large group, and they were all armed. I don't think we could have done anything.' Matthew paused, and then, with his gaze fixed on the floor, added, 'We thought they might arrest us too, and so fled before they could. We all became separated in the darkness.'

'It was Judas,' said Philip with bewilderment in his eyes, after Matthew had finished speaking.

'What do you mean, *it was Judas*?' asked Mary, as confused as I was.

'He betrayed Jesus and led the group to us in the

garden. He'd left during the meal, but we thought he'd just gone to buy some provisions or something.'

'Are you sure?' I asked, finding it almost impossible to believe that one of the Twelve could have betrayed their master.

Matthew nodded. 'He must have told the chief priests where we'd be. It was the temple guard who arrested him.'

We all stood in stunned silence, confused and our confidence shaken by Jesus surrendering himself to his enemies. I suddenly asked, 'Where has he been taken?'

'We don't know for sure,' replied Matthew, 'but my guess is the guards will take him straight to the high priest.'

'To the temple?' asked Lazarus.

'More likely to Caiaphas' house at this time of night,' answered Philip.

'What will they do to him?' asked Mary in a strained voice.

'I don't know,' said Matthew quietly. 'I don't know.'

After another pause, Matthew suddenly said to Philip, 'We need to find the others.' He turned back to me. 'We thought they might have come here as you're so close to the Mount of Olives.'

'If they're not here, they've probably gone back to the house in the Upper City where we ate the meal,' said Philip to Matthew. They immediately decided to return there, though not leaving before they had told us the location of the house.

'Should we gather together all who are followers of Jesus?' Lazarus asked the two men, as we reached the courtyard door.

'I don't know,' said Matthew once again, 'but whatever you do, be careful. They may not be content with only one arrest.' And I thought of the plot to kill Lazarus – and felt sick to the stomach.

Once Matthew and Philip had headed off in the direction of Jerusalem, we did the only thing we could think of: we hurried the short distance to Simon's house. Soon, not only Simon, Rachel and James had been awakened, but others also loyal to Jesus – Jonathan, our uncle John, and Judas the Potter. They all left their wives and families to join our hastily convened meeting. Had Matthias not been at the temple for the Passover, he would also have been called upon to join us.

'What will they do to him?' I asked, repeating Mary's earlier question after we had recounted all we knew. I added in a quiet voice, 'We know they want to kill him.'

'They won't be able to kill him,' replied Lazarus angrily, although I wasn't sure whether his ire was directed at our leaders for wanting it or at me for voicing it. 'But I don't understand why he didn't he do anything to stop them arresting him,' he went on. 'Surely he could have called down fire from heaven as Elijah did, or used his power in some other way?'

Judas, clearly as perplexed as my brother, added, 'Or why did God not send the angels at his command to protect him?'

We all, however, instinctively looked to Jonathan for answers. He was our synagogue leader, and – more importantly – the one who understood better than any of us not only the Scriptures but also the workings of power within Jerusalem. 'I believe Lazarus is right,' said

Jonathan. He had watched, as we all had, Jesus calling Lazarus from the tomb, witnessing first-hand Jesus' authority and power over death. 'I, too, believe that he can't come to harm at their hands. So we have to believe that he has some reason in allowing himself to be arrested. He will, I'm sure, be brought in front of Caiaphas and probably Annas too. Annas may not officially be the high priest any longer, but he still wields considerable power in the city.'

'What of the Sanhedrin?' asked Simon.

'He may well involve the Council – who knows? – but if he does, it can't be until first light at the earliest.'

Our discussions continued, although all we knew for certain was that Jesus had been arrested on the authority of the Jewish leaders. And even though we longed to be able to do something – *anything* – straight away, we would have to wait until dawn. Jonathan assured us that he would go into Jerusalem as early as possible to try to seek out Nicodemus, who was both on the Sanhedrin and a believer. But what did happen before we dispersed, however, was that both Jonathan and Simon led us in prayer, crying out to the God of our fathers to vindicate his chosen one, the Anointed One, the Messiah. And Simon departed with these words: 'Who knows – maybe these events will become the triumph of the Lord? Do not the Scriptures themselves say, *No one who hopes in you will ever be put to shame, but shame will come on those who are treacherous without cause*? We must put our trust in the Lord.'

I heard in Simon's words echoes of my father, but sleep eluded me for the rest of the night. I found myself again and again silently mouthing the words that had been prayed earlier. Mary tossed and turned, and both of us spent the night longing for the first signs of grey to peep around the hangings over the window. I kept on trying to calm myself with Jonathan's assurances that nothing of significance was likely to happen before morning came. If only that had been true.

Chapter 24

The darkest hour

"'In that day," declares the Sovereign LORD, "I will make the sun go down at noon and darken the earth in broad daylight… I will make that time like mourning for an only son and the end of it like a bitter day."'
(Amos 8:9–10)

AD 33 – Friday 3ʳᵈ April

Hearing for the second time the nearby crowing of one of Bethany's cockerels, meant it was close enough to morning for me to finally get up. If first light hadn't yet come, then it wouldn't be long. In the darkness I could hear Mary also stirring.

'Have you slept?' I asked, as I fumbled for the clothes that would be lying nearby.

'No. Have you?'

Even though Mary couldn't yet see me, I shook my head in the darkness, and added a simple, 'No.'

It didn't take long for the two of us and my brother to be ready to leave for Jerusalem. The usual routine of baking the first bread of the day was dispensed with. As the twilight of dawn began to give the household objects in the courtyard their shape and size, I brought out raisin cakes, offering them to my brother and sister. Mary shook her head, and Lazarus only took one, nibbling it without enthusiasm. I quickly threw some feed on the courtyard stones. The hens seemed to be the only ones interested in eating. Then, for a third time, the cock crowed to announce the morning. And I wondered where Jesus was at that moment, and what was happening to him.

We had just closed the door of the courtyard behind us when Simon and James joined us. We set off on the familiar road up to the brow of the Mount of Olives, the grey light gradually strengthening and turning the dark shapes around us into the trees and rocks we knew so well. As we began to descend the other side of the hill, Jerusalem rose ahead of us, dark and strangely forbidding. Although sunrise would soon be upon Bethany, it would still be some time before the morning sun rose high enough above the Mount of Olives for its light to fall on the enormous stones of the Temple Mount.

We finally arrived in the south-western corner of the Upper City, and found the house to which Matthew and Philip had given us directions. A serving girl quickly took us to the upper room, and through the door we heard lowered voices, speaking urgently. They ceased instantly when she opened the door. Every face that met us was, for a moment, filled with dread. But it was swiftly replaced by relief. 'Shalom, friends,' began Simon.

If we'd hoped for light to be thrown on the hours since Passover, we were to be disappointed. As we joined the fear-filled conversations, our grasp of events remained as murky as the cramped streets of Jerusalem at dawn. The only thing clear was that, as expected, Jesus had been taken to the sizeable house of Caiaphas, the high priest, only a short distance away in the Upper City.

As I stood talking to Simon and James in the dimly lit room, I noticed my brother suddenly looking puzzled. He made his way over to me. 'Where's Peter?' he asked.

I glanced around, and couldn't see the big fisherman either. 'I don't know,' I replied. 'Why don't you ask Andrew?'

But when Lazarus questioned Simon Peter's brother, he just shrugged his shoulders. 'I haven't seen him since the garden. I don't know.'

Those last three words seemed to characterise much of our conversation – fuelled by rumour and speculation rather than solid facts. When John, one of the Twelve, returned a short while later, however, he did at least bring us some news, albeit unwelcome.

'They've just taken Jesus to Pilate,' he said. 'They're at Herod's Palace.' He was breathing rapidly, doubtless having run from the governor's residence, just to the north and on the western edge of the Upper City. We didn't need to ask who he meant by *they*.

'Where's Simon Peter?' asked Philip, echoing my brother's question.

John shook his head. 'He managed to follow Jesus into the courtyard of the high priest's house. But he left suddenly before I could speak to him again. That's the last time I saw him.'

John's news brought the crowded room to life again, with discussions breaking out in the little knots around the room. Mary turned to Simon, who – together with James – had not left our sides since Bethany. 'Why have they taken Jesus to Pilate?' she asked. 'He hasn't even criticised the Romans, let alone broken any of their laws!'

Simon let out a deep sigh and paused, as if he had

some hesitancy in sharing what he knew. But Lazarus also knew the answer, and had no such qualms about our sensitivities. 'The Sanhedrin can deliver a death penalty,' he said, 'but Pilate's the only one who can give permission for it to be carried out.' But he added, with defiance in his voice: 'Do they honestly think their plans will work against Jesus?'

It was impossible to know exactly what was going on in my brother's head. I guessed, however, that even now Lazarus was imagining some glorious intervention by the armies of heaven to establish God's true anointed king.

Given Lazarus' blunt words, Simon no longer had any reason for reticence. 'Lazarus is right,' he said. 'We've known for a long time that the high priest and the other leaders have wanted to silence Jesus.'

'But what Mary says is also right,' I countered. 'Jesus has never spoken against Rome or violated their laws.'

'That's as maybe,' replied Simon, 'but do not think that our leaders have no influence with Pilate.'

'Jesus knows what he's doing,' asserted Lazarus. And I wished that I shared my brother's confidence.

A short while later, several of us left the upper room to make our way towards the opulent palace, built by Herod the Great, where Pilate's power was exercised. Simon cautioned us to keep our distance; we didn't yet know if the Jewish leaders were planning further arrests. I felt scared, and kept glancing around, as we brushed shoulders with passers-by. *What if they were with Caiaphas?*

We stationed ourselves on the corner of a side street, maybe thirty or forty paces from the main entrance to Herod's palace. The light in the sky had strengthened, and although it was still early – maybe still not yet an hour after sunrise – the streets around us were already beginning to get busy. We could only guess what was happening behind the imposing doors of the palace, in front of which Roman soldiers were standing guard. But it wasn't long before a large and noisy group emerged.

'It's Jesus!' whispered Lazarus, whose greater height afforded him a better view of what was happening. 'Soldiers are escorting him.' Although Mary and I both craned our necks, all we could see properly was the sizeable number of chief priests, scribes and temple guards accompanying the soldiers, whose metal helmets we could just about make out. When the group had disappeared from sight along one of the streets heading east, my brother turned quickly towards Simon, with his greater knowledge of the politics of our city. 'Where do you think they're taking him?' he asked.

'I can't imagine that they're going to the temple – not with Pilate's soldiers guarding him. Maybe the Antonia Fortress?'

'What about Herod Antipas?' suggested James, who had largely been silent up until that point. 'He's in Jerusalem for Passover, isn't he, and at the Hasmonaean Palace?'

The impressive building, constructed by Herod's predecessors, lay in the direction in which the crowd had gone. But to me that didn't make sense. 'Why would Pilate be sending him to Herod Antipas? Herod only has power in Galilee and Perea, doesn't he? Surely he has no authority here in Jerusalem?'

'Why are we discussing this now?' asked Lazarus impatiently. 'Shouldn't we be following them?'

'Yes, but not by walking in front of the governor's residence,' warned Simon.

'If we cut down near Uncle Jacob's house we can approach the Hasmonaean Palace from the south,' suggested Lazarus, obviously anxious to be doing something other than standing still.

James nodded, evidently sharing some of my brother's impatience, and Simon agreed. As we wound our way through the familiar streets of the Upper City, I listened to the men attempting to fathom the reasons behind Pilate's move.

'I thought there was no love lost between Pilate and Herod,' began James.

'That's right,' his father replied. 'It's no secret that Antipas and others in his family have felt that Pilate's over-stepped the mark in some of the decisions he's made. Their complaints about him may have won them support among the Jews, but done little for their dealings with the governor.'

'Do you think Pilate is trying to get Herod's favour, then?' suggested James.

'Maybe,' replied Simon. 'It certainly wouldn't do him any harm to show Antipas some deference, particularly as he doesn't have the support of Sejanus any more. And after all, everyone knows that Jesus is a Galilean, and that *is* Herod's responsibility.'

As they continued talking, I glanced at my sister. She was looking horribly pale, and was paying no attention to what was being said. She would be caring little for the reasons behind what was happening. Her mind would be on the man at the heart of the unfolding events.

It quickly became clear that Pilate had indeed (whatever his motives) sent Jesus to the ruler of Galilee. We soon found ourselves, however, heading back to where we started. Whatever had happened at the Hasmonaean Palace, Antipas had decided to send Jesus back to Pilate. We debated whether to return to the upper room or go to my uncle Jacob's house. But none of us wanted to lose the only certainty that we had: the knowledge of where Jesus was. So we went back to our previous vantage point, on the corner of the side street.

It was probably little more than an hour since we'd arrived in Jerusalem. But every moment dragged. It was agony. Keeping our distance, and waiting for any word, any sign, of what was happening behind the high walls of Herod's palace. *What were they doing to Jesus?* Even though we couldn't see beyond those walls, we could at least see what was happening at the gates.

'Who are they?' asked Lazarus, as a sizeable group, dressed in common tunics and cloaks, streamed into the governor's quarters.

'I don't know,' answered Simon, 'but I can see who's bringing them.'

'The chief priests?' said James.

'Yes,' replied Simon, 'and I suspect that they're ensuring that Pilate only hears what they want him to hear.'

And it wasn't long before the shouting began.

Although the voices from the courtyard behind the walls were mostly indistinct, we could nevertheless hear the mood of the crowd that had, it seemed, been gathered to sway the Roman governor. The jeering sickened me, knowing that Jesus was somewhere inside – alone – and

ostile crowd. But the noise soon
me: *Barabbas!*

ame was unfamiliar to me, it was
ae Romans captured him recently,'
. 'He's well-known for inciting revolt

pening?'
reply was the familiar three words: 'I

te long for the shouts of the crowd to
ering again. But the next words we clearly
iling ones, repeated again and again: *crucify*
went cold. *Were they calling for this Barabbas
– or someone else?* There was little point in
ons that the others were no better placed to
while we all stood quietly, straining our ears.
shouting stopped. My heart was pounding as
yes on the nearby gates.

After what felt like an age, men began streaming out
through the gates, talking and jeering loudly. And my fears
for Jesus' safety only increased – for they had the look of
those who had got what they wanted.

'Stay here,' whispered James. Without waiting for
a response, he left us and wove his way through the
onlookers, making his way over to those emerging from
the palace. He drew alongside a couple of men, appearing
to casually question them. He then gave a nod of thanks,
but his expression darkened the moment he turned
away and began weaving his way back to where we were
standing.

'Pilate gave in to them,' he said furiously. None of
us could bring ourselves to voice the word *crucifixion.*

Despite the almost overwhelming sense of dread in my heart, part of me simply could not believe the implication of his words.

'Let's wait and see what happens,' said Simon grimly.

Could there still be deliverance even now? I wondered to myself. We stood in silence, all wrestling with our own unspoken doubts and fears, our eyes fixed once again on the same spot: the gates through which Jesus would presumably, at some point, emerge.

Great God in heaven, I silently prayed, *are not all things possible for you? Defend and deliver your faithful servant, Lord. Hear my prayer!* Mary's lips were moving but making no sound. I knew her heart was also begging the God of our fathers for mercy. And still we waited.

If I had still believed, however, that Jesus could not die, that there might still be some sudden reversal – some miraculous, glorious arrival of the hosts of heaven to bring deliverance to the Lord's anointed – then those beliefs were shattered when I finally saw him. Soldiers brought him out through the gates, and what I saw shook me to my very core, leaving me scarcely able to breathe or stand. I heard Mary's choked cry at my side, and turned to see my brother reaching out to support her as her legs began to crumple. For we could barely recognise him.

'What have they done to you, Lord?' I whispered in horror. Though I needed no answer. Even from where we were standing, I could see that his face was badly bruised and bloodied. On his head was some sort of cruel travesty of a crown, drawing blood.

'*Lord, have mercy!*' I heard Simon gasp.

I thought he only saw what I did. But then James, with shock on his face, murmured, 'He's been flogged.'

I closed my eyes and laid my hand on my brother's shoulder to steady myself, and heard, as I did so, an agonised wail from Mary. *Flogging? No, dear God!* The mere thought of it almost overwhelmed me. It would have been no ordinary whip, but one embedded with pieces of bone, to tear the flesh of the victim. And it would have been merciless. We had all heard tales of those for whom a flogging proved fatal.

But if that were not horrific enough, my eyes, when I opened them again, could now see the ultimate abomination. There was a heavy, coarse beam of wood lashed across Jesus' shoulders. The beam meant only one thing – crucifixion.

I could not believe what I was seeing. *How could this be happening?* But my mind was numb and unable to think straight. Instead, I looked on as Jesus, barely able to walk, collapsed under the weight of the wood. A soldier strode over to the rapidly growing crowd, and hauled out a bystander. He was dragged over to where Jesus was struggling – trying, but failing, to lift the crosspiece. Two other soldiers quickly transferred the heavy beam from Jesus to the stranger, who had no choice but to carry it on Jesus' behalf. They then pulled Jesus to his feet, pushing him roughly forward, undoubtedly keen to waste as little time as possible getting to their destination. It would not be a long journey, but we all knew where it would end.

We could do nothing other than keep following Jesus, each of us silenced by shock. Soon we found ourselves part of what had become a procession. A steadily increasing number of onlookers were joining those behind Jesus, and there were also two further victims to be crucified. Together we descended rapidly through the Upper City, into the crowded streets below. I walked on in a daze, with my arm around my sister. And it wasn't long before I heard not only Mary sobbing, but the wailing of many of the women of Jerusalem who had joined us. They were grieving over the one who had, less than a week earlier, wept over their city. I suddenly wondered if they had sons or daughters or brothers or sisters who had been healed by the hands of Jesus.

As we went out through the city walls, leaving behind the narrow, heaving streets, we were suddenly under an expanse of clear blue sky. In front of me was the place used by the Romans for their crucifixions. It was a small rocky hill, just outside one of the gates in the city's western wall. It was a place of death, not only because of the regular executions, but also because its rocks could be hewn to make stone tombs for the wealthy. We called the place *Golgotha* – the skull – because of its shape. And the name felt grimly appropriate.

To most Jews, crucifixion was an abhorrence – a shameful and degrading atrocity from which we would shield our eyes or flee. But Rome excelled at brutal deaths. We could escape their blood-soaked tournaments but not their executions – for they did not want us to. We found ourselves standing in an appallingly public place, beside one of the roads that ran into and out of the city. But this time, although we stood a little way off from the rocky mound, we could not and would not flee. But neither could we watch.

Mary clung to me and I wrapped my arms around her, wanting to protect her from the nightmare in which we were trapped, but not knowing how. The crowds around us included familiar faces, many of them tear-stained, and as the murmuring suddenly dwindled to nothing, I could guess what was coming.

The harsh metallic *clank* pierced the air, as a heavy mallet struck one of the nails that secured each victim to the rough wood of the cross. Mary clung to me more tightly and I could feel her shaking. I put an arm around her head in a vain attempt to shield her, not only from the hammering of the nails, but also from the screams and curses of the men whose torture had only just begun. But Jesus' cry, when it came, was different. Its agony was mingled with a plea for mercy. Not for himself, but for the ones who wielded the mallets. Even now, Jesus was like no other.

I continued to keep my eyes tightly shut, knowing that the soldiers would soon be lifting each of the crosses, to complete the gruesome act of crucifixion. I couldn't bear to think of Jesus suffering such humiliation and torture. But at last I summoned the courage to open my eyes and raise my head, as if I had to prove to myself that the nightmare was actually happening. And I saw him, on the central cross between two others.

I finally spoke. 'How long will it take?' I asked, my eyes still fixed on Jesus but my voice sounding far away.

Simon answered quietly: 'He has been weakened by the flogging, but it will still be some hours. But they will not keep the bodies on the crosses on the Sabbath, so it will have to be over by sunset – and that is a mercy.'

And so began our agonising vigil. I took a quick look up at the sky, and judged the sun to be half way between sunrise and noon, and then looked around at the crowds. Mary, who came from the town of Magdala, was watching a little distance away. With her were other women who'd also followed Jesus from Galilee. The disciple John was close to the foot of the cross, and near him, the mother of Jesus. I could not even begin to comprehend what she must have been feeling. I had seen first-hand a mother's deep grief for her son when Esther had grieved for Levi. But this was different. *How could any mother look upon her son on a cross? And how could* this *mother look upon* this *son?* But she, like us, could not abandon him either.

But if some in the crowd shared our pain, there were others who pushed the sword deeper into our hearts. 'So you'd destroy the temple and build it up in three days, would you?' said one of the bystanders in a voice heavy with sarcasm. I wanted to cover my ears to drown out the ripple of laughter that followed, but the mocking didn't end there. It wasn't long before the arrival of men dressed in the robes of scribes and chief priests. Their looks of smug satisfaction sickened me. It wasn't enough for them to send to the cross a man who had only ever shown love and spoken the truth. They had to come to gloat, to declare to the man who had dared to challenge them that they had won.

'He saved others, but he can't save himself!' shouted one with derision.

'If he really *is* the Messiah, the King of Israel, then why doesn't he come down from the cross? *Then* we'd believe in him!' The words of the scribe were met with further jeers.

But beside me, I heard Lazarus muttering angrily, 'Why can't they just shut up and leave him alone? Haven't they done enough already?' I laid a hand lightly on his arm, to dissuade him from responding in a more vocal way, and felt him shaking with anger. I could also see that he was finding it hard to hold back his tears.

But the tormentors didn't stop. The stinging taunts continued. 'He trusts in God, so let God deliver him if He wants to! After all – ' continued the speaker, pausing, as if for effect: ' – he said *I am the Son of God.*' And that was the cue for not only the soldiers, but also one of those crucified with him, to join in with the cruel mocking.

'I can't bear it,' whispered Mary, struggling to catch her breath through her sobs.

'Come, sister,' I replied softly, and for a while I steered Mary away from the crowd, Simon walking with us whilst James stayed by Lazarus' side.

And just as we reached the edge of the crowd, we spotted the familiar, if grim, face of Jonathan coming towards us. He looked over to where the three crosses were silhouetted against the sky, and I had never before seen such pain on his face. He did not use our customary greeting, *Shalom*. And neither did we. There was no peace, no well-being in that place.

'Jonathan, yours is a welcome presence,' said Simon.

'But too late to make any difference,' he replied with sadness, and then began to relate what he had discovered in the hours since dawn. Where the information had come from, I did not know, though he had friends on both the Council and Herod's staff.

'The Sanhedrin met as soon as it was light, but from what I hear the outcome was decided long before even the first council member arrived. I think they still feared what the crowds might do if they got wind of this. That's why it's all happened so quickly. I don't know if it was a full council or not. They only need twenty-three not the full

323

seventy-one for a decision after all. All I know is that they agreed to put Jesus to death. And that neither Joseph nor Nicodemus were part of it.' Although I knew a few men by the name of Joseph, I didn't know to whom Jonathan was referring. But neither did I care – and Mary didn't seem to be listening.

'But what was the charge?' asked Simon.

'Blasphemy.'

'But Pilate would have thrown that out as an irrelevant Jewish scruple, surely?'

'Indeed, but somewhere between the house of Caiaphas and Herod's palace it became something of more interest to Rome,' continued Jonathan grimly.

'Which was?'

'Telling everybody not to pay taxes to Caesar – '

'That's a lie!' replied Simon with indignation.

' – and claiming to be the Messiah,' continued Jonathan, adding pointedly, 'a king.'

'So they make him out to be some sort of revolutionary – another Jewish Zealot to be crucified along with the rest.'

'From what I hear, though, the governor saw right through them. Whatever the Jews say, Pilate is nothing if not shrewd. He apparently tried to get him released. He even offered them a choice of Jesus or Barabbas.'

'And our leaders chose Barabbas!' said Simon contemptuously.

Jonathan continued. 'And just to ensure they got what they wanted, they told Pilate that if he let Jesus go, then he was no friend of Caesar.'

'They know how to manipulate him,' replied Simon, this time with anger. 'His position with Tiberius is precarious enough with Sejanus gone.'

'He's upset our leaders too many times already to risk doing so again, especially now.'

'A bad report to Caesar could be the end of him.'

Although I heard their words, they washed over me. I cared little for the twisted process in which the instruments of justice had simply become a tool for the powerful. I glanced at Mary whilst the men continued speaking in low tones. It seemed that all life, all joy, all strength had been drained from her. And then I lifted my weary head and looked once more at the cross.

Son of David. How could the glory of the Messiah be turned into such hideous shame? It felt as if everything I held dear was crashing down. It never entered my head that this abomination could be part of God's plan.

Jonathan eventually left us when two others – obviously among Jerusalem's rich – arrived. He joined them, standing a little way off behind the main body of the crowd. A first and then second hour slipped past, punctuated by pain-filled cries from the two outer crosses, and by words from the lips of Jesus that I was too far away to catch. But when noon arrived, so did a darkness that was as inexplicable as it was unnerving. I heard cries of fear as the light of day faded with neither warning nor reason. It felt as if it were night, though without the full moon of Passover. Those who had been content to stand and idly watch another Roman crucifixion hurried away, scared. But we returned quickly to Lazarus and James. I could feel the chill in the air, and whispered fearfully, 'What's happening?'

And in the deep gloom I heard Simon reply, 'I don't know, child, I don't know.'

We stood in silence, barely able to make out the outline of the cross on which Jesus hung. And once again, my heart raised a plea to heaven: *Let it end soon. Please, let it be over.*

But still the hours passed. Until suddenly the darkness was pierced by a loud cry: 'My God, my God, why have you forsaken me?' I recognised the voice of Jesus, and it plunged me into yet another horror. *Had God abandoned Him? Surely that could not be! But then why his cry? Where was God when we needed Him most?* I felt an iciness inside me. It had nothing to do with the cold that accompanied the dark. Beside me, Mary was weeping softly.

Before the end came, however, another cry rang out. But this one was different. I could just about make out a soldier raising something to the lips of Jesus, to give him a drink. And then I heard it.

'It is finished!'

It sounded like a strange, inexplicable cry of triumph. As I stared, bewildered, at the cross once more, Jesus lowered his head.

Suddenly we had to grab each other as the ground shook violently beneath us. It was as if the foundations of the earth itself were being shaken. And when the quaking was eventually stilled, I knew that it was finally over.

Just as quickly as the darkness had descended it lifted again. Rays of sunlight streamed down into our world once more, and onto the rocky outcrop and the three crosses. The central figure was now marked by the stillness of death, whilst those on either side continued the agonising struggle to raise themselves to breathe. I heard Simon speaking quietly to James. But Mary, Lazarus and I just stood silently, each of us staring numbly at the central cross and at the man who still hung there, not being able to take our eyes from him now that he was dead.

I felt a gentle hand on my shoulder, and tore my gaze away from Jesus. Simon's cheeks, like ours, were wet with tears. 'Stay here,' he said simply. 'I'll be back shortly.' And he walked across to Jonathan and the men I assumed to be Nicodemus and Joseph. It wasn't long before Jonathan and Simon had re-joined us with one of the two men – introduced to us as Nicodemus – whilst the other disappeared through the gate into the city.

Despite my numbness, I still felt confused when Nicodemus approached us. *What does he want with us?* I thought, only wanting to be left alone with my grief.

'You're Lazarus, son of Heli?' began Nicodemus, and my brother nodded silently. 'If Pilate will permit us to take Jesus' body, we want to see that he receives a proper burial. Joseph of Arimathea, who is also a believer, has gone to petition him now, and I see no reason why Pilate should refuse him. Joseph also has a new tomb close by where we may lay Jesus. The Sabbath will soon be upon us, so we do not have time to make full preparations, but we will do what we can before the day ends. I know of your family's business, and, if you are able, we would like to purchase the necessary perfumes for the burial from you.'

'We have myrrh and aloes,' said Lazarus quietly, 'but take them freely. I want no money for them.'

The older man laid a gentle and fatherly hand on my brother's shoulder. 'No, I will pay you the full price,' he said. And then, echoing words spoken by David a thousand years earlier, he added, 'I will not give as an offering to the Lord something of yours that costs me nothing.'

Nicodemus' dignity and graciousness touched my heart. Despite my emptiness, the kindness that he was showing to Jesus in death moved me to further tears. It was a small reminder of beauty and love amongst such ugliness and hate.

Lazarus and James soon departed with Nicodemus for the family workshop in the Lower City, but Mary and I lingered, with Simon by our side. Like the other women who stood nearby, we were not yet ready or willing to say a final goodbye to the one we all held so dear. We embraced and wept with the women from Galilee.

'We will also tend to Jesus' body after the Sabbath,' said Mary Magdalene.

'Mary and I will help you,' I replied.

An older woman, Joanna, touched my arm lightly and gave me a gentle smile. 'Go back to Bethany and rest, sisters. We know that you gave our Lord a place to lay his head in these last days. Please do us the kindness of now letting *us* care for his needs in death.' I nodded and we kissed each other.

Simon glanced over at the sun, as it dropped lower in the sky. 'We must leave for Bethany soon, Martha, if we are to be back before the Sabbath begins.'

I knew he was right. After a final glance at the cross, we finally turned to leave, loud screams of pain in our ears, as the soldiers hastened the deaths of those hanging on either side of Jesus. They, too, would need to be removed from their crosses before sunset.

The short journey back to Bethany was largely made in a dazed silence. There was, after all, nothing more to be said. At least, that's what I'd supposed. As my thoughts drifted to Lazarus and Nicodemus and to the myrrh and aloes that my brother would be supplying, the memory of the almost overpowering fragrance of Mary's nard came to mind. It felt as if a lifetime had passed since then. *But what was it that Jesus had said after Mary had anointed him?* I thought hard for a moment, and then it came to me: *When she poured this perfume on my body, she did it to prepare me for burial. That was it!*

And as we finished our climb to the top of the Mount of Olives, I suddenly whispered, 'He knew.' Simon turned to look at me, puzzled. 'He knew... Jesus knew he was going to die,' I said with bewilderment. But I couldn't see beyond that. I had been prepared to accept a different Messiah – but not a crucified one.

Chapter 25

The curtain

'The punishment that brought us peace was upon him,
and by his wounds we are healed.' (Isaiah 53:5)

AD 33 – Friday 3rd/Saturday 4th April

There had been no time to prepare for the Sabbath, but that didn't matter and I didn't care. Rachel and Simon opened their home to us that evening, and we gladly took refuge with those who shared our grief.

'You must eat,' insisted Rachel, as she held out the basket of unleavened bread towards me.

Despite not having eaten since the previous evening – *had the Passover really been only a day ago?* – I still felt no hunger. I took a piece of the fresh, flat bread to please our hostess rather than to appease my stomach. But Rachel's eyes had also been reddened with crying. Mary shook her head when the basket was passed to her, but when I touched her arm, she acquiesced. Like me, though, she only nibbled the bread with indifference. Both my brother and sister were beyond any comfort I could give. But I felt I had to be strong for them, though I didn't know how.

Our meal had none of the usual weekly celebration, barely even an acknowledgment that this was a special

Sabbath because of the Passover. Still, I took comfort in being with those who were walking the same path as us. Though any conversation that evening was usually in response to the phrase that Lazarus kept repeating: *I don't understand.* None of us did.

The following morning, the three of us did what we'd previously only ever done during sickness: we skipped synagogue. The news of Jesus' death would have reached Bethany the previous day, before the Sabbath had begun. We couldn't face the stares, the questions, the whispering. I remembered what I'd overheard when Lazarus had died: *he's healed the blind – couldn't he have stopped him dying?* And I wondered what they would be saying now.

But if we couldn't face joining our neighbours in worship, then they still came to us. 'Shalom, dear friends,' said Salome, as she walked into the courtyard with her husband, bearing a dish of chick peas and vegetables.

'We missed you at synagogue,' said Judas. He paused. 'Not that we expected you.' The compassion in his voice touched me, and soon Mary, Lazarus and I were weeping again on their shoulders. It wasn't long before Jonathan's wife, Naomi, arrived with grilled fish. They all treated us as if we had had a bereavement in the house, as if we had lost a close member of our family. And it felt like we had. We wept once more when my uncle and aunt arrived from the other side of Bethany. But even the kindness of our friends and family could not lift us from our desolation – though I could at least see that they, too, were grieving.

I had never felt so bereft and alone. Even when Lazarus had died, we'd still had Jesus. Even though we'd had to wait, we had still known that we would see him again. But who did we have now? Who could we turn to, to explain to us the workings of the God whose painful ways were more inscrutable than ever? I had known from my childhood that our people had in the past rejected God's prophets. But it seemed inconceivable that we could reject the Messiah. *But is that not what we had seen the previous day? And if we had not only rejected but killed the Messiah, then what did that mean for us as the people of God?* If rejecting the prophets had resulted in the exile of our people, expelled from the Promised Land and all they held dear, I dreaded to think what judgment might now befall us.

But shortly after the Sabbath had ended and darkness had fallen once again, one final visitor knocked on our door. It was Esther, the woman who for a few short years had been my mother-in-law. Although she was no longer a young woman and had been further aged by the loss of Levi, she still had an inner beauty that was a soothing balm to my wounded soul.

We sat together, and after she had asked after us and heard our sorrows, she paused, as if unsure how to proceed. 'Matthias, as you know, is busy this week at the temple, with the Feast,' she began hesitantly. 'But he sent us news just before the Sabbath.' We waited in silence, and I found that my curiosity had been piqued, despite my grief. 'He told us that something strange, even terrible, happened at the temple – on the afternoon of Preparation Day.' She paused again.

'What was it?' asked my brother, obviously sharing my curiosity.

'The veil of the temple – the curtain...' continued

Esther, but still with seeming reticence. I immediately imagined in my mind's eye the huge curtain, hanging in the Sanctuary, which marked the point beyond which priests were not permitted to go. It was the entrance into the Holy of Holies, the very presence of the Almighty.

'Go on…' said Lazarus.

'The curtain was torn – completely – from top to bottom.'

'Torn?' I exclaimed, dumbfounded. 'How?'

'Not by any human hand,' replied Esther. 'At least, that's what Matthias said.'

'And what happened then?' asked Lazarus, as taken aback as I was.

'I don't know,' said Esther. 'The message was only a short one.'

Mary, who had appeared as if she wasn't listening or wasn't interested, suddenly looked up. 'What time was that?'

'Around the ninth hour,' replied Esther, 'at the time of the evening sacrifice.' My mind raced. *That was three hours after noon.*

But Mary made the connection before I did. 'The time at which Jesus died.' And Esther nodded.

I continued wondering at the meaning of the news that Esther had brought us as I lay awake in my bed that night. *Was the tearing of the curtain part of God's judgment? Or was there some deeper meaning that was hidden to us?* Any answers eluded me, and I finally dropped off into a troubled sleep, still in the dark.

But morning was coming.

Chapter 26

A new day

'You will not abandon me to the realm of the dead, nor will you let your holy one see decay.' (Psalm 16:10)

AD 33 – Sunday 5th April

Resting on the Sabbath had done nothing to dispel the weariness of grief. The aching of our limbs matched that of our hearts as we made our way back into Jerusalem, after not only the Sabbath had ended but a new morning had come. We spoke little. *What was there to say?* We had no particular plans for that day – or for the uncertain future that now lay ahead. We only wanted to be with those who had loved Jesus. And so we were heading for the house in the Upper City where we'd met them before the crucifixion.

The spring sunshine felt unseemly, almost blasphemous. *Why wasn't creation mourning with us?* If I'd had any energy, any spark of life still burning within me, I would have screamed at the sun to stop shining, to darken its face as it had done two days earlier. But I was numb. And the only clouds were not black or threatening. They simply dappled an otherwise clear blue sky with splashes of white.

My thoughts often drifted to the women who would

have been at the tomb earlier that morning. I wondered if their hearts had broken afresh as they tended to the body of Jesus.

None of us could face the temple courts, where we might catch sight of some of the Jews responsible for the crucifixion. So we entered through one of the more southerly gates. It also felt strange and wrong that men and women were still bustling through the narrow streets of the city, going about the affairs of the first day of a new week, as if nothing had happened. *What were they doing? Didn't they know that Jesus was dead?* And anger flickered inside me. Thankfully, we soon began our ascent into the less crowded streets of the Upper City.

Our route took us past the tomb of David – the memorial that Herod had built to my childhood hero. The mightiest king in our history had deserved a magnificent tomb. *But what about the one we'd believed to be the greatest king of all? Would his final resting place continue to be the tomb hastily supplied by Joseph?* In death, as in life, Jesus owned nothing. The clothes he'd worn were his only belongings – and even those had been taken from him at the end. The soldiers at the foot of his cross had gambled for them. *He'd deserved our all, but we had taken all he had, and the only thing we had given him in death was a borrowed tomb!*

When we arrived at our destination, we found the door into the courtyard of the sizeable house still locked. We knocked loudly, and, after a short wait, Andrew opened the door. After a furtive look around, he closed the door and locked it again behind us. 'Come upstairs quickly,' he said. But there was something on his face and in his voice that I was at a loss to understand. We followed him across the courtyard and up the steps to the large room where our friends were gathered. But we were not prepared for what we found.

The surprise – the shock – was the difference we could instantly feel: a complete change of mood that was utterly unexpected. Gone were the weeping, the looks of despair, and the low despondent murmuring. Instead, our entrance suddenly seemed to be the cue for everyone to start speaking rapidly and all at once. Amongst the clamour, I heard someone say, 'You're speaking nonsense!'

But also claims that I couldn't believe. 'The tomb is empty.'

'The body's not there.'

And two more words that changed our world forever. 'He's alive.'

It took some time for us to piece together the story. 'We went to the tomb just as dawn was breaking,' began Joanna.

'But when we got there, the stone was rolled away and the tomb was empty!' continued a woman I recognised as another Mary.

'There were angels!' said Joanna excitedly.

'So you say,' cut in Thomas from the back of the room. From the murmurings that followed, he was clearly not the only one dubious about the women's story.

But if most of the men remained unconvinced, it certainly wasn't all of them. 'But the tomb *was* empty,' insisted John. 'Peter and I saw it for ourselves. All that was there were the grave-clothes.'

Although the voices of dissent were temporarily silenced, as soon as Mary Magdalene repeated her story about having seen Jesus after thinking he was the gardener, the room became noisy – and divided – again. It was evident that virtually all the men gave little credence to Mary's words. Her frustration was obvious as she insisted again and again that what she'd said had really happened.

One person in the room, however, was strangely silent. I'd never seen Peter looking so quiet or withdrawn. He'd always been the one who was impetuous and quick to speak. He'd run to the tomb with John and found it empty. He'd even gone inside and seen the grave-clothes. And yet here he was, sitting by himself on the edge of the room, seemingly unwilling to meet our gaze. When he did occasionally glance up, I caught a haunted look in his eyes. As if something more than that morning's news was on his mind, for he alone remained silent. Only later did I hear what had happened in the courtyard of the high priest's house and of his three-fold denial of Jesus.

But Peter's silence was quickly set aside. I only really cared about one question: *what had happened to Jesus? Could what Mary and the other women were saying really be true?*

'Martha! I saw him!' exclaimed Mary Magdalene to me, grasping my hands. 'He spoke to me. He told me not to hold on to him. He said he was going to his Father – to *our* Father!' Only two days earlier, I'd seen her tears and the look of utter hopelessness. But now her eyes were bright and full of life. And I wasn't sure what to say.

It was clear to me that something extraordinary must have taken place. And from the look of my brother and sister, they had already accepted that the impossible had happened. My own thoughts were less sure. *Yes, if Lazarus had been raised from the dead, then death was no insurmountable barrier for God. But why had neither Peter nor John seen Jesus – or even the angels – at the tomb? If Jesus were alive, why wouldn't he have shown himself to them? But then again, was it really unthinkable that, if Jesus were alive, the women showing him a final act of devotion might be the first to find out?* I just didn't know what to think.

With each new arrival at the house, including that of Simon and James later in the morning, the stories were re-told and the discussions re-ignited. Although Lazarus and Mary both appeared content – and eager – to listen to it all again and again, I felt the need for something familiar and tangible. And so I took refuge out in the courtyard in the one thing I knew better than any other.

'Shall I slice the onions whilst you bake the bread?' I suggested to the servant-girl who worked in the house.

She smiled gratefully, 'That would be lovely.'

I soon found myself joined by some of the other women, as together we prepared and cooked what food there was to hand. The news of the empty tomb had not only stirred people's hearts, but also re-kindled their appetites.

Not that there were any recognisable mealtimes during the day – there was too much coming and going. At some point Peter left, and it was only when Lazarus reappeared through the courtyard door that I realised, with a jolt, that I had not seen him for a while.

'It's true,' he whispered to me excitedly, drawing me aside. 'The tomb's empty!'

'You've been there… *by yourself*?' I exclaimed, with a mixture of alarm and disbelief, the plot to kill him never too far from my mind.

His familiar look of exasperation returned. 'Martha! Will you *ever* stop worrying? I'm not a child. Did you even hear what I said? The tomb *is* empty!'

I allowed myself to relax slightly and finally gave him a little smile. I'd loved his fervent loyalty to Jesus, and shouldn't have been surprised. He was never going to be content with merely receiving momentous news second-hand when he could witness it for himself. And despite my struggle to believe, I suddenly realised that the awful despair in my heart was no longer there.

'Any angels?' I asked, almost mischievously.

He grinned back at me. 'No.' But then, after a moment, he added with feeling, 'but I believe he's alive.' And I did not doubt his sincerity.

As the day wore on, others departed. Thomas stormed out for some reason, and I didn't see him again that day. Then shortly after, I overheard a man called Cleopas talking to Matthew. 'We must leave now if we are to be home by nightfall,' he said reluctantly.

'Where do you both live?' asked Matthew.

'A village called Emmaus, replied his companion. 'It's about seven miles from here.'

'The Lord be with you,' said Matthew as they walked together to the door of the courtyard.

'We'll return again soon,' replied Cleopas – although none of us expected that to be within a few hours.

It was the return of Peter some time later, however, that changed everything. Most of us were outside in the courtyard in the afternoon sun when he was let back in.

'I've seen the Lord,' was as far as he got before our gathering erupted again. In an instant he was being deluged with questions as to where and when and how. All he would say, however, was that he'd been on his own when Jesus had met him. I wondered if, once again, he'd been to the tomb – or even to the garden on the Mount of Olives where Jesus had been arrested.

I heard the voice of Andrew call out, using the name for his brother that he'd used all his life. 'But Simon, if Jesus is alive, when and how did it happen?' And again, a host of voices started speaking at once.

Peter held up his hand for quiet. 'I don't know. I don't understand it any more than any of you do. But brothers, sisters – ' He paused, looking around at us all, his face radiant. Then he said, with triumph in his voice, 'It is true! The Lord is risen!'

Despite our further questions, he would still not be drawn on what Jesus had said to him. But we could see the transformation that had taken place. The haunted look had gone. Now there was only peace and joy. Whilst some had dismissed the testimony of the women, the words of Peter seemed to be accepted as true. And my sister's face had an expression of longing which I understood: *If only we, too, could see the Lord!*

Although our neighbours Simon and James left to return to their families shortly before nightfall, I did not even suggest to either my brother or sister that we return to Bethany that night. They would have refused to leave – and I wanted to stay. We would be able to find beds for the night, anyway, at the house of my uncle Jacob. It was, after all, only a short distance away in the Upper City. Once again I found myself preparing food with the other women in the courtyard, grilling over the open fire some fish from the market, which I'd flavoured with oil, salt and dill. Others baked more unleavened bread.

It was an hour or two after nightfall that we heard

the sudden banging on the door. Those upstairs hurried down to join us, having heard the disturbance below. The door was unlocked once more, and even in the fire-light I could see that the faces of Cleopas and his companion were reddened, and could hear that they were out of breath. As Andrew quickly locked the door again behind them, he exclaimed, 'The Lord really has risen – Peter's seen him!'

'So have we,' gasped Cleopas, as the new arrivals both tried to catch their breath. And they both began to speak excitedly, one after the other.

'He walked with us along the road to Emmaus – '

'But we didn't recognise him at first.'

'He explained the Scriptures to us as we walked together.'

'It felt like our hearts were burning within us!'

Once again, it took some time to hear the whole story. An unknown traveller had joined them and asked them about all that had been happening in Jerusalem. He then chastised them for being slow to believe all that had been written in the prophets about the Messiah. When they reached Emmaus, they invited Jesus – still unrecognised by them – to stay with them as the day was almost over, and had then sat at the table together to eat.

'He took the bread, said the blessing over it, and then broke it and gave it to us,' said Cleopas. 'And then it was if our eyes were opened.'

'We saw the scars in his wrists and knew it was Jesus!' And we continued to eagerly talk together about all that had happened.

Until, that is, we heard the familiar voice that had the power and authority to still all others. 'Peace be with you.'

The talking ceased in an instant. And we froze. Because there he was. Jesus – suddenly, shockingly, unbelievably – standing in our midst. No-one had unlocked the door. We stood in startled silence, all staring at him, as if he were a ghost. *This was the man I'd last seen hanging bruised and bloodied – and dead – upon the cross.* Whatever we'd been told by those who'd said he was alive, our reaction at coming face to face with him was one of shock, even fear.

'Why are you frightened,' he asked us, 'and why are there doubts in your mind?' He lifted his hands – with their scars. 'Look at my hands – and my feet. It really *is* me.' He looked around at the stunned faces with a radiant smile. 'Touch me – I'm real, not a ghost! Ghosts don't have a solid body like mine.' And then he held out his scarred hands to us to see and feel, and even lifted his outer clothing up slightly to reveal his similarly-scarred feet. But still we stood there, dumbfounded. Too amazed, too unnerved – not knowing whether to weep or to shout for joy. So Jesus spoke again. 'Do you have anything here to eat?' Within moments a plate was being held out to him, with a piece of the fish I'd grilled still on it. We stared at him as he ate it, proving to us just how real he was. And I thought I caught a familiar look of approval on Jesus' face as he tasted the fish.

'It's one of Martha's, Lord,' added Andrew suddenly, his face breaking into a grin. And then we were all laughing and crying together, our doubts and fears finally dispelled, as we all accepted for ourselves the truth that would change our lives forever. Jesus was alive!

That evening with Jesus was one that we wished would never end. For, as he'd done on the road to Emmaus, he began to explain how everything that had happened to him was a fulfilment of what had been foretold. It was all there in the Law of Moses, the Prophets and the Psalms – the three parts of our Scriptures. And we understood for the first time the truth that we'd previously been unable to see: that the Messiah had to suffer and die before rising from the dead on the third day.

I could echo the words spoken by Cleopas: my heart burned within me. And it felt as if the divide between earth and heaven had melted away.

But as abruptly and inexplicably as Jesus had stood among us, he was gone. Our rejoicing, however, continued. Although we were too exhilarated to be tired, the evening eventually had to come to an end. After lengthy and joyful farewells, we wound our way back to my uncle and aunt's house, wondering if we would have to raise them from their sleep. We would have a story to tell before we finally lay down that night. We had seen the promised Messiah walk amongst us. But now we had witnessed with our own eyes what were surely the most momentous events that our world had ever seen – or would ever see. Not only the death of God's Messiah, as foretold by the Scriptures, but also his rising to life on the third day.

'*I am the Resurrection and the Life.*' I softly murmured the words of Jesus to myself, as my brother knocked loudly on the door and called out my uncle's name. 'Yes, Lord,' I quietly prayed, 'I believe.'

Chapter 27

A new world

'I will also make you a light for the Gentiles, that my salvation may reach to the ends of the earth.' (Isaiah 49:6)

AD 33 – April/May

In the six weeks that followed Jesus' resurrection, we saw him again a number of times, as did others. Not that we had any way of predicting beforehand who would see him, or when or where. It could as easily be beside a lake as in a house, to an individual as to a group – or to five hundred or more. We didn't understand how he could suddenly appear, and just as suddenly disappear. Or where he went each time he left us. But what we did understand more and more each day were the Scriptures that spoke of him. We searched God's Word together, seeing familiar words in new ways, as if we had been blind before, or the meaning was hidden from us despite being in plain sight all the time. And, of course, whenever Jesus was with us, we soaked in all that he taught us, as dry and thirsty ground soaks in rain.

'It couldn't be plainer,' said our friend Jonathan excitedly one day, as we ate at his house with Simon and Rachel. 'The prophet Isaiah speaks of the suffering servant. The rabbis never knew for certain to whom the words applied, whether to Isaiah or to our nation or to another. It is all so clear now that he was speaking of the Messiah, of Jesus!' And we listened as the leader of our synagogue recited, from memory, words that had been read out on the Sabbath many times over the years.

'This is what the Sovereign LORD says:

Surely he took up our pain
  and bore our suffering,
yet we considered him punished by God,
  stricken by him, and afflicted.
But he was pierced for our transgressions,
  he was crushed for our iniquities;
the punishment that brought us peace was on him,
  and by his wounds we are healed.
We all, like sheep, have gone astray,
  each of us has turned to our own way;
and the LORD has laid on him
  the iniquity of us all.'

Jonathan paused, letting the ancient words – written hundreds of years before – sink in. My brother murmured, 'John the Baptist called him the Lamb of God.'

Jonathan nodded. 'The one true and perfect sacrifice for sin – for *all* our sin.' And we fell silent, awed by the simple truth, so recently grasped but almost too astounding to believe: Jesus had died *for us*. His cry of abandonment on the cross came from a psalm that foretold his suffering. The cry was testament to the truth that he was bearing the just punishment of God – punishment that we deserved and should have borne.

'But what about the curtain in the temple?' asked

Lazarus suddenly. 'It was torn from top to bottom when Jesus died.'

But this time it was Simon who answered. 'It was a sign for us. A sign that God's presence is now open to us through the Lord Jesus. Even though we have sinned, we may now approach our holy God without fear.' Then Simon continued, 'Unclean as we are, we have been made clean by him – clean enough to enter the Holy of Holies.' And the man who had once been known as *Simon the Leper* paused and smiled. 'His touch has the power to make not only our bodies clean, but our hearts as well.'

But it was not only our understanding of Jesus' death that grew in the weeks that followed. We learned that we, too, like Jesus, could now call God our father. And even more remarkably, more wonderfully, could address the Almighty as *Abba*. Our Creator was nearer, dearer, that we could ever have imagined or dreamt. But we also began to grasp more of what it meant that Jesus was His Son.

It seemed incredible that we, as Jews, could think that Jesus shared the nature of God. We had always been taught that there was one God. Our proclamation each Sabbath, etched on our hearts and minds, was that *the LORD our God, the LORD, is one.* And yet Jesus being God's Son, unthinkable as that was to us, was the only thing that made sense of all we had witnessed. Not that we pretended to understand how it could be so. But, as my father Heli had always taught me, how could we ever expect to fathom all the mysteries of the One who created the heavens and the earth. I remembered the conversation I'd had with him, when he had laughed at my question as to whether God was like him. He'd responded by asking how a small man on the Lord's vast earth could possibly contain the immeasurable love of God. And yet we had met a man for whom that *had* been possible, a man in whom the earthly and the divine, the mortal and the immortal had been woven seamlessly together. He had walked among us as a man, but when we had met him, we had met God.

'I don't understand it,' grumbled Lazarus, as we walked back from Jerusalem to Bethany one day.

Mary threw back her head and laughed. 'And you never will, dear brother!'

And as we all laughed together, I looked up and saw a single swallow rising and swooping in the sky. My father, Heli, had been right. We would never understand all of the ways of the Almighty – but that didn't mean that we couldn't trust Him. And I remembered my father's favourite phrase. The Messiah *had* come – and his name was Jesus. And nothing would ever be the same again. It was not just our world that had changed. It was the whole world.

But if the Messiah had come, we slowly began to realise, to our sorrow, that that didn't mean he was going to stay. And he spoke of leaving us.

Finally, there came a day (forty days after his resurrection), that was to be the last time we would see him on earth, before he returned in glory. Although the winter rains had long since passed, and the dry season was upon us, plenty of white, fair-weather clouds were still drifting lazily across the sky. Jesus met us in Jerusalem, but we didn't stay there. He led the Eleven (as they had become known), and some other believers like ourselves, along the familiar road up the Mount of Olives towards Bethany, though that wasn't where he was heading.

One of the questions we'd discussed frequently, of course, was what was going to happen next. Some wondered whether there would still be a glorious re-establishing of our kingdom – and if so, when. The question was put to Jesus, just after we'd reached the top of the Mount and had begun to go down again. 'The Father alone has the authority to set those dates and times,' he began, and then smiled at us. 'And they are not for you to know.' He then stopped, as if he'd reached his destination, and looked at each one of us in turn as we gathered around him. And when he began to speak again, we could hear the finality in his voice. 'But you will receive power when the Holy Spirit comes on you; and you will be my witnesses in Jerusalem, and in all Judea and Samaria, and to the ends of the earth.' And with that, he raised his hands and blessed us. As he did so, he was lifted up before our very eyes, until a cloud hid him from our sight.

He'd told us that he would return to his Father – and now he had. But still we stood staring into the sky, not wanting to accept that he had finally gone. Suddenly, however, we felt the presence of others with us, and found ourselves joined by two men in white.

'Angels!' whispered Lazarus to me excitedly, although I had already guessed that. I felt my heartbeat quicken.

They addressed their words to the Eleven. 'Men of Galilee, why do you stand here looking into the sky? This same Jesus, who has been taken from you into heaven, will come back in the same way as you have seen him go.' And then, as noiselessly as they'd arrived, they were gone, leaving only the sounds of birds in the nearby olive trees, an early summer breeze rustling through their leaves, and the distant barking of one of the dogs that roamed Bethany's streets.

After brief farewells, we parted company with the Eleven and the others, who were returning to Jerusalem. We promised that we would join them again in the city the following day, to wait and to pray together in obedience to Jesus' command. But, significant as the day was, we needed to return home to attend to some everyday tasks of living.

The three of us watched as our friends disappeared over the top of the Mount of Olives. We then turned to leave. 'You go on ahead,' I said to my sister and brother. 'I won't be long.'

As they headed off towards the village, I stood for a little while in silence, raising my face to the bright sun and letting its rays warm my smiling face. For a few moments, as I basked in the sunshine with my eyes closed, I tried to imagine the glories of heaven. The only certainty in my imaginings was that Jesus was now there. But whatever the truth of heaven's unseen glory, I nevertheless felt its peace resting in my heart.

When I opened my eyes again, I looked around at the fields that lay nearby. The barley harvest was almost over, but soon the wheat would be ripe and ready for harvest, and we would be enjoying the first fresh figs of the year. As I took in the sights of the countryside surrounding Bethany with which I had been familiar since my earliest days, I reflected on just how much had changed for me. I had begun my life as a daughter and then a sister. I had supposed – until Jesus came into our lives – that my identity as a woman would first and foremost be one of a widow, and, if I were fortunate, possibly a wife once more. And yet now I knew the greater plan for my life. It wasn't that I was no longer those things, but now I was first and foremost a believer, a disciple, and a witness of the risen Lord. I thought of my sister Mary, sitting at Jesus' feet – the place of the disciple and previously the preserve of men alone. And I remembered Jesus' commendation of her. *She had chosen the better place, the right place, as I had now, too – and as any woman could now do.*

I smiled to myself, as once again I thought of the person who had changed our lives beyond recognition, the person whom my father had taught me to expect from my earliest days. *When the Messiah comes…* And I whispered with a joy that my heart could barely contain, 'He has, Abba. He has.' But any further thoughts of the future at that point were not to be.

'Martha!' My brother's cry interrupted my thinking, as it had done on that sunny afternoon in Bethany only three years earlier. Both my brother and sister had stopped on the edge of the village, and were looking back towards me. 'I'm hungry,' he called out.

My sister chimed in, 'And so am I.'

Another smile came to my face as I began to walk towards them, feigning innocence. 'So?'

'*Martha!*' My brother's face broke into a big grin as he said my name again with exasperation.

Yes, I was now a disciple of Jesus and the world had changed forever. But even those momentous truths did not alter the simple fact that, out of my sister and me, I was still – and would always be – the better cook.

The Family Tree

The family of Martha's mother, Susannah (Galilee and Bethany):

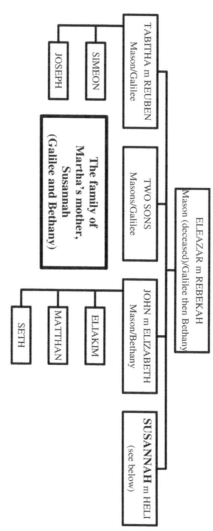

The family of Martha's father, Heli (Jerusalem, Bethany and Jericho):

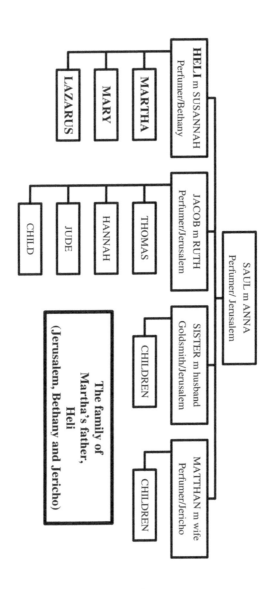

Other families and individuals in Bethany:

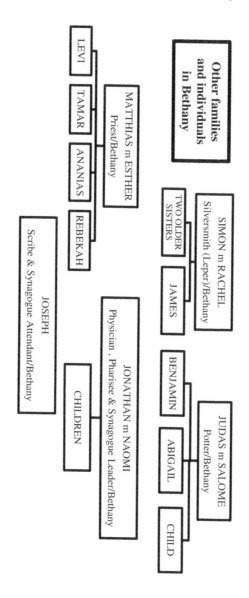

Other families and individuals in Bethany

MATTHIAS m ESTHER
Priest/Bethany

LEVI

TAMAR

ANANIAS

REBEKAH

SIMON m RACHEL
Silversmith (Leper)/Bethany

TWO OLDER SISTERS

JAMES

JOSEPH
Scribe & Synagogue Attendant/Bethany

JONATHAN m NAOMI
Physician , Pharisee & Synagogue Leader/Bethany

CHILDREN

BENJAMIN

JUDAS m SALOME
Potter/Bethany

ABIGAIL

CHILD

Note: All names are those used in English Bibles today. As the New Testament was written down in Greek (although many of its words would originally have been spoken in Aramaic), Jewish names in our New Testaments are English (or Latinised) versions of the Greek rendering of Aramaic (or late Hebrew) names, possibly based on Hebrew originals. So Jesus comes from Iesous which comes from Yeshua which comes from Yehoshua (or, Joshua).